Wild Sex
for
New Lovers

———❦———

Graham Masterton

A SIGNET BOOK

SIGNET
Published by New American Library, a division of
Penguin Putnam Inc., 375 Hudson Street,
New York, New York 10014, U.S.A.
Penguin Books Ltd, 27 Wrights Lane,
London W8 5TZ, England
Penguin Books Australia Ltd, Ringwood,
Victoria, Australia
Penguin Books Canada Ltd, 10 Alcorn Avenue,
Toronto, Ontario, Canada M4V 3B2
Penguin Books (N.Z.) Ltd, 182–190 Wairau Road,
Auckland 10, New Zealand

Penguin Books Ltd, Registered Offices:
Harmondsworth, Middlesex, England

ISBN: 0-7394-1544-1

Printed in the United States of America

CONTENTS

Prologue

So You've Decided to Say "Yes" . . . Now What?

"If you had asked me, an hour before we first went to bed together, if I was ever going to have a sexual relationship with this man, I would have laughed in your face!"

That was Sharon, a 27-year-old nurse from Madison, Wisconsin, talking about her very passionate affair with Michael, a 32-year-old investment consultant.

Sometimes the start of a sexual relationship can take you completely by surprise. You might have known a man for months and months, and liked him, but never really thought of him as a bed partner. Or you might have known him for less than an hour—like the businesswoman who was prosecuted for making frantic and abandoned love on a transAtlantic flight to a man she had never met before they bumped into each other in the check-in line.

It's impossible to generalize about what triggers a sexual affair, because it depends so much on personal circumstances. You might have been dating for a while, and suddenly, inexplicably, the moment seems right. Or, this might be your first-ever date, and suddenly, inexplicably, you know that you want to make love to him.

You might be feeling rejected and blue, and are looking for somebody to help you make it through the night. You might have been drinking. You might be perfectly sober, and suddenly see some quality in Mr. Familiar that you never saw before: a touch, a smile, a word of understanding. You might have gone to a singles bar or a drama club or a writers' circle, specifically looking for a man you want to go to bed with. You might even be high school sweethearts who suddenly realize that now is the time to turn dating into mating.

However it happens, your whole life is going to go through a Richter-scale upheaval. You are going to have to re-appraise your sexuality so that you can make the very best of this exciting and arousing new relationship.

If you've never had a sexual relationship before, you're going to have to ask yourself what your expectations are, and whether you know enough about sex and lovemaking to give your lover a really good time in bed. If you're the veteran of several previous relationships, you're going to have to make sure that you don't bring to bed any sexual problems or prejudices from your past affairs.

No matter what your sexual history is, you're going to have to ask yourself how far you're prepared to commit yourself—physically and emotionally—to the man with whom you will now be sharing your bed (or your couch, or wherever passion happens to overwhelm you.)

Many women find themselves completely unprepared for a new sexual relationship, which is hardly surprising since every sexual relationship is wildly different. Gina, 27, a legal assistant from Los Angeles, California, said, "Going to bed with John was so totally unlike the sex I'd had with my previous boyfriend that I found myself wondering if I was ever going to get used to it. His foreplay seemed to go on forever, and he did things to me that Nat had never even thought of doing. After our very first night together, I was woken up by something tickling me. I was sleeping facedown, and John had gently opened up my legs and was stroking my anus with a goose-feather that he must have plucked out of the pillow.

"I lay there for two or three minutes, pretending that I was still asleep. I was enjoying every second of it. In fact it really turned me on. But the truth was that I didn't really know how I was supposed to react. Nobody had ever touched me like that before, and I didn't know if I was supposed to show him that I was shocked, or excited, or if I was supposed to laugh.

"As it was, he started to stroke the lips of my pussy with it, and then my clitoris, but it was wet by then and it didn't tickle so much. I pretended to wake up, and I turned over, and he was kneeling there, completely naked, with a huge hard-on, smiling at me. I'll always remember it, but I looked at his balls and they were so big and tight and I really felt like reaching out and taking hold of them in my hand.

"But again, I wasn't sure if it was the right thing to do. If he'd like it or not. You read so many things about treating a man's balls as if they're precious eggs, and not squeezing them too hard, I was afraid to do anything at all. And I didn't know if it would be too forward of me. You know—considering this was the first time we'd ever slept together.

"All the same, he climbed on top of me, and he smiled, and he said, 'So you're ticklish, are you?' and he slid that huge cock so far up inside of me that I couldn't help shivering. He made love to me, and it was very, very good, but all the same I still didn't know how to make love to *him*. What kind of attitude to have. Like, after he'd climaxed, and we were lying on the bed together, I didn't know whether I ought to touch his cock or not."

Gina expressed the same uncertainties about how to deal with a new sexual relationship as scores of other women, from age 17 to 47. Many of them had read sexual self-help books, and some of them had watched self-help videos, but more often than not they found that instead of feeling more confident about how to respond to a new lover in their life, they felt considerably more anxious.

The problem was that so many sexual self-help books—although they are well intentioned and often highly informative—tend to lay down hard and fast rules of sexual response. I can't count, how many lists I've read in books and magazines, such as "The Twenty Sex Truths about Men," "Eleven Things that All Men Find Irresistible," and "Sixty-Nine Ways to Blow His Mind in Bed."

You'll often pick up inspirational ideas from these lists, and there's no doubt about it, we all think that lists are fun. But that's all they're meant to be: inspirational and fun. You shouldn't think that the advice they give is carved in stone. If some of the sexual acts that they suggest don't appeal to you, or if you simply don't see the point of them, then don't worry about it. Your new lover won't be disappointed so long as you are confident in your own sexual ability and— most important of all—you're clear in your own mind what you're prepared to do to him and what you're prepared to let him do to you. In other words, your sex life is your call.

Every sexual relationship is unique, because it depends on so many factors apart from the simple act of making love. It depends on your age, your experience, your aspirations, your physical appearance, your confidence, your emotional makeup. It depends on what you're hoping to get out of your relationship and what you're prepared to forgo. It depends on your job, your social status, where you live, and what kind of community you live in.

Sexual fantasies exist only in fantasyland, with no other considerations to affect them except for how erotic they are. Margot, 33, a travel agent from Detroit, Michigan, told me that she had always fantasized about a man taking her while she was baking! "I guess it sounds kind of strange, but I do a whole lot of baking for my children on the weekend, and ever since David and I were separated—well, I guess I've had sex on my mind quite a lot of the time. I'll be standing at the kitchen counter with my hands all covered in flour and some tall, strong guy will come up behind me, and lift up my skirt, and pull my panties halfway down my thighs. He'll be wearing nothing but a T-shirt, and he'll force his cock up me before I know what to do.

"He'll fuck me from behind for a little while,

and I'll be bending right over with my face against the pastry board so that my cheeks are smudged with flour. Then he'll take his cock out and lift me right up onto the counter, and climb on top of me. He'll open my legs wide and he'll push himself back into me, as far as he can go.

"I'll kiss him and grip the cheeks of his ass with my floury hands. He'll have one of those tight, small hard asses I really love. I'll rub flour all over it, and all over his balls. We'll both be gasping and grunting and saying all dirtiest words that we can think of. I'll pick up an egg and break it behind his back, so that it all slides down between the checks of his ass. I'll break another, and another, and smear all that slippery egg white around his asshole. Then I'll take hold of my wooden spoon and I'll slowly push the handle up him, stretching him wide.

"I'll push it deeper and deeper, until he has this incredible climax, and I have an orgasm, too. Then we'll just lie there, on the kitchen counter, covered in flour and pastry and eggs, and we won't have to move."

Of course the reality is that Margot's fantasy will have to remain a fantasy. At the moment she doesn't have a sexual partner, and even if she did, the presence of her two young children in the house on weekends would make her Betty Crocker–style erotica impossible.

So, like all of us, she has to adjust her sexual

expectations to her actual lifestyle and surroundings. And this is why she shouldn't feel
worried if she can't live up to the lists of sexual shenanigans that she reads about in books—
even in *my* books. I know very well that some
of the erotic variations that I suggest are arousing to think about, but—for any woman who
lives in a suburban household with a husband
and a dog and the usual number of children—
the occasions when you will ever have the
chance to try them out will rarely be as often as
you might like.

Sometimes there are practical considerations
that are extremely dull but which we all have
to take into account, as is the case with Moira,
a 32-year-old bridal consultant from Palatine,
Illinois. "I read *How to Drive Your Man Even
Wilder in Bed* and I was really turned on by the
idea of waxing my pussy. I don't know why. I
think it was what you said about exposing yourself completely to the man in your life . . . you
know, showing him that you were ready for sex.
I didn't have a boyfriend then, I did it for myself, the complete Brazilian wax. I loved it, and
I used to stand in front of the mirror in my bedroom closet and masturbate, imagining what a
man would think about it, if he could see it.

"Then I met Rod. He's eleven years older than
me, and he works for a large insurance company. He's very vigorous, very fit. He may have

gray hair but he's a great lover. We met at his cousin's wedding, because I was taking care of the bridal gown and all the bridesmaids' dresses. What can I say? We just clicked. There was a chemistry between us, something that had never happened to me before.

"He was quite formal. He invited me out for dinner, and he was so charming. There was something about his eyes that told me that I was going to go to bed with him that night. I can't exactly describe what it was, but his eyes twinkled, like he was really interested in what I was saying and who I was. It was so different from that look that most men give you. They spend the whole evening staring down your cleavage and in the end you feel like saying, 'Have you lost something down there?'

"We went back to Rod's hotel, and when I undressed I could tell he was very excited by the way I looked, with my bare pussy and all. He was very, very hairy. Hairy chest, hairy cock, hairy balls. It was almost like making love to an animal, you know? It was quite a turn-on, but I've never really gone for very hairy guys. I'm more of a Chippendales fan, me. You know, the smooth six-pack look.

"The next morning he was sleeping, lying naked on the bed, and I guess I was feeling mischievous because I took out my nail scissors and I trimmed his pubic hair until his cock and his balls were almost completely bare. He looked so sexy that I sucked his cock and licked his balls, which woke him up, naturally! But just as I was rubbing him up to a climax, he looked down and saw what I'd done to him, and he went ape.

"He was scheduled to play racquetball with his boss that morning, and they all took showers together after the game. And there was no way that his boss wasn't going to notice that he had had a very close shave! I said I was sorry, and he forgave me, but our relationship never really recovered. I guess there were all kinds of things wrong with it, right from the beginning— the age difference in particular. But I learned that you can't impose your own idea of sexiness on other people . . . you can't expect somebody to dress some particular way or look some particular way just because it turns you on."

Moira was right. What she did to Rod was innocent enough, and dozens of other men might have found it highly erotic. I suggested nearly 30 years ago that women could drive their men wilder in bed if they shaved their pubic hair, and these days it's a rarity to find a fashion model or a *Penthouse* centerfold or even an ordinary businesswoman who isn't bare down there. But these days, with men becoming increasingly interested in skin care and physique and general grooming, more than 35 percent of the males I've talked to have admitted to "some trimming" of their pubic hair and more than 8 percent regularly shave their pubic area completely.

Jack, 35, a high school coach from Scranton, Pennsylvania, told me that he regularly waxed and that all of his girlfriends "go wild for it." He said, "Women are shy of touching a man's cock and balls, but if they're completely bare, it's like you're showing them off explicitly, you're saying here they are, look at them, touch them, feel them, suck them, they're all yours. Usually women never get a real good look at a man's cock and balls—even their husband's—because they're hiding inside this briar patch. One thing I've learned from the women I've loved is that they're incredibly curious about men's sexual organs, half attracted toward them and half afraid of them. Like, one minute your cock is huge and hard and exciting, and the next minute it's all floppy and wet and no good for anything. Women like to see that; they find it interesting. And if your cock and your balls are completely visible, women feel that they can touch them and stroke them and *discover* them. You'd be amazed the number of women who like to suck your cock after you've finished making love, when it's completely soft, and they can get it all in their mouth, and maybe one of your balls, too."

All the same, Moira didn't observe one of the

basic rules of first-time love, which is not to assume that your new lover has the same sexual fantasies as you do—especially when your sexual fantasies impinge on his personal space. In a fantasy situation, Rod may have been highly excited by having his pubic hair clipped. But he lived in the real world, as all of us do, where he had to strip down in front of his boss. What Moira did was just as serious a breach of sexual etiquette as a man giving his new lover hickeys all over her neck. Hickeys either look juvenile or sluttish, and these days, no woman wants to look like either of those things, or has to.

This book will show you, in very simple terms, how to behave in bed (and out of it) with a man you've met and decided you want to make love to. At the same time, I hope it will also show you how to attract a man that you really want, and how to make him feel that his very first night with you was the night that his life changed forever.

I was already married when I met my present wife. I was editor of *Penthouse* and *Penthouse Forum* magazines in those days, and she was my editorial assistant. We were brought together by the classic Christmas party situation: a little too much to drink, a little too much letting-down of hair. But what she did on that first night we spent together was a revelation.

Not because she was sexually experienced—she wasn't. She confessed later that some of the things I wanted to do (like oral sex) she had never done before.

But what she brought to bed that night was an eagerness, an enthusiasm, a willingness to enjoy herself. Later on, as our relationship progressed, she told me things she liked and things she didn't. But that first night, she threw herself into the passion of our first lovemaking without any inhibitions at all, and that was what won me over forever. It was her sexual bravura.

There is nothing more off-putting than a woman who insists on getting undressed in the bathroom, and then rushes into bed with her nightie on, so that she can't be seen. Sex is all about display, and confidence, and feeling good about yourself. Then there's the woman whose firm hand keeps pushing her would-be lover away from vital parts of her body. She's not comfortable with the feel of her own vagina, its wetness, its responses, and that's why she doesn't want anybody else to touch it, either.

There's the woman who just lies on the bed and waits to be fucked. She's not a myth, believe me. Over dinner, she was animated and sparkling and batting her eyelashes. Now she's just lying there, naked, in the belief that her nakedness is proof enough that she wants to have sex. She may gasp when you enter her. She may even whisper, "yes, oh, yes," once or twice. But she never commits herself, never participates, never puts herself out on a limb.

Any exciting relationship requires risk-taking from both partners, whether it's a friendship or a business deal or a game of tennis. Risk equals excitement. When you decide to enter into a new sexual relationship with a man, you can't play it safe. If you want safe, go back to macramé. Sex by its very nature is dangerous. You're going to take off all of your clothes in front of a strange man and allow him to push his erect penis up inside your vagina. You're allowing him to enter your body and, ipso facto, your entire world. You have to be fairly sure of what you're doing— what you're letting yourself in for—and how far you're really prepared to go.

Men have some pretty funny ideas about ownership, even today. You may know from experience that some men whom you thought of as one-night stands believe that, because you foolishly allowed them to make love to you once, you belong to them forever. They never stop pestering you for a repeat performance, and if you refuse, they tell everybody that you're frigid, or that there's something seriously wrong with you.

There *is* something seriously wrong with you: you got yourself involved with them in the first place. You have to learn how to assess potential bed-partners more judiciously. How to separate the losers from the not-so-bads from the real knee-weakeners. The fact is, though, that men are just people—which takes us back to what we were saying about fantasy. It's easy enough to have a daydream about a gorgeous construction worker with a huge bulge going halfway down the left leg of his Levi's. But even gorgeous construction workers have real personalities, and real problems.

The great secret of giving a man the very best first night of his life—and of keeping his sexual attention for many more nights to come—is that you should *never assume that a man knows what he's doing in bed*. Remember, he may know how to make love, but he doesn't yet know how to make love to *you*.

No matter how experienced and sophisticated he may be, every man is looking for you to give him guidance. He's looking for you to give him hints and clues to what turns you on the most. He wants to know how intense and committed you want to be; and what you're prepared to do with him and what you're not.

The beginning of a new sexual relationship is critical—whether you're a virgin, setting out on your very first sexual experience, or whether you're a woman with a whole string of broken relationships behind her, looking to find a genuine long-term affair, and even marriage.

On the very first night, you set the whole tone of your forthcoming relationship (unless, of course, you're just looking for a one-night stand.) You show your new lover what you need and what you expect. You also show him what really turns you on—and what really turns you off.

As one female psychiatrist told me, "Men need to be shown what to do, especially when it comes to sex. If you don't make it abundantly clear that you don't want him to chew your nipples like Starbursts, he'll go on doing it. If you don't tell him that you want your clitoris stroked, not rubbed like Aladdin's magic lamp, then his touch will never ease up."

This doesn't mean that you should openly criticize his sexual performance. If you do that, you'll probably never get to see him again. But if he's doing something you find painful or uncomfortable, a little "ouch!" followed by a little laugh usually does the trick—or simply a shift into a new position. If you make your movement look eager rather than irritated, you won't put him off his stroke or make him feel that you're being critical, and if he has the slightest sense he'll realize why you've done it.

Similarly, if you want him to try something that excites you, you can guide him with your hands or simply by the way you move your body against his. Or if you still don't get the response you're looking for, whisper it into his ear. "Why don't you . . . stroke my back/ suck my nipples/ kiss my pussy . . . ?"

It's very important to get your new lover used to the idea that you need plenty of gradually mounting stimulation. I know this isn't easy the first time you make love. You will both be intensely aroused and the sheer excitement of having him inside you for the first time will make it almost impossible for you to think about pacing yourself. But make sure that you show him very early in your sexual relationship that you expect him to take his time when you go to bed together, so that your lovemaking lasts longer and you *both* get the satisfaction that you deserve.

Even today, with men's magazines full of more information about sex than ever, I still hear that old complaint that "he just pushes himself inside me, jiggles up and down until he comes, gives me a kiss on the cheek, and falls asleep." It's such a cliché that you can hardly believe that men still act that way in bed, but many of them still do . . . and when you start a new sexual relationship it's crucial that you don't allow your lover to fall into bad habits.

Sexologist Sarah Lewis, a fellow contributor for the European magazine *Men Only,* told me that she always encourages her new lovers to learn the art of sensual massage. She does this simply by producing a bottle of perfumed massage oil and asking the man to caress her with it. She has never known a man to decline the offer, and she says that even the least dextrous of men can give a girl a highly stimulating time when their hands are good and oily. The main point is that it slows men down, because they're having such a good time smearing oil all over your body.

"I like a man who knows what he's doing with his fingers and the palm of his hand," she says. "This means slowly and sensuously stimulating every part of my body until I'm really begging for it. A man can do this by rubbing oil into my skin using circular movements, and remembering to give me light touches on my breasts until I'm fully aroused. He shouldn't go near my clitoris, just keep teasing the rest of my body.

"Then he should fondle my back all the way down to my bottom, kneading the flesh on either side of the spine."

Sarah's trick is to suggest to her new lovers that they try some secret sexual techniques that even very few women are aware of. Her lovers are almost always willing to play along because they feel that they will learn something that will give them the ability to arouse every woman they ever meet. They don't feel as if she's belittling their skill in the sack because, well, if even *women* don't know about these techniques, how are men supposed to?

"Press your thumbs into the top of her skull—this will send energy straight to her crotch. Smooth her forehead, over eyebrows, under eyes and over cheeks. Rub your palms over her breasts, then gently suck on her erect nipples. Stroke her arms and make sure you cover her back with oil—believe me, she'll be wetter than the plains in the rainy season.

"Now press a point on her inner thigh, two inches or so down from her pussy. You should have a finger on her inner thigh and a thumb on the outer part of her thigh, and hold her like this for thirty-odd seconds. At the same time, you should tell her what a beautiful sex goddess she is, and how you want her to have the biggest orgasm of her life, but you need her help.

"For a woman to experience a microcosmic orgasm, she needs to slow her breathing down. While you fondle her, she should take a deep breath in and hold to the count of three, deep breath out and hold to the count of three. When she breathes in she should push her belly out, and when she breathes out she should hold her stomach in. While she's doing this, put your palm on her stomach and massage it. Get it right and she'll experience all kinds of erotic sensations."

If your new lover feels that he has really satisfied you sexually, then he will leave you with a feeling of warmth and achievement, and the desire to see you again as soon as possible. You might have been lucky and found a man who is already very good in bed—an experienced man who knows how to arouse you and how to make you feel like a sex princess. In which case, there isn't much you have to do to guide him in bed except to show your appreciation when he does something that really turns you on. Again, just because he's terrific and he knows all the moves, don't be tempted to do nothing more than lie there and passively enjoy what he's doing to you. Even if you don't feel that you're very experienced, and you're worried that you might do something wrong (such as squeezing his balls too hard) show him that you're aroused and enthusiastic. You may not think that you're an expert, but your enthusiasm will more than make up for any lack of expertise. You know how to talk dirty, don't you? You know how to moan and wiggle? And you know how to dig your nails into a man's buttocks and bite his earlobes?

In any case, by the time you've finished reading this book you should be just as good in bed as any man you're ever likely to meet. You should be able to show him that you have sexual talents of your own, and that he can't rely entirely on his experience of other women to make you happy. He has to make love to you like an individual—not just another conquest.

On the other hand, if your new lover is clumsy, or awkward, or uncertain of himself, there's a lot you can do to give him confidence. You can use different positions to make him feel more in control of your lovemaking (even when, secretly, it's you who's running the show). Later in this book, I'll give you at least three guaranteed ways of making your lover feel harder and last longer. You will always bolster his feeling of virility by paying particular attention to his cock, as if it's the hugest, hardest, most exciting cock you've encountered in your life.

However, the single greatest anxiety that women have about new sexual relationships is how to handle their lover's sexual equipment. I have talked to literally dozens of women on the subject of what they find most daunting about starting a love affair, and over 80 percent of them said that they "weren't at all sure" how to touch, fondle, or stimulate a man's penis.

Kate Taylor, who writes a very witty sex instruction column for *GQ* magazine, said, "The first time I ever tried to play with a man's cock, I was hopeless. I was eighteen, which for me was a very naive age (I still thought that *blow job* meant *blow*), and the poor man in question wasn't much better. After half an hour of pulling and squeezing that a Hungarian fish-gutter would have been proud of, my arm-muscles were in spasm and there was no sign of a result. Finally, I sat back, exhausted. 'Shouldn't you have come ten minutes ago?' I asked him. He looked down at his bruised and battered willy. 'No,' he said, 'I think I should have left.'

"Then a boyfriend had the sense to buy me your book *How to Drive Your Man Wild in Bed*. It was a godsend. I devoured it, and by the time I finished it, I was superb. I knew that the best way to excite a man's cock is not to touch it at all, but to cover the surrounding areas with teasing, feather-like touches that seem to concentrate all of a man's psyche on his poor, ignored organ. I know when to squeeze and when to pull and best of all, when to stop.

"I know that there is nothing worse for a man than having a hand still clamped around his genitals long after he has spent himself. With all that sensitivity it must feel as if he's caught in a demented milking machine. I was suddenly the Kenny Rogers of hand jobs—I knew when to walk away and when to run."

By the time you have finished reading this book, you too will have Kate Taylor's expertise—and a little more, too. Since writing *How to Drive Your Man Wild in Bed* I have talked to more than a hundred men of five different ethnic origins about the sexual manipulation that excites them the most. I have also discovered

some extraordinary sexual massage techniques
that are not at all difficult to learn but that will
have any man desperate for more. I guarantee
that if you use any one of these techniques on
your first night of loving, you will have him
hooked forever. Or, at least, for as long as you
want him.

Contrary to what some sexual pundits say, I
believe that you can learn good basic sexual
technique from books, in the same way that you
can learn good cookery and How to Speak Span-
ish and how to fit a new plug into your Christmas lights.

When you make love to a man, you do have
to know (roughly) what you're doing, from the
moment your eyes meet across a crowded room,
to the moment when you both lie back on the
pillow, sweating and panting, and wondering
where it goes from here.

You don't need to learn very much to be a
good lover. Most of it is common sense, combined with a little basic anatomical knowledge,
and one or two tricks that will make your lovemaking memorable. But once you have these,
you will have sexual confidence, and it's confidence that makes a woman really terrific in bed.

Confidence gives you the ability to control the
way your relationship develops. Confidence
makes you a tigress in bed, and gives you the

nerve to expect your lover to behave like a tiger in return.

Jayne, 32, who runs a beauty parlor in Milwaukee, Wisconsin, said that she was always shy and retiring when it came to making love. "I know why. When I was around eighteen or nineteen I was very overweight, and none of the guys ever wanted to date me, because I was so fat. Then when I was twenty, the weight began to drop off me. I started to look really pretty, and the guys began to show an interest.

"This guy Greg asked me for a date. He was blond-haired and very tall, and captain of athletics. All the girls at college swooned over him. So you can imagine how I felt when he wanted to go out with me. We dated two or three times and on the fourth date he took me back to this motel. He didn't ask, he just took me there, and I wasn't brave enough to say no.

"I'm not sure that I *would* have said no, because I was totally infatuated with him, but the point is that he didn't even give me the chance.

"He put on some music and gave me a drink and then he started to dance with me, and kiss me, and slowly undress me. That was the very first time that a man had ever taken my clothes off. That was the very first time that a man had ever seen me completely naked. So you can imagine how I felt—petrified.

"Greg undressed. He had a great body, very

muscular, with a flat stomach and thighs like Hercules. His cock was sticking right up and it was enormous, and red. I'll never forget how red it was. He kept on dancing with me and his cock kept bumping against my stomach and I really didn't know what to do. I didn't dare to touch it. But after a while, Greg sat back on the bed, and held his cock in his fist, and said, 'How about a little *antipasto?*'

"I didn't know what he was talking about. I wasn't completely innocent. I knew about oral sex. There was one girl at high school who won a bet by giving a blow job to every boy in the ice-hockey team. But I didn't expect to get down on my knees and start sucking Greg's cock on the very first night we slept together.

"He said, 'Come on, don't tell me you're shy,' and he took hold of my hand and pulled me down onto the bed next to him. I kissed him, and ran my hands through his hair, and tried to act all romantic and sexy, but he took hold of my head and forced it downward. He said, 'There are girls in college who would pay money to have this monster in their mouth.'

"I kissed it, and licked it a little. But Greg got impatient and tried to push it into my mouth. I almost gagged. He said, 'You don't know what the hell you're doing, do you?'

"It all went wrong after that. Greg tried to put on a rubber but then his cock went soft and he started to get angry. I got dressed again and asked him to take me home. Greg never spoke to me again after that, and word got around college that I was frigid. Well, we all know where *that* story came from. But it destroyed my confidence completely. I really began to believe that I *was* frigid and that I was absolutely no good in bed.

"It was only when I left college and started training as a hairstylist that I met a man who showed me that there was nothing wrong with me at all. John was older than me, thirty-six and divorced. He took me out to dinner, and concerts. He didn't push me, ever. But the night came when he asked me if I wanted to come back to his apartment.

"I nearly said no, but he was so gentle about it that I decided it had to be now or never. I was useless in bed. I lay on my back with my arms around him and just let him get on with it. I was so tense that I got a cramp in my left leg. But John was tender and loving and if he was disappointed he didn't show it. Afterward, he said, 'That was beautiful,' and held me in his arms and for the first time I realized how much of a pleasure sex could be—not just because of the sexual act itself, but because of the closeness, you know—the sharing."

All the same, it took Jayne years to overcome her sexual reticence. "I read women's magazines and books about sex but I always had the feeling that other women knew something about sex that I didn't. Every time I went to bed with a man I was worried that he was going to think how frigid and ignorant I was." And all because some swollen-headed jock had treated her as if she were a five-dollar whore rather than an innocent and pretty young girl whom he should have treated with tenderness and respect. If anybody was ignorant and impotent, it was him.

But you *will* meet men whose sexual competence leaves a whole lot to be desired, and if you refused to go to bed with all of them, you'd probably find that, most nights, you'd be going to bed on your own. Just because a man isn't quite sure how to encourage you to give him oral sex, or how to caress your breasts without kneading them like two handfuls of baker's dough, that doesn't mean that he's a sexual write-off. He can learn, the same way you did. He can be taught, he can be shown. If he's cute and you like him, then it's worth the effort, isn't it? Michaelangelo didn't paint the ceiling of the Sistine Chapel the week after he'd first picked up a paintbrush.

There's another side to the start of a new sexual affair . . . the emotional side. To begin with, of course, your body chemicals make the physical act of lovemaking so exciting that you're close to being mentally unstable, and you tend to ignore your emotional needs. But this is the time when you ought to be thinking about how much of yourself you're prepared to invest in this new relationship. Sometimes a brief sexual fling can lift your life out of the doldrums caused by a broken marriage or a broken affair, loneliness, or worry about money. Once you've been made to feel sexy and confident and valuable again, you may not feel the need to continue the affair. Your emotional needs may lie elsewhere, with a different kind of person. So it may be unwise, in those first heady days of sexual excitement, to commit yourself too much. Even the hottest affair can suddenly cool.

I'm often asked how far a woman should go to show a man that she likes him, and that she's eager to develop a much more serious relationship with him. Maybe you're the kind of woman who can happily enjoy a one-night stand with a man, kiss him goodbye, and never see him again. There's nothing wrong with that, if you've got the self-confidence and the strength, and you're always prepared for that one-night stand who might unexpectedly steal your heart and never give it back.

But from all the mail I've received, and all the questions that I've been asked, it's more likely you're the kind of woman who feels that when you commit yourself sexually, you make something of an emotional commitment, too. I'm not necessarily talking about love with a capital *L*. I'm not necessarily talking about marriage. But I am talking about a relationship that is more than athletic, more than a spasmodic exchange of bodily fluids. Because the very best sex comes out of understanding, mutual respect, mutual interest in each other, and genuine friendship.

"I broke up with David," said Mariella, 28, a television production assistant from New York City. "He was wonderful in bed. He could open the doors to heaven. But apart from that, we had nothing in common at all. When he had clothes on, he was boring, stuffy, arrogant, prejudiced, and selfish. I miss him sometimes. I'm almost tempted to call him up, for the best fuck you could ever imagine. But I can't stand his attitude. And I'll bet that he doesn't even remember my name."

However, if you meet a man you really like, and who obviously likes you, you can use your lovemaking as a way to start making emotional connections, and strengthening them, every time you meet and make love. You can use your mutual sexual attraction as a starting point for building a relationship that will last for a very long time, if not forever.

Very few couples seem to want to work at their relationships anymore. They want it all handed to them on a plate, without making any effort to build real communication with their partner. Nobody said that a long-term sexual relationship was easy. It isn't. But the sexual and emotional joys that you will get out of it are profound.

I have talked to several couples recently about the fad of so-called "sweet cheating"—when husbands and wives who feel that their sex life has become stale give each other permission to go and date other men and women. It's a kind of updated version of swinging from the 1970s. It's not really cheating, they argue, because their partner says it's okay, and they all protest that it's improved their marriage. "If you think we were turned on before, you should see us now!" a reader wrote to the magazine *Woman's Own*; and another wrote, "My husband almost became a different person when we finally decided that was what our marriage needed. Since having my first brief affair a year ago, my husband really treats me special now, and nothing is good enough for me. He has also become a much better lover, and at the rate he's going, those affairs won't be necessary anymore, except maybe to keep him on his toes!"

This lady had been married for only four years, and already she was looking for other men. Which goes to show that relationships that are based purely on sexual attraction, without emotional compatibility, are unlikely to last for very long.

Really exciting and long-lasting sexual relationships are founded on complete honesty, on
talking, explaining, guiding and being truthful.
Sometimes you may feel like nothing more than
a fling or a one-night stand, and then there's no
particular obligation on you to be 100 percent
honest. You can pretend that you're William
Randolph Hearst's illegitimate great-great-
granddaughter, or that you once recorded a duet
with Cher. But if you're looking to lay the foundations for a genuinely solid partnership, always
tell the truth.

Tell the truth about who you are; and what
you are; and what you're looking for. Tell the
truth about your sexual appetites. Reading between the lines of the *Woman's Own* reader's letter, when she says *"we* finally decided that was
what our marriage needed," you can imagine
who really made the decision. She was tired of
him, and wasn't prepared to put the effort into
rejuvenating their sex life. So he felt that he had
to give her permission to go out and have affairs with other men.

Maybe it excited him at first. "Gee, my wife's
been fucking another man and she still comes back
to me." But the end result of infidelity—whether
it's "permitted" or not—is always corrosive. It
always leads to break-ups and heartache. It's always a betrayal of trust.

If you know how to fall in love—if you're

prepared to be selfless and sharing—then you can have a relationship that's almost magical. A British poet, Craig Raines, recently wrote that good sex isn't a speech, it's a conversation. The whole point of this book is to show you how to meet a new lover and start a sexual relationship that has every chance of developing into love and companionship, and all the erotic excitements that love and companionship can bring.

Celia, 26, a computer salesperson from Akron, Ohio, told me that her three-year relationship with Carl, 32, had left her feeling "worthless." Carl was a domineering personality who expected her to do "anything and everything" whether she was aroused or not. Sitting on the couch watching television, he would open his zipper and expect her to kneel in front of him and give him oral sex, and if she didn't make a show of swallowing his semen with exaggerated relish, he would slap her.

"I don't know why I stayed with him. I don't. I blame myself. But I was very young when I met him, only nineteen years old, and I knew nothing about sex and nothing about men. I was dependent on him and I mistook my dependence for love."

Carl would start having sex with her in the middle of the night when she was asleep and unprepared for it.

"I'm not going to lie to you. Sometimes I

thought it was exciting. To wake up, and find that you're being forcibly fucked. But I talked to my closest girlfriend, Sylvia, and she was horrified. She's not a feminist or anything, but she said, you have to give your consent, otherwise the guy's raping you. Then I told her about the oral sex and she was just about ready to go over and kill him.

"Sylvia gave me the strength to leave Carl; but even when I met John my head still wasn't straight, not sexually. John is only a year older than me, the sweetest, nicest guy you could ever meet, but I guess I was still looking for that dominance, you know? Every time we made love there was something missing. But then I realized what it was. It was fear. And it was humiliation. I hated it, but at the same time it was a turn-on. Carl caught me on the stairs once, halfway up, and grabbed my hair, and forced his cock into my mouth, and made me suck him. Then he fucked me, but I had an orgasm that I'm never going to forget. I wouldn't have cared if I'd died, right at that moment, because that was ecstasy.

"So, with John, I had to relearn how to make love. I had to learn how to show him what I wanted when we went to bed, and that was very difficult, because Carl had never cared what I wanted. I had to overcome my hatred of oral sex. It took months before I managed to lick

John's cock—and then I only licked it. But I told him all about my problems with Carl, and how I was trying to get over them, and once he understood, he was wonderful. He was tender with me, he took his time, and he never once lost his temper.

"The day came when he was going down on me, licking my pussy, and I shifted myself underneath him so that I could take his cock into my mouth. I sucked it slow and gentle, and rubbed it, too, so that I could really relish it, instead of having it forced down my throat.

"He came so gently. Just a shudder, and it all flooded out. I didn't swallow it. I let it drop all over my face instead. Forehead, cheeks, eyelashes, chin. It was so warm, and it smelled so beautiful. John came up from the end of the bed and his face was all wet with my pussy-juice. We kissed, and massaged our bodily fluids all over each other's faces, and licked each other's fingers, and that was when I knew that sex was all about sharing, not taking what you wanted without asking, and not submitting to it, either.

"I never thought that I would ever give oral sex to a man again, but it's not the oral sex, it's the man that makes the difference. John and I do all kinds of things together now—things I never even did with Carl. I love anal sex, especially when it hurts a little bit. Carl tried it, but I never allowed him to do it, and most of the

time he was too drunk. We like having sex out-
doors, too—whenever we can find someplace
private.

"But the most important thing is that we have
this closeness. We can walk into a room and
everybody knows at once that we're a couple,
we're together. That gives me such strength. If
you asked me to give advice to anybody starting out on a new sexual relationship, I'd say,
don't worry so much about the sex, think about
the friendship. Friends who fuck, that's the ideal
formula."

1

First Night Fever

There's always a little madness about the first time you make love, no matter where it happens, or when. While I was researching this book, I talked to dozens of women from all over the country—from Washington State to New Hampshire. Women from all kinds of backgrounds—business executives and social workers and cashiers and homemakers. No matter what their background, they all agreed that when they started a new sexual relationship with a man, they felt as if they were on a roller coaster, out of control of their own sexual feelings, and simply unable to say no.

This roller-coaster feeling, of course, is the real joy of sex. But at the risk of sounding like a wet blanket, it's important not to let yourself get carried so far away that you forget what you've always wanted out of a sexual relationship, and what *he* will be expecting out of it, too.

You may be interested in nothing more than

a one-night stand—in which case you don't have to be so careful about what you say and how you behave. But even one night stands can be a whole lot more exciting if you really know what you're doing and what you want out of them. And you never know—that one-night stand may turn out to last for a thousand and one nights.

"I slept with Jack to help me get over my broken affair with Wayne," said 28-year-old Carole, a legal secretary from New York City. "All I wanted was to know that I was still sexy, and that I could still get a man into bed if I wanted to. I liked Jack, but honestly I hardly knew him. He worked in a different department from me and we used to meet only once or twice a week in the elevators.

"But after that one night together, I was totally infatuated. His lovemaking was so different from Wayne's. He wasn't just having sex, he was making love to me. He was looking at me, talking to me, listening to me, touching me, always trying to think up new ways to make me feel excited.

"We met each other the next night, and the next. Now we've been together for five and a half years and it's still as good as it ever was. Not bad for a one-night stand, huh?"

Not only will you enjoy one-night stands even more if you're really good at giving a man what he wants, you will increase your chances of one-night stands blossoming into longer-term relationships. Many women end up having a series of one-nighters or very short flings because they don't have the sexual knowledge and the confidence to be able to sustain their affairs beyond three or four dates.

"I always start to feel afraid," said Sylvia, 26, a model from Dallas, Texas. "If a man starts getting serious with me, I'm going to wind up disappointing him, and I'm going to get hurt. The thing is, I'm not at all confident that I could keep a man satisfied for very long. I know about sex but I'm not sure that I know what men want when they take me to bed. One of my boyfriends broke up with me because he said having sex with me was boring. I don't know if he said that just to make me feel bad, but I keep thinking that maybe he was right."

Sylvia usually broke off her relationships as soon as her lovers looked as if they wanted a longer-term affair, and of course that gave her the reputation for being promiscuous, and a tease. That meant that very few of her lovers thought of her as a prospective long-term partner, and so her chances of ever finding a long-term lover or a husband were becoming more and more remote.

She needed to break the cycle by learning what she wanted out of sex and how to give her lovers what they wanted—and, more than that, how to be *sure* that she was giving them what they wanted.

Christine, 22, a student from San Jose, California, wrote, "I'm always so afraid of doing the wrong thing in bed. I can't imagine what it must be like to have a penis, what it feels like. I always seem to be squeezing my boyfriends too hard and hurting them, or else I'm not squeezing them hard enough, and they complain that I'm not giving them any sensation at all."

Sylvia and Christine are by no means alone. In spite of all the sexual self-help articles in women's magazines, they still feel unsure of themselves when they're actually faced with having to arouse and satisfy a man.

Because of that, I've been working on several ways to help you start a new sexual relationship with complete confidence in your ability to stimulate your lover the way that he really likes to be stimulated; and learn how to build on your first night's lovemaking so that your relationship becomes hotter and stronger every time you meet. Even if it eventually fizzles out, you should enjoy it so much that you always look back on it with pleasure and pride, as an experience that excited you and enriched you, with very few regrets.

To achieve this, you have to be well prepared for that very first encounter, even if you have no idea when it's coming. It may take you by surprise, but it should never catch you with your panties around your ankles. Once he's actually got you into bed, it's too late to wish that you had taught yourself to stimulate his nipples and manipulate his penis (and *what* was that I read about testicles being like small, sensitive eggs?).

It's a question of preparing yourself, in every possible way. I'm not just talking about using condoms to protect yourself against pregnancy and sexually transmitted diseases—which of course are an absolute must if you intend to sleep with a man for the first time. I'm talking about preparing yourself physically and mentally for lovemaking, so that you are skilful, confident, and exciting in bed, and so that you bring out the very best in the men who are making love to you.

These days, we consider it essential to eat sensibly and exercise and keep ourselves groomed. These are prerequisites for a healthy, happy, energetic life. We practice at tennis, we practice at golf. We wouldn't think of trying to bake a strawberry pavlova without making sure that we knew how to do it. Yet we don't train ourselves in any way for sex, which, apart from being technically more difficult than playing golf or baking a strawberry pavlova, has far-reaching implications for our future well-being. If you drive into the rough or your pavlova doesn't rise, well, it's irritating but it's not life-shattering. Whereas a relationship that breaks down because of sexual difficulties can affect you forever. I'm speaking from personal experience because one night with my wife, nearly 30 years ago, turned my entire life upside-down.

We all know that first encounters can be really wild, and no matter what cautionary advice people give you about it, you're probably going to go ahead and do it anyhow. But if you know how to handle yourself (and him) you'll have a very much wilder time, believe me. *And* you'll also have the ability to develop that first encounter, if you want to, into a really full and satisfying relationship.

So how can you acquire all of this skill and all of this knowledge?

There are dozens of "how-to" sex books, from the frivolous to the medical, and you can learn a whole lot from any of these. There are plenty of instructive videos, some of them nothing more than thinly disguised pornography, but some are highly educational. And there's nothing wrong with pornography, whether it's thinly disguised or not. You can learn a great deal from some of the classic porno movies such as *Deep Throat* and *Debbie Does Dallas.*

But very few books or videos give you any real idea of what a man is looking for on the very first night that he makes love to you. And none of them gives you an insight into what a man finds attractive about you and what you can do to really turn him on. There was a time, not so long ago, when a woman could capture a man's attention if she obviously wasn't wearing a bra. These days, several sex writers have caught on to the fact that if you tell the new man in your life that you're not wearing panties tonight, he'll be understandably excited. But times change. Carla, 27, a travel agent from San Francisco, California, told me that "[the line] which really makes the guys sit up and pay attention [is] I'm thinking of having rings in my nipples. What do you think?" The reply, she said, is always the same. "They make a strangled noise and their tongue drops to the floor." If you don't want to be *quite* so upfront, however, you can always ask the guy you've got your eye on if he has a tattoo. Even if he doesn't, you can tell him about yours: that sweet little bluebird, and wouldn't he like to know where it is? I promise you, he won't leave you alone all evening.

The way to catch a man's attention and hold it is to make him feel that you're sexually daring—to scare him a little. That will make him feel that he has to be very good in bed to satisfy you, and that will make him work extra hard to please you. You should always have the upper hand, right from the beginning of your new relationship, even if you don't show it. There may be times when you want him to take control of your lovemaking, when *you* want to be dominated, but this should always happen under your own terms.

Greta, 31, a beauty consultant from Philadelphia, Pennsylvania, told me that she was sexually excited by dominant men. "The trouble is, men aren't naturally dominant these days. They always feel that they have to be polite and politically correct, even in bed. You have to go a long way to find a caveman who's going to drag you off by your hair and fuck you in his cave. But sometimes you feel like having sex like that. It's a woman thing. It's nothing to do with rape. It's all to do with being *taken*."

But when you first meet a new man, you can make him *feel* dominant and *act* dominant with the come-on lines you use. As I've said before, every sexual encounter is different, and as amusing as it is to make lists, they can only be used as rough guidelines to the kind of things that you ought to be saying to attract the men you want. Here is a list, though, of the 10 most effective things you can say to a man if you want to attract his sexual attention. Forget about the female equivalent of those corny lines like, "Did it hurt?" "Did what hurt?" "When you fell from heaven." You need to arouse his most basic male instincts, such as protectiveness, lust, and self-

interest; and you need to initiate an ongoing conversation. The trouble with most come-on lines
is that they don't lead to anything else. Lines
such as the one I mentioned usually elicit nothing more than embarrassed laughter or a blank
stare.

Remember that in spite of any apparent
bravado, the men you meet are likely to be just
as nervous and reticent as you are, and that's
why I always place so much emphasis on *guidance*. Guide him into a conversation, and then
guide it the way you want it to go—into greater
flirtation and greater intimacy—then guide him
(if you still like him) into bed with you.

The Top Ten Come-On Lines
(And How To Follow Them Up)

These lines have all been tried and tested in the
field, and while some of my women researchers
argued about the sequence in which we have finally arranged them, all of them agreed that they
were much more effective than the usual lines
that they had been trying on men.

1. *You look like you know about sports cars.* Even
   if he says "not a thing," you can still pursue your line. *I'm thinking of buying a new
   sports car and I was wondering if a Porsche*

would suit me. Then allow him to pontificate on the comparative merits of various sports cars. *Do you think it would be asking too much for you to come take a look at some cars with me?* Suggest a time and a date and arrange to meet him at a Porsche dealer, where he can sit in all of the cars and look under the hood and discuss turbochargers. Don't forget to stand very close to him, and when he's talking to the dealer, look up at him as if you're seriously impressed by his automotive knowledge. The dealer may even take you out for a test drive, when you can suggest that *he* drive, to show you what the car can do. I don't expect you to have the money for a Porsche. All you have to do is tell the dealer that you'll think it over, and afterward, over drinks or lunch, flatter your new man friend by saying that you loved the way he handled the Porsche, but it's much too powerful for you. You've guided him into a situation where he believes that he's dominant, and that you're relying on his masculine expertise and protectiveness, whereas in fact you've simply manipulated him into coming out on your first date.

2. *Which gym do you go to?* Not "do you go to a gym?" or "I'll bet you go to a gym."

The secret is to pay compliments *indirectly.* If you're asking him which gym he goes to, it's obvious that you think he looks physically toned-up and attractive. *My gym's closing down and I don't know where to go.* The chances are very high that he'll invite you to come along to his gym. If he says he doesn't go to a gym, but that he simply jogs: *I stopped jogging because I couldn't find anyplace nice to jog.* He will then tell you where *he* jogs, and if he's so impervious to your come-on line that he doesn't ask you to come jogging with him, ask him if he would mind if you tagged along, to see what it's like. Your first date may be pounding the sidewalks, but after the jogging there are always showers, and breakfast together, and after breakfast— who knows?

3. *Do you think these porcini mushrooms are good for linguine?* This is your supermarket come-on line. A man shopping on his own with a single basket is highly likely to be unattached. But make sure you check first what kind of items the man is carrying in his basket. It's no good asking a man about prosciutto and fresh tuna if he's buying fish sticks and cans of Spam. *I have some old school friends coming for lunch on the weekend and I'm trying to cook them some-*

thing really impressive. What's your favorite Italian food? Whatever he says, pretend that you've never cooked it before, or never cooked it really well, even if it's only spaghetti bolognese. *Do you have a secret for great spaghetti bolognese? Do you think you could let me have your recipe? I really want to make this lunch into something special.* You arrange to meet him to give you the recipe, and if he checks out okay, you suggest that he come over Friday evening to try a sample batch. And if it's really good, which I'm sure it will be, your relationship can start to develop from there. He feels he's given you some good advice, and in return you've fed him well.

4. *I couldn't help noticing your hands.* "Why?" he'll ask you. "What about my hands?" *They're a very interesting shape. Do you see how your index finger is exactly the same length as your ring finger?* "No, I never noticed that before. What does that mean?" *Well, my grandmother used to be able to tell people's personalities from the length of their fingers. She wasn't a palm reader . . . she didn't believe in any of that. But if your index finger and your ring finger are exactly the same length, it means that you're very well balanced and reliable, but it also means that you're always having to take the responsibil-*

ity for other people's mistakes. "Oh, yeah?"—
and this is the moment when you take
hold of his hand and lay it in the palm of
your hand, and there are few better ways
of making instant physical contact with a
strange man than this. *This long middle finger means that you're very passionate about
everything in your life, but that you don't like
to show it.* And so on, and so forth. You
can play this line for all it's worth, because
you're not directly complimenting the guy,
you're simply saying gosh, look at what
your hand tells me. You finish up by sug-
gesting that he ought to have a deeper,
more detailed reading, because he could
change his whole life around if he did.
Just see if he can resist it—because, after
all, you'll be talking all about *him*, and
men's favorite subject is always themselves.

5. *Can I ask you something? If some wealthy
woman you didn't really like very much offered you a weekend skiing in Aspen, would
you go?* This is always good: asking him
to make a moral judgment. But this particular conundrum is subtly loaded, because it suggests that you've been offered
a free weekend away by a wealthy man
you don't like, and you're asking him to
rescue you. *It's my boss. My friends all say*

that I'd be crazy not to go . . . but I don't know.
"You shouldn't go if you don't like the
guy. What's the point on going away for
the weekend with somebody you don't
like?" *That's what I think. So long as you're
with somebody you like, it doesn't matter
where you go. And the trouble is, he's going
to expect me to be so grateful that he'll want
to get me into his bed.* "You can't do that!"
He'll be growing indignant by now, especially if he likes you. "Say you can't go."
You'll be able to improvise nicely from
here, because you'll have stirred up his
protective instincts. *But he's been pestering
me for so long . . . and he knows that I'm not
doing anything this weekend.* "Maybe you
are. Maybe you're going someplace with
me. That'll show him." This come-on line
was actually used by 26-year-old Rhoda,
who works for an electronics company in
Silicon Valley, and she said that it worked
so quickly that "it practically took my
breath away . . . if there's one thing a man
doesn't want to see, it's an attractive
woman falling into the clutches of another
man."

6. *I've forgotten my glasses . . . you couldn't read
this menu for me, could you*? You don't even
have to be near-sighted to try this come-
on line. If your relationship develops into

something special, it's very doubtful that
he'll ever notice that you never wear
glasses. Having a man read a menu for
you is a surprisingly sensual experience,
especially since you can stare at him ad-
miringly while he's doing it, and let out
one or two "mms" of anticipation when
he reads out something especially tasty.
You ought to be quite sexily dressed for
this one, in a low-cut dress or short skirt.
Many men find the combination of a really
sexy look with some sort of minor hand-
icap, like poor eyesight or deafness, to be
extremely erotic. It gives them a prime opportunity to be protective and dominant—
so they think, anyhow—and to keep other
men at bay. You can try the same come-
on line at the theater or the airport or the
bus station, wherever there are programs
and flight announcements and travel
schedules in very small print.

7. *I'm doing a survey of all the kinds of things
that men like most about women, and you look
like somebody who could help me.* "What's it
for?" *It's for a national database that is going
to help everybody from cosmetics companies to
serious psychiatrists. Any contribution would
be really valuable.* And don't pause here!
*For instance, what was the first thing you no-
ticed about me? Was it my hair? My eyes?*

My lips? My dress? You can get very intimate very quickly with this come-on
line, especially if you behave in a cool,
professional-sounding way. You can actually get him to tell you how much he likes
the look of you, without actually begging
for compliments. *Do you like smaller women
or fuller-figured women? Do you like breasts
bigger than mine or smaller than mine?* The
answer to this question is always electri-
fying. Then you can suggest that maybe
you and he could get together and talk
things through in a little more detail. And
then you can take it from there. . . .

8. *I'm so sorry, I couldn't help noticing your after
   shave. It's gorgeous. I've been trying to buy
   to present for my favorite uncle, and he'd love
   a fragrance like that. Well, actually, he's a real
   individual, very young for his age, a little wild,
   and that is exactly the smell that would suit
   him.* Again, flattery by innuendo, rather
   than directly. You're a charismatic guy, just
   like my wacky uncle, whether my wacky
   uncle really exists or not.

9. *My friends over there bet me I wouldn't dare
   to come up to you and buy you a drink. But
   I decided it was worth the risk.* With any luck,
   he will collaborate with you, so that you
   can win the bet.

10. *You're Harve Roberts, aren't you?* Having previously taken the trouble to find out his name. *One of my friends was talking to me about you.* "Oh, yes? What did she say?" *Well, that would be telling tales, wouldn't it?* "Oh come on, who was it? What did they say?" You see how interested men are in themselves, and what other people think of them? *It wasn't anything. It was all good, anyhow. It was really all good. I swear it.* "So what did she say? Come on, tell me. I'm going to find out sooner or later." *I can't tell you. But she said you were very big in whatever it is you do.* "Big?" And that's when you give the quickest glance down to his pants, and then up again, and then smile, and then say, *Well, I guess some women have all the luck.* Start to walk away, but I'll bet you that he'll call you back. This is what I call a bantering come-on, where you tease the man and make him do most of the running. It's riskier, but it depends on the situation where you meet. In a crowded bar, or the back room of a house party, it can work very, very well. Natalie, 28, who works for an online media company in Los Angeles, California, said, "I'm a strong person, so when I see a good-looking man I'm not going to pussyfoot around. I like to tease him and

flirt with him, but I also know that I have to bolster his ego, make him feel confident and virile. I see a whole lot of women who put men down. A lot of the time, they don't mean to. They like the guy but they don't want to show it, so they go to the opposite extreme and start being rude to him. In the end they never get anyplace at all, because in reality they're scared of starting a new relationship and they scare off any potential lovers, too. A man likes to feel good with a woman, comfortable, as if he's controlling the whole scene. It doesn't matter if he really *is* controlling it. That's not the point. The whole point of coming on to a man is to make him feel encouraged."

Another incredibly important point to re-member—and you'd be amazed how many women forget to do this—is to *smile*. Smile with your lips and smile with your eyes. One smile is worth a thousand come-on lines, no matter how ingenious they are. You can practice your sexy smiling in the mirror at home, whenever you don't have anything better to do. Pout and look vampish. Try to put yourself into the mind of a man who's just met you. Is he going to find you an attractive woman to be with? Is he going to think that you're seductive?

Once you've found and flirted with your new lover-to-be, what next? How do you progress from light conversation to making love? This is where all of your self-control comes into play, even if you may feel like throwing caution (and your panties) to the wind. You can be as forward and wanton and sexually creative as you like, even on your first date, but the most important point to remember is that you're in charge of yourself, you're in charge of your own body and your own destiny. You need to make your first night as hot and feverish as possible: a night that he'll never forget.

When he gets around to inviting you back to his apartment, house, or hotel room, you should show pleasure in your eyes. You know how to look pleased, don't you? But say nothing, and ask him for a last drink before you go. Take your time over that last drink, too, so that you build up his anticipation. Be warm and affectionate, but whatever you do, don't rush. You may be aching to feel his cock inside you, but don't show it, not yet.

You can be forward and wanton by the way you talk to him, by the way you hold his gaze with your eyes. (How many times have I mentioned eye contact so far? It's *essential* to show him all the time that you're interested in him.) You can be forward and wanton by touching him, by putting your hand on his knee, by sitting with your legs crossed so that your skirt rides high. You can give him little downward flutters of your eyelashes, you can lick your lips with the tip of your tongue. Yes, you can be as cornily flirtatious as you like. But most important of all, you should make sure you *shine*, sexually—that you show him by your enthusiasm and your brightness that you're all woman, which is what you are, right?

Take that shining back to his apartment with you (or wherever you go). He should feel that he's brought back a prize. And certainly don't stop showing an interest in him—in who he is, what his tastes are, where he likes to eat, where he goes on vacation. You don't need to get too personal, not on your first date, but it's worth finding out if he shares the same kind of interests as you do, and if he's the kind of man you might like to spend a little more time with.

Different woman have different approaches to going to bed with a man for the very first time. Kathleen, 24, an interior decorator from Charleston, South Carolina, said, "If I manage to fix a date with a guy that I really have the hots for, then I'm afraid that there's no stopping me. I don't believe in all of this stuff about waiting until your third or fourth date before having sex with a guy. What's the use of going out to dinner with a guy three or four times and then discovering that you don't get on very well in bed? What do you do then? Say 'goodbye, it's been nice'? If you got on well before you had sex, you're going to lose a friend as well as a lover."

Kathleen had some ingenious ideas for making a first night unforgettable. "You want to catch the guy's attention, right? You want to make him think that he's discovered a woman who's something really special. The more handsome a hunk he is, the more you have to make yourself really individual, because a handsome hunk is going to have had plenty of women before you, and you want to make yourself stand out in the crowd, so to speak.

"I've always liked John. He runs his own specialist joinery company, and I first met him because we use him to make custom-built closets and fireplace surrounds for our customers' homes. He's very bright, very well educated, but he's brilliant with his hands, too. A natural carpenter. The second I saw him I thought, *wow, I have to get to know this man.* He has short blond hair, and glasses, and the bluest eyes you ever saw. He's always lightly tanned, because he likes to sail, and his arms have all these gorgeous golden hairs on them. And he always has this great *smell* about him, like fragrant wood.

"I met him at a house that we were remodeling in the Charleston Heights area. I made a point of taking a taxi there, instead of driving my own car. There were just the two of us there, as well as the client, of course. When we'd finished running through the specifics, and said goodbye to the client, I asked him if he could give me a ride back to the city, because my car was in the shop. That gave me a good ten minutes to get to know him a little better, and try to work some of my magic on him.

"He started to talk about the job, but then I said, 'Do you think that working with wood— you know, molding things, shaping things—do you think that makes you a better lover?' He looked at me surprised, and he laughed, but I'd introduced the idea into his head that sex would be possible with me, if he happened to be interested. He said, 'I don't know . . . I don't think a man is qualified to judge his own performance, do you?' So I smiled and said, 'Maybe you're right. Maybe you need somebody else to judge it.'

"It was almost twelve. He said, 'I'm real hungry. I didn't have time for breakfast today. How about some lunch?' So we had lunch together, crab salads and a couple of glasses of wine, even though I never usually drink wine at lunchtime, and I suspected that he didn't either. Without saying a word, we both knew that I wasn't going to be spending the afternoon matching color swatches and he wasn't going to be carving any oak.

"We talked so much, I couldn't believe it. He told me all about his business, and his family, and how much you could learn from handling natural materials. We didn't say anything particularly sexual, but because I'd already shown that I was interested, we didn't have to. All I had to do was look into his eyes and give him my famous flirtatious look from under my eyelashes.

"After the meal, he said, 'Listen, I live just around here. I have to pick up some tools for this afternoon, do you want to come around and see my apartment?' I said, 'You have to pick up some *tools*?' And we both collapsed laughing. There is nothing sexier to my mind than laughter. It brings you so close together.

"We drove around to his apartment. It was lovely, in a beautiful old historic building, on the top floor, with sun shining in. There were polished wooden floors, wonderful furniture, and old paintings of Fort Sumter and ships and Indian canoes and stuff. I didn't wait. I didn't want to wait. I took hold of John's hand and led him through into the bedroom. It was all white-painted, with an enormous bed with white covers on it. He took me in his arms and kissed me, and that was the very first kiss, and it went right down to the soles of my feet, believe me. And his woodwork *did* make him a better lover. His hands were so strong and controlled.

"I unbuttoned his shirt. He's very lean and muscular, and he was wearing this spotless white tee over his suntanned skin. We kissed some more, and he unbuttoned my dress, all the way down. He cupped his hands over my breasts, and then he unfastened my bra. My hair's very dark but I have very pale skin, which is why John was amazed that my nipples were so red. He said they looked like ripe strawberries. I unbuckled his belt and tugged his Dockers down. Underneath his white boxer shorts, his cock was sticking up like a hammer-handle. I gripped it quite firmly through his pants and said, 'Is this one of the tools you have to pick up?' I kept my grip on his cock while he kissed me again, and fondled my breasts. He had a really arousing way of rubbing my nipples in between his finger and thumb, and very slightly pulling them at the same time. And I knew he liked the way I was holding his cock. I don't think many women realize that men like having their cocks held hard. They hold them really hard themselves, when they jerk off. They enjoy tickling and teasing, too, but not when they feel like an urgent fuck.

"He stepped out of his Dockers and I pulled down his shorts. His cock was magnificent, fully hard, with a gorgeous plum-colored head, and big tight balls. His hole was already wet with juice, and I can't tell you how wet *I* was!

"I slipped off my own panties. They were cream-colored silk, with a lace edging. I wrapped them around his cock and slowly started to masturbate him with them. The silk acted as sort of a lubricant, so I could grip his cock really hard, and give him deep, forceful downstrokes. All the time I said, 'I'll bet you've been dying to come in my panties, ever since you first saw me.'

"Then I slid my panties down and wrapped them around his balls, and I massaged his balls through the silk. This always turns men on so much. But it turns me on, too, because it gives me the chance to feel them and fondle them and get myself hot before they start fucking me. I love foreplay, all that sexy messing around before you finally get down to it, but men always want to get right down to it. So the best way to slow them up is to start the foreplay yourself. No good lying there, and then complaining that he didn't stroke your breasts or kiss your kneecaps. You can slow things down for yourself, so long as you've got the self-control.

"I lay back on the bed, still massaging his balls, and he climbed on top of me. He was so turned on he was dripping his love juice onto my stomach. Then I dropped my panties, and put his arms around him, and kissed him. And when he slipped his tongue into my mouth, I bit the end of it, not too hard, not to hurt him too much, but hard enough so that he couldn't take his tongue out.

"I only did it for a moment, but it's a good tease. And it does hurt a little, so there's a touch of S&M in it, and a touch of 'who's the boss around here?' if you know what I mean.

"He kissed my neck and my breasts. He was a very good, slow lover, who wanted to relish everything. I have quite big breasts, and he cupped each of them in both hands and licked my nipples until they were so stiff that I thought they were going to pop. He bit them, too—not as hard as I'd bitten his tongue—but it was a little reminder that S&M can work both ways.

"I did something then that always stuns men, the very first time that they make love to you. Usually, they expect to stroke your outside thighs and then work their way around your knees and up your inner thighs until they finally reach what they're looking for. But I opened my legs as wide as I could—almost doing a split—and I opened up the lips of my pussy with my fingers, stretched them open, so that John could see right up inside me, and how wet I was, and how much I wanted him.

"I took hold of his cock and guided it in between my legs, and there we were: big purple cock and bright pink pussy-lips, all shining with our own desire for each other. And we paused, and I gently stroked the back of his neck with my fingernails, and said, 'Is this what you really want?' All he did was smile—the same way he smiled when I asked him whether working with wood made him a better lover—and he sank himself into me, and I could see him sinking inside me, inch by inch, until his blond pubic hair was touching my pussy, and all I could feel was this huge hard cock filling me up. He made my eyes water.

"He started to push himself in and out of me really hard, really quick. But I reached around and gripped the cheeks of his ass, and dug my fingernails right into them, and started another rhythm of my own, slowly, holding his ass when he was right up inside me, and only letting him pull out of me when I was ready. I stuck my fingernail into his asshole, too. It's sharp, and it hurts a little bit, but I've never met the man who doesn't like it. And when you really start getting serious, you can cram two or three fingers up his asshole and really give him hell. He may feel sore afterward, but you'll give him the climax of his life.

"Anyhow, I slowed John down, and we carried on this gentle, rhythmic fucking, with the sun shining on us, and the traffic noises down in the street outside, and the wind chimes jingling. I could just see myself in the gilt-framed mirror on the other side of the bedroom, my legs spread wide apart, and John on top of me, with my fingers cradling his balls.

"We fucked harder and faster, and at last John climaxed. His cock went into spasm and I could almost feel his sperm shooting up inside of me. He lay back on the bed, panting, and I lay beside him and played with his half-hard cock for a while. Then I took it into my mouth and sucked out the last of his sperm, sucking quite hard, because I knew that he was going to be feeling very sensitive, just about then. I licked his balls and I even poked the tip of my tongue into his asshole.

"He thought it was all over, but it wasn't. Men often tell girls that they have to have a climax at least three times a week or else it's going to affect their health. Well, I needed an orgasm right then and there, and it was John who was going to give it to me.

"I sat astride his face, with my legs pinning his shoulders down on the bed. I said, 'If you were a carpenter, and I was a lady, would you love me anyway?'

"I reached down with my fingers and opened my pussy right in front of him. It was full of his sperm and some of it dripped down onto his chin. But he lifted his head and stuck out his tongue and he licked my spermy clitoris, and then he licked all around my lips, and pushed his tongue into my pussy-hole. Then he began to understand what I wanted from him, sexually. No holds barred. No *holes* barred, either. He slipped his finger into my pussy, until it was all wet and juicy with a combination of his sperm and my juice, and then he pushed it up my asshole, no warning, but it was so slippery that it didn't hurt me. In fact, it was ecstasy itself.

"Then he started to lick my clitoris again, much more intensely this time, and I knew that I wasn't going to be able to hold out much longer. My muscles began to twitch and that feeling started to rise up inside me, so all I could do was cling onto the headboard and see where the roller coaster would take me. John's chin was dripping. He was licking my pussy and all of his own sperm as well. And at the same time his finger was working inside my asshole ... I can't tell you what kind of a feeling *that* gave me. Like my whole insides were tender and tingling.

"I had an orgasm so intense that I think I almost shook the whole bed apart. I tried to lift myself off John, but he said, 'No,' and held my thighs, and licked and sucked my pussy like a man who hasn't had a drink for weeks. When he was finished, he said, 'Nothing is ever going to taste as good as that again. Me and you, mixed together.'

"I was lying close beside him, with my hair spread across his shoulder. I said, 'Who said it isn't? We could do this again tomorrow if you like. I'd hate to think it was a one-lunch-hour stand.' He smiled again, and said, 'I guess.' But I went across to my pocketbook, where I'd left it when I came in, and I took out a red ribbon. I tied it around his balls, and said, 'That's to remind you, the same way we used to tie a knot in a handkerchief, when we were kids. When you take off your pants tonight, and look in the mirror, you'll know who wants you.'

"He opened another bottle of white wine, and we sat out on his balcony, naked, and talked. The sun was warm and I guess you could say that I felt pretty much at peace with the world. John kept his red ribbon around his balls and I guess the idea of it must have turned him on because his cock kept getting stiff. In the end, we couldn't stand it any longer and we went back inside and made love again—furiously this time. Good hard fucking. We ended up sweaty and gasping for breath but we were holding each other tight. He stroked my hair and said, 'Do you know something? You've really made me understand what I've been missing. It's not sex. It's a sexual relationship. It's a woman who thinks for herself.'

"I don't know how long my affair with John is going to last. He still has plenty of pretty young women around him, not to mention wealthy and sex-starved older women. But every time we make love, I always try to think of something special to excite him . . . something to remember me by, until the next time. It can be as simple as leaving my panties tangled up in his bedclothes, so that he finds them after I've gone. Or leaving him a little card with a sketch in it of me fellating him, saying 'Mmh! Hmh! Guess what I forgot to do! Next time, okay?'

"I know I'm very forward, but whatever they say, men like forward. They're all shy underneath. Not weak, but afraid of making mistakes. And they all think that women are the stronger sex. Why do you think men ever beat up on women? Because they're afraid of them. You don't beat up on people you're not afraid of. Women are strong, yes. I'm strong, and I'm not ashamed of making the first move with a man. But I know when he needs to believe that he's in charge, and that's when I back off. You can do anything you like with a man, but never belittle him."

Women are endlessly inventive when it comes to making an impression on their new lovers. Janie, 23, a costume designer from Chicago, Illinois, impressed Paul, 24, an architect trainee, when he came around to her apartment. "I knew Paul for over six months before anything happened between us and although I could tell that he liked me—like he didn't think I was a total dog or anything—he never did anything but

wave and say hi and chat about design. I'm not
very good with conversation or come-on lines
or anything like that, and I couldn't find any
way to tell him what I felt. Like, he's so cute.
He's tall, with this floppy hairstyle, and this
smile that could melt your heart. So one weekend I simply invited him back to my place. I
said I had pizza and some great new CDs and
all my friends were out of town, and would he
like to come over, that's all.

"I wore a short, short skirt and a little crop
top, and bare feet. I knew he liked the way I
looked as soon as I opened the door. Anyhow,
I didn't come on to him right away. We sat
around and played music and drank wine and
I heated up a pizza for us. I asked him what
music he liked and what he liked to do on weekends, stuff like that. I never ask boys about their
families. I like to show them that I'm interested
in *them*, that's all—not where their folks live or
what their sister's doing in college. Paul started
to talk about his work and there was obviously
something upsetting him. One of his designs had
been trashed by one of the senior partners and
he was very sore about it. So I asked him to
draw it for me on a big sheet of paper. He really
lit up while he was doing it, and I really listened, and tried to understand what he was talking about, because this was his big passion. If
you take a real interest in a man's big passion,

then you'll soon become part of his big passion, too.

"He said to me, 'You're the first person I've really been able to talk to.' I said, 'That's because I like you and I can see that you're really committed.' He said, 'I like you, too.' And he took me in his arms and kissed me, right in the middle of the kitchen, and I couldn't even put my arms around him, because I had a glass of wine in one hand and a slice of pizza in another.

"We kissed again and again. It was like we were both suddenly hungry for each other. I put down the wine and dropped the pizza on the floor and we were practically eating each other alive. He slid his hands under my top and caressed my nipples and it was such an incredible feeling. I could feel how hard he was, right through his corduroy pants.

"I wanted to go to bed with him right there and then, but I'd made up my mind that I was going to make an impression on him—one that he'd never forget. Even if he went to bed with a hundred other girls after he'd been to bed with me, I wanted him to remember this evening forever. So I asked him to open another bottle of wine, while I went into the bedroom and showed him what *my* big passion was.

"He wasn't long, but it didn't take me long to get myself ready. When he walked into the bedroom I was wearing nothing but long white lace gloves, long white lace stockings, and a white lace G-string. I said, 'My big passion is costume design, and this is my design for a virgin on her first night in a house of ill-repute.'

"We both laughed, but Paul was so turned on. He came over and held me and kissed me, and then he started to pull his own shirt off. He squeezed and fondled my breasts while I unbuckled his belt. I reached down into his open pants and rubbed the flat of my hand against his cock. He was so big and hard I couldn't believe it. I pulled his pants down further, and took his cock right out. All the time he was kissing me as if he wanted to swallow me alive— that's if I didn't swallow him first!

"I slid his cock underneath the elastic of my G-string until it was up against my pussy. Then I slowly rolled it from side to side, so that he could feel my pubic hair and my wet pussy lips. He actually groaned, and said, 'Oh God, I want to fuck you.' I lay back on the bed and he climbed on top of me. He started to pull down my G-string but I said, 'No, you don't have to do that.' I opened my hand and showed him that I was holding a small pair of nail-scissors. All he had to do was cut the elastic, and my pussy was completely exposed.

"I think my gloves and stockings really turned him on, too. He fucked me quickly the first time. He thrust his cock so deep inside me that I could feel him touching the neck of my womb, which always gives me these weird, sexy shivers. His balls thumped against my bottom, and every inch of him was tense and tight. He climaxed in less than five minutes. But he didn't leave it there. He lay beside me and started to caress and fondle me, touching my face, touching my lips, touching my neck, touching my nipples. He ran his hand across my stomach and slid his fingers down inside my stocking-tops. Then he began to play with my pussy, gently stroking my clitoris, gently tugging at my pussy lips, and slipping his finger up inside me. One finger, then two fingers, then three, gradually stretching my hole wider and wider.

"He was so tender, and yet he gradually opened my pussy up like a flower, holding my lips wide apart. He leaned over my pussy and started to lick my clitoris, incredibly gently, almost *too* gently. I looked down and I could see the tip of his tongue barely flicking at it. But my orgasm caught me by surprise. Usually I can feel it slowly rising up, until it finally washes all over me, but with Paul it came like a sudden spasm, almost as if I'd been electrocuted. One spasm followed another, and then another, and then another, and Paul gripped my thighs to keep me still and kept on licking me and licking me and then I had the orgasm to end all orgasms. It was like a nuclear bomb going off in my body.

"I thought I couldn't take any more, but as soon as my orgasm was over, he climbed on top of me again and his cock was just as hard as it was before. He pushed it into me much more gently this time, and it felt beautiful. I was so juicy inside that it simply *slid* in, right up to the balls. I reached down and played with his balls while he leaned forward and kissed me and breathed silly little things in my ear. He was slow this time. He drew his cock almost all the way out and rubbed it against the entrance to my pussy. Then he worked it back in, pressing it against the sides, with all kinds of different motions. I tightened my muscles with every stroke he made, so that he could really feel it, and it wasn't long before I could tell that he was getting close to another climax. The only thing was, *I* was, too! Every time I tightened my muscles, I could really feel his cock up inside me, and this feeling was beginning to grow, deep between my legs, until I knew that I wouldn't be able to stop myself from coming.

"We came almost together. Paul came first, and then me, and my pussy contracted so much that I almost squeezed his slippery cock right out of me.

"I didn't stop there, though. As he lay back on the bed, I knelt between his legs and gave his cock and his balls a long, slow, lascivious wash with my tongue, gently sucking his soft cock to make sure there wasn't any come left behind. I almost managed to make him hard again!"

Many other women have told me that their new lovers were very aroused by only partial undressing, rather like Janie with her gloves and her stockings. Margot, a 34-year-old executive at a utilities company, said that the first time she made love to her husband-to-be, she was wearing thigh-length woolly stockings and a thick red turtleneck sweater. "It still turns him on to see me dressed like that. He said that fumbling with my bare breasts inside my sweater was one of the most erotic sensations he could remember." Other women have made love in fur coats, evening gowns, and even wet-suits. Carmen, 28, a teacher from Kansas City, Missouri, said, "Men are always aroused by body suits. They love unfastening the studs between your legs, which leaves your cunt completely exposed. I think it turns them on more than total nudity."

We'll look in more detail at ways to make a stunning sexual impression on your first night with your new lover, and also at ways in which you can make sure that he'll want to come back for more. But right now let's go back and see what you can do to prepare yourself for lovemaking *before* you meet that man of your erotic dreams.

2

Is There Sex Before Sex?

If you were fairly confident that you were going to be invited to join some friends for a wonderful vacation in the Caribbean later this year, but your swimming was only up to dog paddle standard, you'd probably make some effort to improve your style, right? Take a few lessons, get in a few hours of practice at your local pool.

You can be fairly confident that sometime very soon, you're going to meet a man who wants to make love to you. So what are you doing about getting into sexual shape? Probably nothing, apart from keeping reasonably fit and eating your muesli like a good girl. But have you been exercising yourself sexually, both body and mind, so that when that unexpected moment arrives and he carries you into the bedroom, you know what you want and how to get it—and, equally important, you know what *he* wants and how to give it to him?

Maybe you're a virgin and you've never had sex with a man before. Maybe you're between boyfriends, or divorced. Maybe you've gone off men for a while. It doesn't matter what your circumstances are, you should always make sure that you're prepared for a sexual encounter— and that means a whole lot more than carrying strawberry-flavored condoms in your purse.

Kathy, 18, a student from Omaha, Nebraska, said, "The first time I had sex with a boy it was a disaster. I'd been to all of the biology classes, I knew how men got erections. I have an older brother, so men weren't exactly a mystery to me. I knew about clitorises and orgasms. I knew about oral sex, too. But I didn't have any idea of how to handle the whole scenario, if you can understand what I'm talking about. I didn't know whether sex was supposed to go on and on for hours, or if it was all supposed to be over as quickly as possible. I didn't know what men expected of me. Was I supposed to thrash around and scream 'yes! yes! yes!' like some of those women in the movies?

"I knew that women take longer than men to get aroused, but how was I going to get aroused enough if a man just wanted a quick one? And what could I do if I didn't have an orgasm? Was it something to worry about, or what? And what if the man asked me if I'd had an orgasm, when I hadn't? What was I supposed to say?"

Kathy's uncertainties were almost endless, and while many of them will eventually be resolved by plain old-fashioned experience, they are shared by millions of women of all ages and sexual situations. Thankfully, the days are gone when women used to write to me and tell me with inconsolable bitterness that after 30 years of marriage they have only just discovered that they are capable of having orgasms. But all the same, Kathy's first sexual encounter was ruined by her lack of confidence.

"I guess the trouble is that I'm naturally shy. So I was amazed when this hunky guy Brad suddenly came up to me in the corridor at school and asked if I wanted to go out with him. I mean, all the girls swooned over him. Of course I said yes, and he picked me up after school and took me to this country-and-western place where they serve hamburgers and ribs and stuff. I don't usually like country-and-western, but if Brad had taken me I think I would have liked Tibetan gong music. He was great company, funny and interesting, and he always made you feel that he really wanted to know what you thought about things.

"We stopped in the car on the way home, down by the lake. Sounds corny, doesn't it? But he just put his arms around me and kissed me and oh, boy, his kisses felt like ten thousand volts. I'd kissed boys before, of course, but now

I felt like I was kissing a man. I knew then and there that I was going to have sex with him, that I *needed* to have sex with him. I couldn't help myself.

"He took a blanket out of the trunk and laid it on the grass. It was a beautiful warm night, all of the stars were out. You couldn't have had a more romantic setting for losing your virginity. Brad wasn't rough, but I think he wanted to have sex as urgently as I did. He unbuttoned my blouse and felt my breasts through my bra. All of the time he was kissing me and sliding his tongue into my mouth. He unfastened my bra and then he was touching my bare breasts, rolling my nipples between his fingers. I thought I ought to unbutton his shirt, too, so I did, and ran my hands over his chest. I touched his nipples, too, and they were as hard and nubbly as mine.

"He unbuttoned my skirt and pulled down the zipper at the back, but I didn't want him to go any further than that. I was very wet between my legs, because I was so turned on, and I didn't want him to find a damp patch on my panties. I didn't realize that he wouldn't have minded at all, in fact, it would have excited him even more. Anyhow, I took off my own skirt and quickly stepped out of my panties, but even then I didn't really want him to touch me between my legs because I was so embarrassed that I was wet.

"I think Brad was expecting me to take off his pants, but again I didn't really know what to do, so I put my arms around his neck and kissed him and that was all, and he had to take his own pants off. Once he was naked, I could feel his stiff cock up against my thigh. It was very exciting but it was frightening, too. I didn't know if I was supposed to touch it or not, or if I did, *how*. So I didn't, and in retrospect I guess he must have found that very frustrating. He laid me down on the blanket and he kissed my lips, and my neck, and my breasts. I felt like I was in heaven, I really did.

"He knelt astride my chest, and put his cock between my breasts and squeezed them together. I looked down and all I could see was this purple cock-head rearing out of my cleavage . . . and he was wet, too. He knelt up a little higher, so that his cock was right over my face. I seriously didn't know what he expected me to do. I knew about oral sex, but was this the right moment? And what if I did it wrong? I gave his cock a couple of quick kisses and I felt very daring and dirty and sophisticated. He stayed there for a while, holding his cock in his hand, so I gave it another kiss.

"He rubbed his cock against my lips, as if he were putting lip gloss on me, but I still didn't have the nerve to take him into my mouth. So he shifted his way back down the blanket, and opened up my thighs, and put his cock into my pussy.

"This was the moment I had dreamed about and fantasized about, and it should have been perfect. Here I was, lying naked on a blanket on a warm summer night, with a really handsome guy just about to push his huge hard cock inside me, and yet I was so unsure of myself that I froze. I lay there and let him do it. I didn't think about him, and how he felt. I didn't realize that he might be looking for some kind of response. He made love to me very slowly at first, his cock sliding in and out of me really sensually. Sometimes he drew it out completely, so that I just feel the tip of it touching my pussy-lips. Then he slid it back in again, all the way up to his balls, so that I could feel his pubic hair right up against me. It was fantastic, so sensual. But I was afraid to touch him, afraid to show him how much pleasure he was giving me.

"He began to push himself in and out of me faster and faster, and harder and harder. He stopped caring about turning me on, and went for his own climax, like a sprinter. He grunted, and tensed up, and then he took his cock out of me and gave himself three or four rubs with his hand to finish himself off. He shot sperm all over my breasts and my stomach. I remember how warm and wet and slippery it was. Then he wiped his cock against the side of my thigh. I didn't know what to think. I'd never read about men doing *that* before. I simply lay there, covered with his sperm, and looked up at him, and said nothing at all. In the end he got dressed and lit a cigarette and waited for me to get dressed, too.

"He said, 'Why did you bother?' I was feeling very miserable and confused, and when he said that it made me feel even worse. I said, 'I like you.' I didn't tell him that I'd never had sex with anybody else. He said, 'Well, if that's what you do when you like a guy, I'd hate to see what happens when you hate him.'

"Of course I wasn't frigid. And I wasn't sexually ignorant, either. Not of the facts. But I had no experience, that's all, and nobody had ever told me what a man really wants when he takes you to bed, and how to make him feel excited. I lay there on that blanket and let Brad do everything. I didn't even say 'mmm-mmm' when he was sliding his cock in and out of me so slowly. I didn't touch his cock. I didn't play with his balls. I didn't press my breasts together when he put his cock between them. I didn't take his cock into my mouth. In fact, I didn't do anything. I lay there and thought of Omaha, that's all I did. No wonder he thought I was useless in the sack. I was."

What you have to realize is that most men have a very limited understanding of female sexual response and very few have enough knowledge and skill to bring out the best in you. If you don't moan and writhe to their every touch, they'll assume that you're frigid, or that you don't find them sexually arousing. Instead of continuing to stimulate you, they'll concentrate instead on their own satisfaction (as Brad did) and they will probably leave you unfulfilled.

That's why it's important to learn the language of lovemaking, both mental and physical. You may be feeling ecstatic inside, but you have to *communicate* your pleasure. It doesn't matter if you're inexperienced. Your new lover won't mind your awkwardness if you're obviously excited by what he's doing to you. Even if you're not normally a very demonstrative person— even if you think that moaning and gasping during sex is ridiculously theatrical—make sure that your new lover knows without doubt that he's making you happy. He can't feel what you feel. He doesn't know that it gives you the most heavenly feeling in the world when he strokes his penis against your clitoris that particular way. So let him know, either by your sighs of delight or by the way you move your hips, or simply by saying "that gives me the most heavenly feeling in the world."

Your responsiveness will turn *him* on, and

help him to become a better lover, because he will very quickly learn which caresses excite you the most. You'll increase his sexual skill and his personal confidence, and the principal beneficiary will be you. Charlene, 25, a teacher from Orlando, Florida, said, "I did what you suggested and started to make little noises when Trent made love to me, and say things like 'oh . . . that's gorgeous,' or 'mmm . . . that makes me feel so good.' I was kind of embarrassed at first, because I never used to talk or moan when men made love to me. I found that it made me lose my concentration, and it always took longer to reach an orgasm. But when I started to do it with Trent, he loved it, it really made him hot. And because he loved it, it began to excite me, too, until I was saying things completely spontaneously. I started to use dirty words, too, and say things like 'fill my cunt up . . . fuck me harder . . . stick your finger up my asshole . . . I can feel your balls all filled up to bursting. . . .' and this really turned us both on. What was more, we started to do more daring things in bed, because we were using our imagination more. I'd say something like 'I want to lick your balls' or 'I want to jerk you off so that you shoot your come on my tongue,' just to excite him, you understand, just to give him a sexy mental picture. But it excited me, too, because I never talk like that, not normally. And I found myself not only daring to say things like that, but to do them, too. One evening I said, 'I'm going to rub my cunt all over your face.' And Trent said, 'You wouldn't dare.' So I sat astride his face, and I opened up my cunt with my fingers, and smeared his whole face with juice. He loved it, and I loved it, too, because he wouldn't stop licking me while I was doing it."

So Charlene found, as you will, that what can start off as simulated expressions of ecstasy can very quickly turn into real cries of passion. If you can pluck up enough courage to vocalize your sexual feelings, you will find that your new lover is very happy to listen, and to be guided by what you say, even if all you say is "oohh-hhhhhh . . ."

Kathy lay on that blanket and—out of shyness and lack of sexual experience—made no attempt to show her appreciation of Brad's dedicated lovemaking (that slow in-and-out rhythm, that's a very thoughtful, effective technique). All the same, he shouldn't have allowed himself to become discouraged so quickly. With a little more persistence and an understanding of *why* she was lying there so unresponsively, he could have aroused her and helped her to let go of her inhibitions and blossom.

The sad part about it was that he *did* like her, a very great deal, and that she *did* like him. It was simply that she appeared so aloof. "I was convinced she was either frigid or a lesbian," he said. He confessed to having ejaculated all over her naked body "to see if I could get some kind of response . . . anything."

Kathy needed to learn the vocabulary of love, which isn't very difficult, after all. When to talk and when to stay silent. When to lick and suck and when to bite. The best moments to moan. The best moments to pant, gasp, shudder, or even scream at the top of your lungs.

You can start teaching yourself how to talk dirty and influence your new lover long before you've met him. You have to become accustomed to verbalizing your most intimate sexual thoughts, and using words that, up until now, you may have considered deeply embarrassing. You also have to associate words with actions.

The most effective way in which you can do this is to find yourself some time alone, when you know that you won't be disturbed, either by visitors or children or the telephone. Put yourself in the mood with a glass of wine, maybe, and some soft background music. Then undress, so that you're completely naked. Sit someplace comfortable, perhaps on a heap of cushions or on top of your bed, but make sure that you have a large mirror in front of you so that you can see yourself full-length.

Imagine that you're making love with a new man, somebody you've never met before. He's handsome, vigorous, just the kind of man who makes you melt. Stroke your cheeks with your fingertips and pretend that they're *his* fingertips. Look into your eyes in the mirror and give yourself the kind of warm, communicating look that he would expect to receive. Pay him a compliment. Say whatever comes into your head. "I love the color of your eyes . . . they're so unusual." "It's really strange . . . I had a dream last week about meeting a man, and he looked almost exactly like you." The trick is to try to imagine that you're him. Try to put yourself inside his mind, and imagine what he would like to hear a woman saying and doing. I call this technique *erotic transference*. It's a way of identifying with your lover's needs and desires so that you will almost always behave in bed in a way that pleases him to the utmost.

Kiss the mirror, keeping your eyes wide open. Lick the mirror with your tongue. Let your eyelids droop and let out the faintest of sighs. Give a little shudder. In other words, try to make him feel that his kiss has gone all the way through you, and touched your clitoris from the inside. Next time you kiss a man for real, try to imagine that happening, what it would feel like.

Whisper "You're making me juicy already." Don't be shy. Remember that this is a man with whom you have already decided to go to bed, and that you're both naked. Kathy, like many young women, was embarrassed because her panties were wet after a kissing session with Brad, but she needn't have been. All women become lubricated when they are sexually aroused (although less so as they grow older) and men find that wetness highly arousing. It shows them that they turn you on, and nothing could be more complimentary than that.

Now you can slow things down. Say "I love the way you kiss, kiss me again." You can keep a man kissing for a very long time, giving you plenty of time to become aroused. Open your mouth, imagine his tongue between your lips. Now, before he starts to do it himself, squeeze and fondle your own breasts, and tug at your own nipples. Say "Every time you kiss me, it makes my nipples tingle."

I talked to literally scores of men about the things that women can do to arouse them, and *all* of them, 100 percent, without exception, said that the sight of a woman caressing herself sexually was an enormous turn-on. It gave them all kinds of explicit messages: look how you're making me feel; you're making me feel sexually excited and uninhibited, and I'm not afraid to show you what you do to me. It also gives the man instant encouragement to fondle your breasts, too. You can fondle them together. Squeeze your breasts so that your nipples stick out and say "Stroke me, suck me, you make my nipples feel as if they're electric."

You can go even further. "Touch my nipples with your cock. You don't know how fantastic it feels, having a hard cock massage your nipples." All the time, in the mirror, simulate these actions. Fondle your breasts and try to imagine what impression it would make on the new man in your life. Don't just knead them . . . lift them up and offer them to him, an erotic gift that he can really wallow in. Urge him to kiss them and lick them. Then say "Lick here . . . lick down my cleavage . . . then you can fuck my breasts with your cock."

Notice that at the same time you're guiding him, encouraging him—and, most important of all, you're *controlling the pace of your lovemaking*, so that by the time you come to actual penetration, you'll have been kissed, caressed, stroked and aroused, and you'll be more than ready for him to slide his penis into you.

Run your fingers lightly down your sides and around your hips. Imagine that *he's* doing it, not you. Close your eyes and give a little shudder, and a quivering exhalation of breath. At this stage keep your thighs closed together, so that he can't immediately climb on top of you and try to penetrate you. This is the time when you can take hold of his penis yourself. He won't feel that you're resisting him (you're massaging his penis, for goodness' sake) but at the same time it will allow you to choose for yourself the moment when you're ready for intercourse.

Grip his penis very firmly just below the glans. Rub it very slowly up and down. Rub it against your stomach and let him fuck your navel. This is especially erotic if you have a navel ring. Move his penis from side to side against your mound of Venus (that is, the plump protuberance just above your clitoris). You can practice this with a penis-shaped vibrator or, failing that, a large penis-sized candle. If he tries to pull himself downward so that he can enter your vagina, simply slide your hand under his testes and cup them in your hand, and then tug his penis upward again, as if to say, "Come on, Fido, behave yourself!"

During the time that you're gripping his penis, you can give him all kinds of erotic compliments, and really build up the sexual tension between you. Hold on to your vibrator very tight and see how sexually descriptive you can be. Let the words come out of your mouth, don't be afraid of them. Used in a hostile context, words like "fuck" and "cock" and "cunt" can sound filthy and aggressive, but in the context of lovemaking they can heighten your excitement and give you an extraordinary feeling of liberation and intimacy. In other words, you ought to feel that you can do anything at all with this man. If he can kiss your vagina, why can't you whisper the word "cunt" in his ear? In the bedroom, between the two of you, you can share anything and everything. Sharon, 24, a computer salesperson from Akron, Ohio, said, "I like to lick my boyfriend's asshole. I do it almost every night, swirling my tongue around and around and sometimes poking it in. He loves it and I love doing it, so what can be wrong with it? It shows him that I love every single inch of him. Mind you, I always make sure that he takes a shower first!" It's that kind of totally uninhibited loving that provides the seedbed for a sexual relationship of extraordinary closeness and durability.

In the mirror, move your hands down between your legs and stroke your inner thighs. Describe out loud how it's making you feel, as if you're talking to your lover. "That's gorgeous . . . that's so good . . . you don't know how much I want you to fuck me." Then move your hands upward and caress the lips of your vagina, the way you like it best. Again, pretend that your lover is touching you, and tell him how he's making you feel. "I adore it when you touch my cunt like that . . . why don't you stick your fingers up me . . . can't you feel how wet I am? It's you . . . you're making me feel so juicy. Just holding your cock, just fondling your balls.

You're so big, I can't believe it. You're hung like a horse."

I have discussed sexual responses in detail with literally hundreds of men, and almost all of them admit that compliments about the size and hardness of their penis are a considerable turn-on. Men are both sexually competitive and sexually unsure of themselves, so if you tell them that "my God, your cock is enormous!" as if you've never seen one so big before, you'll make him feel proud and confident and you'll improve his sex drive enormously.

As you caress your vaginal lips and stroke your clitoris, practice saying things like, "I want your cock up inside me . . . I want it so bad . . . I want you to fill my cunt up with solid cock . . . I want you to fuck me and fuck me until I'm sore." You can improvise, of course, by describing things that really excite you. "I want to feel your balls bouncing against my butt." "I want you to fill me up with gallons of come." Every woman has her own erotic images, and they're not always the same from day to day; but you should learn to describe what turns you on as graphically as you possibly can.

This is not only an opportunity to teach yourself to excite your lover-to-be, it's an opportunity to excite yourself. It's important that you touch yourself intimately and explore the erotic sensations that your body can give you, and to

stimulate yourself as often as you can, so that
you're constantly aware of your sexuality. You
may not always masturbate yourself to a climax,
but you can give yourself hours of pleasure by
fondling yourself, and by trying to imagine what
your new lover is going to feel when he first
sees you naked, opening up your legs for him,
exposing your vagina, inviting him to push his
erection inside you.

Try to imagine what it's like to be *him*. Try to
imagine what effect your looks and your body
and your lovemaking are having on him. Try to
imagine what he would really like you to do to
him (but may be too cautious to ask).

Here are the six intimate acts that men most
want you to do to them, but will very rarely ask
outright.

1: Taking his penis into your mouth, licking
it, and gently sucking it. This is the all-
time favorite sexual stimulation that men
adore. It most often has nothing to do with
asserting their sexual supremacy or making you kneel in front of them. Most oral
sex is performed lying down, in any case.
To a man, it is evidence of your willingness to be totally intimate with him, and
besides that, it feels very good indeed.
More than that, though, it is a sexual act
that he can *see*, and men are highly

aroused by visual stimulation. Jack, 36, an
engineer from Detroit, Michigan, said,
"When Patti performs oral sex on me, I
very rarely come to a climax. The sensation I get from being licked and sucked
isn't usually strong enough to bring me
off—not unless she's really rubbing me
with her hand, too. But it turns me on just
to lie back and watch my cock going in
and out of her lips, and her tongue
swirling all the way around my cock-head,
and her teeth biting into it like an apricot.
I could lie there and watch that all night."

2: Making love to his penis with your
breasts. Many women seem to be afraid
to fondle and caress their own bodies during sex. Yet your body is the instrument
you use to make love, just like a cellist
uses her instrument to play a concerto.
And again, because they are so visually
responsive, men are excited by seeing you
licking your lips, touching your own nipples, smoothing your hands down your
sides, rubbing your thighs. These are all
visible indicators that you are feeling sexually aroused, and they really get the message. If he thinks you're turned on, he'll
be even more turned on, and he'll turn
you on even more, and so on. Audible and
visible signs of arousal have an escalating

effect that can lift your lovemaking to really ecstatic levels.

Hold your breasts in both hands and use them to massage his penis, teasing the glans with your nipples, and then squeezing the shaft in your cleavage. With his penis deep between your breasts, grip them and rotate them as if you were running in slow motion. Some baby oil or massage oil can greatly enhance his enjoyment of this experience, and yours, too! You probably won't be able to massage him to a climax, but you can bring him pretty close.

3: Masturbating him. Strong, firm masturbation will always arouse him. The trouble is, you may not have the same stamina as he does, nor the same intimate knowledge of how to grip his penis so that it pleases him the most. Not yet, anyhow. Men are always deeply impressed by women who know how to masturbate them really well, and even if you're only half-good at it, you'll have him coming back, begging for more.

4: Playing with his balls. There are so many warnings in sex books for women about the incredible delicacy of men's testicles. In fact, you can fondle them quite robustly, provided you don't try to do it by surprise. You have only to make a feint toward a man's testicles and he will double up like a cheap pocketknife. It's an automatic self-protective instinct, which leaves a man feeling shocked and disconcerted, and embarrassed, too. His testes have to be on the outside of his body, in his scrotum, in order to keep his spermatozoa at an ideal temperature. Unfortunately, this means that he is hyper-sensitive about any sudden or unexpected movements that may threaten his virility. Jim, 34, a private airline pilot from Galveston, Texas, said his girlfriend Marie had impressed him the very first time they had sex together because she had been "such an enthusiastic ball-sucker." He said that "most girls are pretty reluctant about giving you head, except for one or two who are really into oral. But you don't often find a girl who really knows how to treat your balls. Marie always approached them real slow, licking up the insides of my thighs, and then cupping them in her hands. Then she would gently lick all around them, especially right underneath, where it's really sensitive . . . that's a feeling that's almost enough to make you come on the spot, a girl's tongue licking you strong and steady just behind your balls. Then she used to take one ball into her mouth, and fondle the other one with her fingers, sucking and licking, not too hard, not too gentle. My cock used to be standing up right against her forehead, but she used to ignore it, it was my balls she was after. It makes you feel worried and aroused, both at the same time, because you spend your whole life protecting your balls, and here you are with your legs wide apart, allowing somebody to suck them and lick them. I mean, supposing she decided to go *scrunch* and bite them off? That's exposing yourself, man . . . that's entrusting your entire manhood to somebody you maybe don't even know very well.

"But Marie—well, what can you say? She really knows how to play ball. She grips them real tight in her hand, so that they bulge right out, and then she licks them with the tip of her tongue, and if you want to go mad, man, that's the way to go. Sometimes, when we're making love, she digs her fingernails deep into my scrotum and scratches me, so that I bleed, and I have to say that really drives me wild. It's pain and pleasure all mixed together, so that you don't know which is which. And when I come, she holds each of my balls between finger and thumb, and she gently milks them, you know what I mean? Not too hard, so that it makes you ache, but hard enough to make you feel that she's squeezing the last drop of come out of you."

Because women are always frightened of hurting their lovers if they touch their testicles, they tend to shy away from giving them some of the most exciting sexual manipulation in the book. The rule is: firmly but gently, and don't do anything by surprise. Massage your new lover's testicles with your tongue, with scented massage oil, with maple syrup, with molasses, with anything you can think of.

Practice by masturbating with massage oil yourself, and imagine what it must feel like for *him*. Or masturbate with strawberry jelly, like 23-year-old Ellie, who works for a TV production company in Los Angeles, California. "I was making waffles for breakfast. But I kept thinking about this gorgeous guy that I'd met at a rehearsal the day before. I was only wearing a sleep tee, and when I sat down to eat, I couldn't help thinking about this guy and how sexy he was, and I started to play with myself. I had some of the strawberry jelly on my finger, and I rubbed the jelly around my clitoris. It felt sticky and good.

I lifted my T-shirt and sat back in the chair and opened my legs, and started masturbating myself more strongly. Then I scooped two fingers in the jelly jar and smeared strawberry jelly all over my pussy. It felt wonderfully messy, and so I scooped out some more. I rubbed it around and around my pussy and it was so sticky and it smelled so good. I knelt on the floor on my hands and knees, and I rubbed strawberry jelly between the cheeks of my ass, and right up my asshole. I kept trying to imagine what it would be like to do that to a man, smother his cock and his balls in strawberry jelly, and lick it all off, and when I did, when I could picture this jelly-covered cock in my mind's eye, I had an orgasm, and I just lay on the floor, rubbing strawberry jelly between my legs and all over my breasts, and it must have been five minutes before I stopped quaking."

Later in this book, we'll go further into the fascinating subject of women who find it arousing to make a mess, and have intense sexual experiences with custard, sunflower oil, whipped cream, saliva, urine, and chocolate bars. But right now let's go on to the next stimulation that men like the most, and that's . . .

5: Massage. Many men, like women, work, and have bills to pay, and careers to build, and because of that, they experience stress. I talked to several masseuses and a professional chiropractor while I was preparing this book, as well as an expert reflexologist. All agreed that gentle massage and muscular manipulation is an invaluable part of lovemaking. Even if you're not a professional masseuse, you can systematically knead his neck muscles and his back and his shoulders, relaxing him and giving him a feeling of warmth, closeness, and well-being. This will enable him to concentrate all of his sexual attention on you, rather than worry about yesterday's unpaid bill or tomorrow's critical meeting with the southwestern sales director. You can practice massage on yourself, with a little perfumed oil. Make sure that you have plenty of time, and that you're sitting someplace quiet and relaxed, maybe with some mood music playing. Massage each of your shoulders in turn, alternately gripping and releasing your muscles, and then smooth your fingertips around and around, pressing as hard as you can into your tensest knots. Massage your breasts, too, and your stomach and your thighs. Keep your breathing slow and measured, fully inhaling and fully exhaling. Imagine what it would be like for your lover if you were to give him this same treatment, and then eventually get around to massaging his penis.

6: Anal stimulation. A man's anus is just as sexually sensitive as a woman's, and you can give your new lover an extraordinary amount of erotic pleasure by touching, tickling, stroking, and licking his sphincter. If your lover is clean and showered, anal stimulation isn't dirty at all, and even if you insert your finger (or fingers) into his anus, you will rarely encounter any fecal matter. A little lubricant always helps, either from your own vagina, or massage oil, or a proprietary lubricant like KY. Some women like to go as far as "fisting" their lovers—inserting their entire hand into his anus right up to the wrist, which can gave a man a stunning climax, but this is something that you're unlikely to try on a first date. Simply sliding your hand between the cheeks of his bottom and gently massaging his anus in a circular motion with the tip of your finger is a deeply intimate caress that he will be very unlikely to forget. Just remember, though, to make sure your fingernails are neatly trimmed, or he'll be unlikely to forget it for a very different reason!

Devote at least an hour every week to sexual thoughts and sexual fantasies, as well as exploring your own body and your own sexual responses. A penis-shaped vibrator or dildo will not only help to stimulate you, it will allow you to experience what it feels like when an erect penis enters you from various different positions, and with differing rhythms and depths of penetration.

Joanna, 32, a telephone salesperson from Austin, Texas, told me that she had bought two vibrators: "the huge, hard model complete with realistic veins . . . it even has squeezable balls" and "one of those soft, squirmy half-hard affairs, which feels just like a man who's had a little too much to drink, but it's really erotic to play with."

The most important thing to remember is that even if you're not currently involved in a sexual relationship, or if you're not getting as much sex as you'd ideally like, that doesn't mean that you have to switch yourself off and forget about sex altogether. In fact, you should do the opposite, and keep yourself in trim, stimulating yourself whenever the mood takes you (and sometimes, even when it doesn't particularly take you.) You go jogging when your body is saying "No! No! I don't want to go jogging!" and you know that it's good for you. Similarly, it's very good mental and physical exercise to arouse yourself to orgasm.

Shelley, 25, a beautician from St. Paul, Minnesota, told me that she masturbates almost every night before she goes to sleep. "It's a self-indulgence, you know? But it's great that we've reached an age when people can masturbate and not feel guilty about it. If you masturbate, it doesn't mean that you're some kind of social misfit, or a pathetic freak who can't find a partner. At this time in my life, I don't want a partner. I've just finished one very complex relationship with a man who gave me a whole lot of grief, and I just want to be calm and quiet and get my head together before I plunge into another relationship. But I like sex, and I like thinking about sex, and I like having orgasms, and so there's nothing better in the whole wide world than masturbation. I have dildoes, yes. I bought them mail-order through a woman's magazine. I have a very long thin one which I use for anal stimulation. I don't use that too often but sometimes I really feel an urge for it. Then I have a vibrating hairbrush, which has bristles on one side and soft rubbery nubs on the other and a very satisfying handle. I fantasize about so many different things when I masturbate, it's wonderful, it's better than watching a sexy video. I imagine what it's like to have two men in my bed at once. I imagine myself stripping in front of a whole roomful of men, and giving them a sex show with my hairbrush . . . brushing my hair and then sliding the handle up my pussy. Sometimes I don't feel like masturbating when I first get into bed, but if I don't, I always find it difficult to sleep. It really relaxes me, settles my mind, and reminds me that I'm a woman."

One of the most constructive ways of preparing yourself for a new lover is by keeping a sexual diary. People who keep a daily log of their sexual thoughts are almost always more informed about their own erotic resources, as well as being better balanced, less stressed, and much more likely to have a successful sexual relationship.

Let's take a look at how you can create your own sexual diary and radically improve your love life.

3

Diary of Delight

Keeping a sexual diary is a highly beneficial self-help device that has already met with considerable approval from leading psychologists and therapists. I've been recommending for years that you should try to make at least a brief note of your sexual feelings every day, and if possible write down your erotic fantasies and your erotic dreams. It is a matchless way of staying closely in touch with your emotions and your physical desires.

If you've never had a sexual relationship before, you will be much more focused on what your needs are and what you want to discover when you first make love to a man. But even if you *have* had relationships before, you can use your diary to chart the progress of your new affair, day by day and night by night.

If and when your relationship ends, you'll be able to look back and see exactly where it went right and exactly where it went wrong. You can relive your erotic highs and lows, and recall those little things that really turned you on. This will allow you to bring to your next relationship a wealth of experiences that you might otherwise have forgotten.

You can keep the smallest notebook, with only a few jottings in it, such as these genuine excerpts from women's diaries. Jean, 24, from Paterson, New Jersey, wrote: "I really have the hots for Peter . . we danced close together last night and I could feel his cock through his pants . . . it was so hard that I felt like touching it but I didn't dare . . . I felt so light-headed it was like I was in a dream . . . I wonder what would have happened if I *had* dared? I was so juicy that my thong was soaked . . . I lay in bed stroking myself and thinking about the way his cock felt against my thigh . . . *He* was ready for sex, when we danced, and *I* was ready for sex . . . I don't think it's going to take much for us to get together."

Lara, 22, from Muscatine, Iowa, wrote: "I read a story in the newspaper about a woman who was supposed to have had sex with three men at once. There were no intimate details in the story but I can't stop thinking about it, how she did it and what it must have felt like. Last night, when I was lying in bed, I kept wondering what it would be like. I took off my T-shirt and lay on the bed nude, stroking myself. Then I rubbed baby oil all over my breasts and played with my nipples. I tried to imagine what it would be like to have a man massaging my breasts with his cock and his balls, and I couldn't believe how turned-on I began to feel. I think that I could have had an orgasm just by fondling my breasts. But then I thought about having one man's enormous cock in my pussy, and another cock right up my ass, and four balls down between my legs, and I started to stroke my clitoris and slide my fingers inside my pussy. Because my fingers with so slippery with baby oil I did something which I've never done before, and I'm blushing as I write this and hope that nobody ever reads it!!! which is to push my thumb into my asshole and rotate it 'round and 'round, deeper and deeper. Of course I've heard about women who take men's cocks up their ass but I always thought it was incredibly dirty the kind of thing that hookers do and I had never realized how good it could feel. My thumb just wasn't enough, my asshole was tingling so much that I felt that I had to have a cock up inside it, deep inside, right up to the balls, so that I could feel the man's pubic hair up against the cheeks of my ass. I was rubbing my clitoris so fast that my hand was practically a blur and I had a sexual feeling between my legs that was out of this world. I fantasized about a man having a climax right up inside me, and what it would be like later when I went to the john and his sperm dripped out of my asshole, and that made me come and come and come. I just had one orgasm after the other. I shouted out loud and Sissy [with whom Lara shared an apartment] came and knocked on my door and asked me if I was okay. My asshole was sore afterward and I found it hard to imagine how you could actually fit a stiff cock into it, but I guess you have to learn to relax. I've decided to buy myself a vibrator to see if I can practice. I feel like I've discovered something really amazing, some wonderful secret pleasure that nobody ever tells you about. Can you imagine my *mom* saying how incredible it is to have a man's cock up your ass? She didn't even tell me about orgasms!! I can't wait until my vibrator arrives, it's supposed to be completely lifelike, with veins and everything. Even more than that I can't wait until I meet the man of my dreams and have a real live cock up inside me!"

Lara found that writing about her sexual experimentation gave her the opportunity to think about it much more clearly, and "it really took away any guilt I might have had about masturbating, because when I read my diary later, it's full of nothing but excitement and pleasure and discovering myself, both my mind and my body." She said that looking back over some of her early entries was not only self-educational but highly stimulating, and had aroused her so much that she had masturbated again.

"I think that writing a diary about your sex life makes you want to try new things so that you'll have something exciting to write about. If I hadn't written a diary I don't think I would have tried half of the things that I have, such as playing with myself in front of the mirror, or using cucumbers or bananas or candles."

Jayne, 22, from Cleveland, Ohio, wrote down her fantasies about having two men at a time. "They would have to do whatever I wanted. They would have to be naked all the time and I would fondle their cocks whenever I felt like it. One of them would have to make love to me while I sucked the other one's cock and then they would have to change places, so that I could suck a cock that had just been taken out of my pussy, and was still slippery with my own juice."

Some months after she had written that, Jayne started a sexual relationship with Nathan, a 24-year-old computer programmer. "It was a great relationship right from the very first night, because I treated Nathan as if he were two men, and I did *everything* with him, sucking his cock and making love to him all around the room. I was so excited about having sex with him that I wouldn't leave him alone. I even came up behind him and fondled him when he was washing his teeth, so that he climaxed into the wash-basin."

Jayne's diary had given her a memorable record of all the sexual acts that she had imagined for the past three years. So even though she wasn't very experienced, she had an erotic repertoire that Nathan, according to her, found "amazing." At the time of this writing, their relationship is still "burning strong and hot, and growing hotter all the time."

Another short but vivid entry: "I have a secret desire to set a record for having the largest number of guys jerk off over my face and into my mouth, preferably recorded on film. I think I must be a slut, but the idea of having all that gooey jism all over my face and dripping down my breasts really does it for me."

You can make brief notes of your fantasies and your sexual self-pleasuring, or you can create a much more lavish album in which you write down your sexual feelings and your sexual experiences in the minutest detail, complete with Polaroids of yourself and any partners you may have had, and any erotic pictures or pin-ups that you might have come across.

I've been shown erotic diaries that women have filled with highly explicit drawings (some of them very skilled), as well as poems and startlingly explicit stories. They may seem pornographic to an outside observer, but they are an

excellent way of working out your sexual curiosity, your lusts, and your unfulfilled needs.
They focus your mind on what you want to
know about sex, and how your love life is developing. You'll find it really surprising what
you can discover about yourself by writing
about yourself.

Ceri, a 19-year-old art student from Indianapolis, Indiana, wrote poetic musings about
what her sex life would be like, and filled a
whole album with exquisite pen and pencil
drawings of male genitalia, some soft, some half-
hard, some fully erect, some of them being licked
by beautifully drawn cats, and one of them being
embraced by a sexy little fairy as if it were a
tree from some enchanted forest.

Chrysta, a 36-year-old divorcée from Lub-
bock, Texas, wrote a long erotic romance with
herself as the heroine, describing her extraordinary adventures in a fantasy world rather like
that of Conan the Barbarian, in which she was
successively raped and ravaged by sweaty, muscular savages and by all kinds of bizarre beasts,
such as a centaur, half-man and half-horse,
"whose erect cock was so huge and strong that
he lifted me right off my feet, my pussy stretched
open unbelievably wide." Chrysta had pierced
nipples and tattoos of butterflies fluttering under
her vulva "gathering around the honeypot," and
another tattoo of a forked devil's tail that started

at her anus, came up between her buttocks, and curled around her back. She had designed these herself, and had taken Polaroids to put in her diary.

Here's another devilish fantasy, which a young woman called Lucy recounted: "It was a warm night with just enough breeze to stir the trees, revealing a full moon. I tried to move but my wrists and legs appeared to be firmly tied. I was naked, spread-eagled on a large roughish stone. I became aware of a tall, thick-set figure striding slowly toward me. His face was partly covered in a leather mask and he wore some sort of leather bodysuit. His body hair was amazing, he had a full curly dark beard, thick hair all over his back, arms, legs, and chest. Swaying slightly as he walked toward me was the most enormous cock I'd ever seen, purple and angry-looking as it emerged from a dense mat of shaggy pubic hair.

"He climbed onto the stone, straddling me and smothering me in his rank animal smell, with just a hint of sulphur. He sniffed me all over like an animal. Then he raked at my body with long horny nails, raising stinging red weals on my tits and my belly. I quivered with exquisite pain and pleasure, and he ran his hands from my throat to my cunt. Then he nuzzled my cunt, his long rasping tongue exploring deep inside me, exciting me as nothing had before.

"He moved purposefully upward, putting one hand behind my head and thrusting his rampant prick into my eager mouth. It was so long and thick that I thought I'd choke, but it was real enough, hot and hard and throbbing. I sucked on it in delight, and probed its eye with my tongue. Then with an animal-like lust grunt, he moved back and roughly parted my moist cunt lips, lifted up my butt, and rammed in his swollen knob.

"He slammed it into me again and again, sending spirals of pain and delight through me with every stroke. I cried out like a wild animal as wave after wave of orgasms convulsed my body. Finally he pulled his shining engorged prick out of me and came in rivers over my cunt and my belly, spurting out a volcano of creamy steaming lava. He knelt above me, swaying, holding his cock in one hairy hand. Suddenly he let fly a stream of steaming golden piss, soaking my hair and stinging my eyes. I gasped in surprise as its saltiness burned my mouth. He hosed his pungent water all over me, sluicing away the sticky love juices from my belly. The heat of its tingling force aroused me once again as it hit my throbbing tits and twitching cunt. All the time he grinned demonically and chuckled like something crazy."

Lucy was one of the quietest, most respectable women you could ever hope to meet—yet her diary revealed that she had persistent fantasies about masochistic sex, only thinly disguised as Satanic allegories. If you have fantasies like Lucy's, keeping a regular erotic diary will help you to describe and understand your feelings, and to realize that you have nothing to feel guilty or "dirty" about. Everybody has "dirty" thoughts, but if you regularly put them down in writing you will be able to trace the underlying themes that arouse you the most, and include them in your next sexual relationship.

You wouldn't necessarily expect your lover to tie you to a "roughish" rock and scratch you all over with his fingernails, but you could show him that you enjoyed forceful sex, and even suggest that you wouldn't be averse to a little mild bondage, or even what is politely described as "water sports"—playing erotic games while you urinate.

Sex is supposed to be the ultimate intimacy, during which you can say whatever you want and ask for whatever you want. Yet many people still feel inhibited about telling their partners about their secret desires. A question that I am asked time and time again is: "How can I tell my lover that I'd like my lover to try this, that or the other?"

"I would love my partner Joe to go down on me," said Marcia, 28, a finance consultant from Tallahassee, Florida. "But even when I lie next to him, and open my legs wide, and run my fingers through his hair, he still doesn't get the hint. He just climbs on top of me and starts making love to me the usual way. The trouble is, it takes me a very long time to get aroused, and he almost never gives me an orgasm. If only he could lick me for five or ten minutes, I know that I could come. As it is, I'm in a sexual relationship with a man and yet I still have to masturbate to get satisfaction."

Instead of despairing, however, or tolerating a life of sexual dissatisfaction, Marcia took my advice and started to write about herself and Joe in a daily diary. She described every act of love— from a few kisses to full intercourse—and how she had felt afterward, on a fulfillment scale of 1–10. What gradually emerged was a very detailed and insightful picture of her relationship, and some remarkably clear pointers to how she could dramatically improve it.

"*Wednesday*—I was almost asleep last night when Joe put his arm around me. He nuzzled my neck and started stroking my back and my hip. Then he lifted my nightdress and started to play with my breasts. He ran his hands down my body and slid his fingertips between the lips of my pussy and gently played with my clitoris. I found this arousing but it was difficult to become too excited because I knew that it wouldn't last very long and that in a few minutes Joe would want to climb on top of me and start having intercourse. I closed my eyes and tried to think of something very erotic. One of my favorite fantasies is having a young man in handcuffs and leg shackles in my bed. I can do whatever I like with him—kiss him, stroke him all over, suck his cock, play with his balls—and he can't do anything to stop me. I can sit on top of him and fuck him, and I can masturbate him until he climaxes. I can sit on his face if I want to. He's mine. But I can't do anything like that with Joe. I don't know why. And sure enough, Joe stopped rubbing my clitoris, pushed me flat on my back, and forced his cock up inside me. He rammed it in and out, and I can't say that it didn't give me *some* pleasure. Of course it did. But it felt so impersonal, as if he could have been fucking any woman, not specifically me. Then he climaxed, and it was all over. I masturbated before I went to sleep, thinking about that beautiful young man handcuffed to my bed, with his tanned skin and his muscles and his huge stiff cock. My pussy was flooded with sperm, and I put my fingers up me and then I licked it and tasted it, and rubbed it on my nipples. The smell of sperm is wonderful, and it really turns me on. I love Joe, but sometimes it seems like we're going noplace at all, sexually. I could be anybody, as far as he's concerned. A whore, an inflatable plastic woman. He doesn't seem to realize that he's making love to *me*. During all of that lovemaking, so-called, he didn't say a single word."

Marcia's diary contains dozens of similar entries. Joe starts to make to love to her, she knows that he's not going to persist very long with his foreplay before he climbs on top of her in the "missionary position," as usual, and enters her. She's not sufficiently aroused, so she tries to excite herself by thinking of her private sexual fantasies.

Marcia's response is understandable, but her diary clearly shows that she's detaching herself from Joe whenever they make love, rather than opening herself up to him. "Opening up" can mean anything from a kiss, or a whisper, to taking off your panties and opening your legs so that your lover can see right inside you—to the ultimate opening-up, which is opening up your heart, and making sure that your lover realizes that you're giving him everything.

Whatever Joe's failings in the past, Marcia closes in on herself, and tries to lose herself inside of her own sexual fantasies, ignoring what Joe might be feeling, or what his needs are. She complains that he doesn't say a single word when they make love, yet she says nothing, either. Joe sounds like a straightforward guy who didn't go to bed with too many girls before he met Marcia, and who still doesn't know very much about the complexities of female sexuality. But he deserves encouragement, not censure, because every man is capable of being a better lover if the woman in his life knows how to bring it out of him.

When Marcia first met Joe, she expected him to be reasonably expert in bed. But Joe was raised in a very strict Catholic family, in which discussions about sex were frowned upon. He had read *Playboy* and talked about sex with his friends, but he didn't really know what to do when he was confronted with a real live naked woman, apart from climbing on top of her, and having strenuous intercourse with her until he reached a climax.

Page by page, Marcia's diary gradually revealed that it wasn't Joe who was the key to improving this relationship, because Joe simply didn't understand that he was failing to satisfy her. He wasn't a mindreader. Unless Marcia showed him what really excited her, he would never find out, and never give her the fulfillment that she was craving. Whenever he failed to stimulate her, she withdrew into her shell and gave him very little indication that anything was wrong, whereas she should have told him, loud and clear, that things were not going well—not in the orgasm department, anyhow.

In spite of all those articles in men's magazines about "how to drive your woman into a state of mindblowing ecstasy," men can still lack skill and confidence when it comes to making love, and sometimes the only way to make sure that your lover understands what you want is to use the sexual equivalent of a bullhorn, or a billboard on Sunset Boulevard. In other words, you have to be very explicit, very flirtatious, and leave your new lover in no doubt at all about what it takes to turn you on, and what he has to do to bring you to orgasm.

Most men are sexually enthusiastic, but enthusiasm isn't everything. They also need guidance, just as women need guidance in the way they handle men. A lot of the time, when men first manage to persuade you to have sex with them, they can't believe their luck, so they rush you into bed and have intercourse with you as fast as possible just in case you change your mind, or you turn out to be a mirage. And, regretfully, if your relationship endures, it's surprising how quickly enthusiasm can turn into routine, without any intervening ecstasy. After months and years together, too many men climb on top of their partners, have intercourse, then go to sleep or pick up the latest John Grisham.

This is why you should keep a diary. Record the good times, and the not-so-good times. Put down your passions, your doubts, your dissatisfactions, your moments of real delight. A diary is not only useful, it's highly therapeutic.

Armed with a diary, you will find it remarkably easy to analyze what's missing in your sex life and what you and your partner can do to put it right. In the margins, incidentally, you can also note down what you've been eating every day and what exercise you've been taking, so that you can see if your diet and your lifestyle have any bearing on your sexual performance and your sexual fulfillment.

For instance, over 54 percent of the population suffer from stress and depression, which directly affects their sex lives. A key factor in overcoming these symptoms is the level of serotonin—a chemical that helps to improve your mood—in your brain. Foods that are rich in serotonin are oily fishes (such as tuna and sardines), potatoes, chicken, cottage cheese, beans, avocados, turkey, and wheat germ.

If you keep an erotic diary, you can keep track of all of those elements that heighten or depress your sexuality, and after two or three months you should have a very clear idea of what you want out of your relationship and how to improve it. Pammie, 26, a hotel employee from Seattle, Washington, told me that she drank "maybe six or seven glasses of wine" every day. It was only when she kept track of her drinking in her diary that she realized how badly it was affecting her sex life. "I fell asleep early every night and woke up every morning with a hangover, and apart from that, I just didn't feel like sex, and I didn't know why." Adding up her weekly wine consumption in her diary, she realized that she was drinking far too much, and that it was seriously affecting her sex drive. She cut down, and her sex life improved "literally within a week."

Keeping a sexual diary is a powerful stress release and can give you enhanced immunity from depression and from clinical illness. James Pennebaker, a psychologist and researcher at the University of Texas, said, "When people write about emotional topics, they go to the doctor less, there is evidence of improved immune function, they are absent from work less, achieve better grades in college, and, if fired from a job, get a new one more quickly." Also, their sex lives are happier and more fulfilling, and they find it easier to disclose their secret sexual desires to the people they love.

Pennebaker has led international research in the subject of psychoneural immunology, which encourages people to sort out their problems through the written word and move on through life in a happier, healthier way. As Oscar Wilde said, "It is the confession, not the priest, that gives the absolution."

Whether we have done it intentionally or not, we have all had results from writing down our feelings. When we were teenagers, we crammed our diaries with our anger at and our dread of a world that we didn't yet understand. Later on, we jotted down our ideas, our frustrations, and our attempts to exorcise the demons of life. And how many times have we been relieved by writing a furiously angry letter? It hardly matters that we didn't send it.

When Marcia read her own sexual diary, she realized that her own negative response to Joe's lovemaking was the one factor that was preventing their intimate relationship from improving. "I was rejecting him, every time he made love to me, and he could sense that I was rejecting him, but he didn't know why. That was one of the reasons he never tried anything more adventurous. If I didn't like straightforward, missionary-position sex, I certainly wasn't going to like anything else! That's what he thought, anyhow. I never showed him how much I enjoyed our lovemaking. I never showed him that I was prepared to go further and try new things."

Pennebaker conducted a rigorous series of trials in which he divided his students into two groups, each of them writing for 20 minutes three times a month. The first group were told to disclose their innermost feelings. The second had to write essays on time management, which was the blandest subject that Pennebaker could think of. The result was a dramatic improvement for the disclosers, not just in general well-being, but in measurable terms. Their grades improved, and they made significantly fewer trips to the university health care center.

Pennebaker repeated his study with professional engineers who had lost their jobs through redundancy, a deeply angry group of super-rational people. The results were very similar, with one notable feature: those who expressed their anger in their diaries went on to find new jobs much more quickly than the others.

My own experience is that women who keep sexual diaries benefit in much the same way—finding lovers more readily, and when a relationship does break up, dealing with their emotions with much less pain and confusion. Also, like the engineers, they appear to be able to move on to the next relationship much more quickly.

"The things you don't deal with have costs," said psychologist John Weinman, a fellow at Guy's Hospital in London, England. "Inhibiting emotion causes deleterious effects. These can be mitigated by forcing a structure on your experiences, giving you a handle on confusing or difficult events. Writing works, and we now know that it does so much better than other creative outlets, such as painting and dance."

Rob Home, from the University of Brighton, England, said, "We've shown, in the most scientific ways possible, the mind-body connection." However, he warns that people who start writing a diary of their deepest feelings often feel worse, in the short term. "This is because they are facing up to something that hitherto they have been keeping from themselves."

The same can happen when you start keeping a sexual diary. Kay, 32, a teacher from Madison, Wisconsin, said, "I found it very erotic when I first started writing it. I drew pictures of orgies and people making love in public, in the street, on buses, things like that. I was so turned on that I had one hand in my panties while I was writing and drawing, stroking myself. But after I had reached an orgasm, I felt guilty and disgusted with myself for writing anything so filthy, and I tore out all of the pages and burned them. A few days later, though, I began to realize that what I had done was very important to my understanding of my own sexual problems, my shyness and lack of confidence with men. I saw that I *did* have confidence, if only I allowed myself to be more flirtatious, more of a sexual show-off, if you like. Because I sorely needed to know that men found me sexually attractive, and that they wanted me. It was a revelation, and it was a revelation about the very soul of my sexuality, about who I was and what I wanted out of life. So I started again, and wrote some more, and drew some more, and now I've been keeping it for six months. I'm not going to show it to you—not because it's triple-X rated, but because it's too personal. It's for me to read, and me to look at, and see myself naked, metaphorically speaking. Not like in a mirror, because a mirror only shows you what you look like. This is like a portrait painted by somebody who really understands me, really knows me, and shows the sexuality underneath the skin."

Rob Home says, "If you are simply using your diary as a way of complaining over and over again, then you will succeed only in upsetting yourself. It is important to work toward insight, self-reflection, and understanding of your feelings and experiences."

Self-help advisor Julia Cameron recommends that you sit down every day and write for 30 minutes, even if you can't think what to write about and you have to write "I can't think what to write about," over and over. If this sounds too arduous, you could start your sexual diary in a simpler way by writing down five sexy things that you think you ought to do, or five sexual fantasies, or a mixture of both—so long as it's five thoughts that address your sexuality and your sexual ambitions. This can be a simple itemized list, such as this diary entry from Fran, 28, a tax accountant from Indianapolis, Indiana:

1: Throw away all of my underwear and buy new sexy underwear.

2: Have the courage to show my boss that I really like him.

3: Learn how to get a man into bed without looking cheap.

4: Learn what men really want me to do to them in bed (and not be scared of doing it!).

5: Learn how to relax and stop being uptight and really enjoy sex.

Here's another list, from Sandra, a 31-year-old travel agent from Seattle, Washington:

1: I want to find out what I've been missing so far as sex is concerned. I've read about so many sexual pleasures but I've never found the right man to try them with. Or maybe I haven't been communicating my needs very clearly?

2: I want to find a lover who will *enthusiastically* accompany me on my journey of exploration. A man who's adventurous and unembarrased by anything.

3: I want to know what it's like to have multiple orgasms. I'm lucky if I get one!

4: I want to know what it's like to have that really fantastic oral sex women in magazines keep writing about. I want to find out what anal sex is like.

5: I want to try bondage and spanking and maybe even group sex. I just don't want to discover all the things that I could have enjoyed when it's all too late.

And Melissa, 24, an assistant at a photography lab in New York, simply wrote:

1: Discover my sexuality. Buy a giant vibrator and have at least one orgasm every day.

2: Read every book on sex I can find, plus watch sex videos.

3: Work on my confidence by looking people in the eye and starting up conversations with strangers.

4: Groom myself from head to toe. Hair, nails, leg wax. Buy new clothes.

5: Flirt.

Sometimes these five things can develop into lengthy fantasy diaries in their own right. Here's Leila, 25, a medical receptionist from Austin, Texas, who started by writing "wish I could make love in front of a mirror" and progressed to flights of fancy like these:

1: I would love a man to date me in the real old-fashioned romantic way, bringing me an orchid corsage and then taking me out to dinner at a swanky restaurant with candlelight and soft music and gorgeous things to eat. He wouldn't have to be particularly handsome but he would have to treat me like a princess, and listen to everything I say. After dinner he would take me upstairs to his hotel suite, with a balcony overlooking the city. I would dress in a long silky robe and when I came out of the bathroom he would be waiting for me with a tall glass of champagne. He would take me in his arms and kiss me, and then he would open my robe and pour champagne over my breasts, so that it ran all the way down between my legs. He would lick the champagne from my breasts and my nipples, and then he would kneel in front of me, licking it out of my navel, and then my thighs, and then running the tip of his tongue down between the lips of my pussy. We would lie on the bed and he would make love to me very slowly, while the moon shone in through the open windows, and we could hear the orchestra playing some dreamy music. He would be lying on top of me, nothing but a silhouette, his muscles tensed, his cock sliding in and out of me, his balls rhythmically beating against the cheeks of my butt, and I would feel the first stirrings of an orgasm deep inside me, and know that he was going to last more than long enough to bring me off.

2: I would love to mud-wrestle another naked woman while a whole lot of men watched us and cheered us. I don't think that I'm bi-sexual, but I find other women's bodies fascinating, especially women with very big breasts, because mine are quite small. I would love to smear the mud all over the other woman's face and hair, and then squeeze her breasts and pull at her nipples. Then I would rub mud all over her stomach and down her back and deep between the cheeks of her butt. She would force me onto my back and open my legs wide so that all the men in the audience could see, and then she would masturbate me with a handful of slippery mud. All the men would be cheering and whooping, but she would be far too strong for me to stop her. I would have an orgasm, and then another, because she wouldn't stop, and then another, and another, until I was exhausted. Afterward, one of the men would come and help me up, and lead me into the showers, and he would gently clean me up, the two of us standing in the shower-stall together, and he would kiss me and soap me all over and tell me that I was the most beautiful girl that he had ever seen.

3: One of the ideas that has always turned me on is meeting a complete stranger and having sex with him without even knowing his name. Like my car breaks down, right in the middle of nowhere, and a guy appears with a tow truck and takes me to his garage in some half-a-horse town where it's hot and quiet and the only other person in sight is an old man sleeping on a rocker. The tow-truck guy is tall and black-haired and very muscular, and he smells of oil and sweat. He puts my car onto the lift, and then he beckons me into the workshop to take a look underneath it. He grabs me with his greasy hands, and forces a kiss on me, but he's so strong and good looking that I find myself responding. He lifts up my skirt and pulls down my panties. Then he turns me around and makes me bend over so that my hands are resting on his tool chest. He unbuttons his overalls and drops them right to his ankles, so that he's completely naked. I turn around and look at him and his body is magnificent, smudged with grease and shiny with sweat, and his cock sticks out from his black pubic hair all hard and red and angry. I never saw such a huge cock in my life, this looks like twice the size of a normal cock, and his balls are enormous, too, big heavy bags. He pushes me forward, opens up my legs, and forces his cock right up me, all the way, right up to the balls. Then he fucks me hard and fast, gripping my breasts, and covering my clean white blouse with his oily fingermarks. After a while, he's starting to pant, and I know that it can't be long before he's going to climax. So I turn around, and kneel down on the filthy garage floor, and take his cock into my mouth, as deep as I can, lollipopping my tongue up and down his shaft and around his balls. He squirts once, right against my lips, so I open my mouth wide while he shoots the rest of his sperm right onto my tongue. I stick my tongue out at him, and show him his sperm. Then I slowly swallow it, and say *mmmmm*, because it tastes delicious. We get dressed, he fixes my car, and I pay him what I owe him and drive off. We both know that we will never see each other again, ever, and that's the way it should be. This was a meeting of bodies, not of minds.

4: I see a good-looking man at a party. He keeps looking at me and after a while he comes over and introduces himself. We small-talk for a while, and then he asks me if I've ever been paid for sex. I say of course not. So he takes out his billfold and says that he'll give me a thousand dollars to come back to his apartment with him. I tell him he's crazy, but the idea has a terrible kind of attraction. After all, it's not like I'm a real prostitute, and he's a very charming, sociable kind of guy. He says he'll make it $1,500, so I say yes, feeling very daring. He takes me away from the party to an apartment someplace. He says he can't take me home because he's married. It's a nice apartment, warm and luxurious, with white leather couches and chairs. He tells me to take off my clothes, all except for my shoes, and pour him a drink. I pour him a Scotch and then we sit side by side on one of the couches and talk. Then, without any warning, he asks me to open my legs, open them wide. All this time he never touches me. He asks me to show him how I masturbate, and so I do, stroking my clitoris with one finger and rubbing my lips with the other. He sits watching me and peels a banana. Then he gives me the banana and tells me to push it up inside my pussy, which I do. He still doesn't touch me and he doesn't touch himself either. I slide the banana in and out, like a cock, and keep on masturbating, and all he does is watch me. There's something incredibly erotic about it, and I tell him that it won't be long before I'm going to have an orgasm. He says "How long? Let's see," and he lights a cigarette, takes two or three pulls on it, and then inserts the filter-tip into my anus, so that it's gradually smoldering away. I rub myself quicker and quicker, closing my eyes to help me concentrate, but every time I open them again he's watching me, and smiling. I can feel the heat of the cigarette between the cheeks of my butt, and somehow that does it for me. I have an orgasm like I've never had before. When it's all over, the man removes the cigarette and crushes it out. Then he takes out the banana and slowly eats it, still watching me. I don't understand what he wanted from me, but he pays me all the same.

5: I'm lying asleep in bed one night when I'm woken up by my bedroom door opening. Before I can reach over to switch on the light, two naked men have climbed into bed with me, one on each side. I can smell them. They smell like animals in heat. Both of them are very muscular and as they take hold of me I can feel that both of them have huge hard cocks. One of them presses his hand over my mouth and says, "You won't scream, will you? We're not going to hurt you. We're going to give you the time of your life." One of them grips my hair so that I can't move, while the other one fondles my breasts and sucks at one of my nipples. Then the other one sucks at the other nipple, so that I have a man sucking at each breast. I try to struggle, but they're far too heavy and far too strong for me, and the sensation of having both of my nipples sucked by different men is beginning to turn me on. One of them keeps on playing with my breasts while the other one climbs on top of me. I try to keep my legs closed but he forces them apart. My eyes are beginning to grow accustomed to the darkness now, and I can see the men's outlines against the window. They're both very tall, and wide-shouldered, like football players. The one who was sucking my nipples takes hold of the other guy's cock in his hand and starts to rub it. Then he takes it into his mouth and sucks it, so deep that he practically swallows it, almost up to the balls. Then—when the other guy's cock is all shiny with saliva—he guides it down between my legs. He opens my pussy-lips with his fingers so that his friend can push his cock into my hole. The feeling is sensational. His cock is so big and slippery and it slides up inside me and keeps on sliding up and up like an enormous snake. He keeps it there, right up inside me, and rolls over, so that he's lying on his back, and I'm on top of him. Then the other guy kneels in between our legs and pulls my ass-cheeks wide apart. I can't see him but I can feel him smearing something slippery between my cheeks and all around my anus. One of his fingers slips up inside my ass and makes me shudder. Then he lifts himself up and I can feel the head of his cock pressing against my anus. It feels much too big and I can't believe that he's going to try to push it in. But he grips my cheeks with both hands, spreading them as wide as they can go, and he pushes harder and harder, and at last his cock sinks into my ass. It hurts at first, and I tell him stop, but he pushes even deeper, until he's halfway inside. I reach behind me with one hand and I can feel his cock buried in my butt, stretching it open. He gives one last push and he's right inside me. I feel completely filled up with cock—one in my pussy and another in my ass, and I can feel their four balls jostling together between my legs. They start to fuck me in a kind of rhythm—one pushes his cock in while the other pulls his cock out. They fuck me harder and harder, and I get more and more excited, until I'm ramming myself up against them so that they fuck me as deep as they possibly can. I can feel an orgasm coming and it's not like any orgasm I've ever felt before. It's right inside me, right up inside my ass. I start to shake like an earth-tremor and then I just come and come and come and I can't stop coming. The two guys climax, too, both at the same time—one in my pussy and the other up my ass—I can feel their cocks throbbing as they fill me up with sperm. Even when they're finished, though, I don't want them to take their cocks out of me. We lie there for a long time while their cocks gradually go soft. The cock slips out of my pussy first, and then I squeeze the cheeks of my ass and there's a delicious feeling as a soft cock plops out of my ass, all spermy and wet. I lie down between them and rest my head on their thighs and suck both of their cocks, one after the other, until they fall asleep.

Leila's five fantasies are extremely revealing and she can learn a great deal about herself from re-reading them. More than anything else, they show that while she is highly sexed, she's always looking for a man to make the first move: the romantic lover with his candelit dinner, the man who cleans her up after her mud-wrestling fantasy, the mechanic in the auto shop, the partygoer who offers her money to behave like a prostitute, the two men who invade her bedroom and then her body.

She has some mild masochistic tendencies—having a lighted cigarette inserted into her anus, for example, and being taken by two men at once. But neither of these scenarios is particularly extreme, especially since she casts herself as a willing partner in both of them. They simply demonstrate that she derives a considerable amount of sexual pleasure out of the idea of being submissive.

All of us have sexual fantasies, and we can use our fantasies to enhance our understanding of our own sexuality and clarify what we're looking for in our sexual relationships. But however vivid and demanding a fantasy may be, you have to remember that it's just a fantasy. The thought of being gang-raped by sweating Visigoths might be highly arousing, but it may not be an experience you'd particularly relish in real life.

That's why it's worth keeping a diary of all of your erotic ideas, and all your sexual experiences, right down to the last time you masturbated, and how. When you read over them, you'll see what your dreams and your expectations were, and you'll be able to compare them with what you eventually get when you find a man. You'll be able to see why you're attracted to a certain personality and a certain look, and a certain way of making love. You'll *know* yourself, sexually, and that will give you an extraordinary amount of power when it comes to starting up a new relationship.

Some of the greatest people in history have been meticulous diarists, and there's a reason for that. Keeping a diary enables them to keep their lives in perspective, to record their dreams, and to enter into new relationships with a clear idea of what they expect and what they're prepared to accept. In other words, a diary is a very good way of preparing yourself for the realities of finding (and keeping) the kind of man you really want.

4

The Morning After
the Sex Before

The first thing you need to know about finding a new lover is that Tarot cards and
fortune-tellers are of no use whatsoever. Forget
about astrological charts. Forget about those 1-
800 psychics. Your passions aren't affected by
the stars, not in the slightest. They're entirely
controlled by your hormones.

Far too little attention is paid to the chemistry of sex. But the fact is that your sexual behavior is triggered by chemical responses in your
brain. If you can understand a little of what happens to you when you meet a man that you
really like (and when you form a relationship
with him) you have every chance of enjoying
the most erotic and possibly the most long-
lasting liaison that you've ever known.

What happens when we experience love at
first sight? Writer Chrissy Iley says, "It's hap-

pened to me. I met him and the world seemed to shrink. I had the notion of being bonded with him in a former life. I thought it was a hormonal trick, and it probably was."

"When I first saw Craig, I almost wet myself," said 24-year-old Polly, from Darien, Connecticut. "I wanted him. I wanted him to take me to bed. I wanted to have his children. I had only just been introduced to him and I wanted him so much I almost wept out loud from frustration."

Dr. Rajendra Sharma, at the Hale Clinic, said, "When we go into a room, we radiate energy. If someone is there that we want to see, waves coincide. Men and women emit pheromones. As soon as the brain smells these, hormones will heighten."

It was possible that Polly was ovulating. In *Anatomy of Love*, author Helen Fisher claims that during ovulation, women can smell a man more keenly. "They are more susceptible to infatuation when they smell male essence and are unconsciously drawn toward it."

As the male musk starts to affect your limbic system—that part of your brain which governs ecstasy and lust—something else is happening as well. Your subconscious is consulting your love map—a mock-up of the ideal man, the man you really want to be with. Chrissy Iley says, "Many times I have met this man who reminded me of that volatile, hypercritical, hot then cold, authoritative and ingenious, infinitely alluring daddy. I recognize the type now. I can smell it. And obviously the hormones are not far away."

When you first meet a man who turns you on, a violent emotional disturbance begins. It is set off by a neurochemical called phenylethylamine, accompanied by dopamine and the hormone LHRH (lueneising hormone-releasing hormone). LHRH controls the release of estrogen and progesterone.

The sexual charge that this cocktail of hormones can give you is enormous. You can feel like the earth is moving under your feet. But don't forget that *your* appearance and the pheromones that *you* are giving off can be equally disturbing to the men you meet.

You can't switch your hormones off. You can't stop yourself from being ridiculously attracted to that good-looking guy with the easy grin and the muscles. But so long as you're always aware that you're being taken on a roller-coaster ride by your own chemistry, and you learn to control what you say and how you behave, you can almost always catch the interest of the men who really interest you—and, more important— hold it.

In Chapter One, we talked about ways in which you can attract and keep a man's attention, and ways in which you can make it clear to him that you're interested in a relationship that goes further than holding hands while you listen to his old Duke Ellington records.

Once you've started talking to a man you like, it's important to show him how you feel, but at the same time it's equally important that you don't frighten him off. Men, like women, enjoy being openly flattered, but only to a very limited extent. What will often arouse their interest more is if you disagree with them, argue with them, and show them that you have a mind of your own. This will not only sharpen their interest in you, it will give *you* some idea of how clever they are, how arrogant they are (or not), and how dismissive they are (or not) of women's opinions. You can learn a whole lot more about a man you like by provoking him into a little verbal swordplay than you can by blinking at him with those big eyes of yours and hanging on his every word.

Men tend to shy away from aggressive, testosterone-charged Valkyries, but they do like their women to have personality as well as looks. I met dozens of gorgeous women when I was editing *Penthouse* magazine, but the woman who really caught my attention was my argumentative young editorial assistant—who later became my wife.

Some women, overwhelmed by their own hormonal response, go way over the top when they meet a man they find attractive and act positively rude. It's often their way of hiding their own feelings and of arousing the man's interest without showing him that they find him so magnetic. *You may make me feel like the whole planet has suddenly turned upside-down but I'm certainly not going to let you believe that you're as sexy as I think you are.*

Occasionally you'll find a man who is mature and experienced enough to realize why you're being so dismissive and sarcastic, and why you're making so many cutting remarks. He'll know that you like him and that you're only trying to stop yourself from showing it. After all, if you *really* didn't like him, you wouldn't even bother to talk to him, would you? On the whole, though, I wouldn't count on the men you meet being sophisticated enough to realize that when you're calling him vain, arrogant, and self-opinionated, you're really telling him that he's handsome, assertive, and confident, and that he turns your knees into raspberry Jell-O.

I talked to scores of men about their first-night experiences with women, and asked them what it was that first attracted them—and more important—what it was that made them want to see these women again. In other words, after their initial lust was satisfied, what special characteristic did these women have that made them more than one-night stands?

Attracting a man to make another date with you takes sexual skill. From what my male interviewees told me, it's obvious that too many women think that once they've gotten a man into bed, they've done all they have to do. The most often-repeated criticism was, "She woke up in the morning looking like she'd had a fight with a grizzly and lost. She yawned and stretched and flumped off to the bathroom like we'd been married for twenty years. She didn't bother to brush her hair properly or put on makeup, and she put her sweater on backward. I felt that now that she'd gotten me to go to bed with her, that was it, she didn't give a damn." Then again, "I tried to talk to her, tried to get a smile out of her, but all I got were grunts. After she'd had about six cups of coffee she told me that she wasn't a morning person. This was one o'clock in the afternoon."

The morning after the first night before (or the evening after the first afternoon before, or whenever you've been lucky enough to make love) is a critical moment in the development of a new sexual relationship. It can be the moment when your hormones decide that you don't really like this guy, after all, and this can cause you intense frustration, depression, and self-doubt. If this happens, this is the moment to cool it and *not* to rush into any further dates or assignations. Give yourself time to think.

But if you discover that he's still just as cute in the morning, then this is the moment for you to show him that *you're* just as alluring as the woman he wanted to make love to last night, if not more so. This is the moment to use good psychology to make sure that you've snared his interest enough to want to see and make love to you again . . . and again. I call this the Sex Hook. It's like the cliffhanger at the end of each episode of *The Bold and the Beautiful*, or at the end of each chapter of a good thriller. Keep your newly found lover intrigued, attracted, a little bemused, and eager to find out more.

Here are the real-life experiences of two men who each went to bed with a woman: why they did it, what the attraction was, and why they wanted to see that woman again. You'll see that each woman used a Sex Hook of one kind or another, sometimes deliberately, sometimes unconsciously. But in every case they aroused enough interest in their new partner to make him eager for more.

As you'll see, the Sex Hook isn't necessarily all about sex. It's about *allure*. It's about guiding your new lover into the kind of relationship that you want to have with him—a relationship from which you believe you will both derive the greatest pleasure, satisfaction, and excitement.

This is Chris, a 27-year-old magazine editor from Los Angeles, California. He met Cindy, a

24-year-old photographer's assistant, at a fashion shoot on the boardwalk at Venice Beach.
"You have to admit that Venice Beach is not exactly a babe-free zone. I have to say it was pretty
hard to concentrate on what we were doing with
all those bikini-clad girls whizzing around us on
Rollerblades. I wasn't really looking for anybody
at that particular time. The month before, my
live-in girlfriend had left me after four and a
half years, and I guess I was still hurting some.
I knew we weren't suited. We were always ar-
guing and throwing each other's clothes out of
the window. But when you lose somebody who's
been so close to you, you still feel like you've
got the flu, very hypersensitive and depressed.
You keep wanting to tell them things and they're
not there to tell.

"Anyhow, during a break I was sitting on a
director's chair drinking a soda when I noticed
this girl kneeling down on the boardwalk re-
loading all of the photographer's cameras. She
was small and blonde, with a pink-and-white
striped top and a pair of tight white shorts. And
white Nike shoes, too. She was very curvy, big-
breasted, a little bit of a tummy, but I've always
been a sucker for that. I don't like my women
to look like anorexics. The only trouble was, she
was wearing this baseball cap with a very long
peak, so I couldn't see her face.

"In the end, I walked up to her and offered

her a soda. She looked up and she had this incredible face. You couldn't call her exactly beautiful, but she had one of those Mariel Hemingway kind of faces—good cheekbones, deep-set eyes, wide mouth, and . . . freckles. I always melt when I see freckles.

"She stood up and took the soda and said, 'Thanks. You're a gentleman.' I said, 'You noticed?' just teasing her a little, and she smiled and said, 'In those shorts, how could I help it?' Now, that's something I really like in a girl. Flirty, with a little innuendo, not too much, but all carried off with a wide, sweet smile. She never stopped smiling, and she was smiling with her eyes, too, and that always makes me feel good. It makes me feel like the girl is really pleased to be talking to me. She paid attention to me, too. There's nothing worse than trying to talk to a girl and all the time her eyes are wandering off behind your left shoulder, searching for somebody handsomer or richer or famouser than you are. That happens all the time in LA, and if you ask me that's why there are so many dissatisfied young women here. Like, they can't *all* date Jack Nicholson.

"I asked Cindy about her job, and about her ambitions. She said she wanted to be a professional photographer one day, and then she asked if she could take my picture. That was when I knew she liked the look of me. Good photographers are always incredibly fussy, and they don't like taking pictures of people who don't interest them. Besides, it gave her an excuse to see me again, to show me the picture when it was developed. I asked her to make sure that it was a truthful picture. A real picture, the way she really saw me. 'That way, I'll know whether you like me or not.'

"After that, we had to continue with the fashion shoot. We were running out of time and light and we still had a whole lot of new outfits to photograph. I didn't have the chance to talk to Cindy again and I didn't see her leave at the end of the day . . . I was too busy making sure that the models didn't walk off with the clothes.

"But sure enough she called me at the office the following afternoon and said she had my picture and would I like to see it? We met at one of my favorite bars. The moment she walked in I knew that I still liked her just as much. She wore a simple white dress, very feminine, with ribbons at the shoulders, and her hair was in a long bob, with a single barrette to hold her fringe back. We had a cocktail and she showed me the pictures. I said, 'Do I look like this to you?' and she said, 'Yes . . . you look confident, but you look sensitive, too. Like you have an inner secret which you can't answer yourself but you won't trust to anybody else. And you look a little sad, too.'

"Well, I thought I was pretty good at flirting, but Cindy had the whole thing worked out to perfection. This was flirting *par excellence*, as far as I was concerned. She made me feel good looking and virile, but she also made me feel that I had my sensitive side, too; and there was the unspoken suggestion that she was the one who could help me get over my pain.

"I've used that same technique over and over, because every woman you meet has some kind of pain, some kind of uncertainty, and even if they love their husbands or whoever they're living with, there's always *something* that their partners don't appreciate about them; or some dissatisfaction in their lives they want to talk about.

"I drove Cindy home and she invited me in to see her portfolio. We opened a bottle of wine and sat on the couch and she showed me some of her work. Brilliant, most of it. People standing in huge empty landscapes. Lonesome, but very human at the same time. Then she showed me a series of nude self-portraits. They were black-and-white, very stark, and I didn't think they flattered her much. All the same, she had a really great body.

"She asked me what I thought. I looked at her and our faces were only inches apart. I kissed her, and said, 'I like pictures of T-bone steaks.

They make my mouth water. But I prefer the real thing.'

"I don't know how long it took us to get into bed after that. Only a matter of minutes, as I recall. Cindy crossed her arms and lifted off her dress, and underneath she was wearing this plain white gauzy bra that you could see her nipples through, and a plain white gauzy thong, which did nothing at all to cover up her pubic hair, which was shiny and blond.

"She unbuttoned my shirt and as she did so she stroked and caressed and massaged my chest and twisted my nipples between her fingertips, almost as if she wanted to screw them off. She was passionate and she made it obvious that she wanted me, but at the same time she was very vulnerable and very feminine, too. I'd say to any woman that it's a great trick if you can manage it. She was all soft and breathy, but looking back on it, she guided me into doing exactly what she wanted me to do.

"I took off her bra. Her breasts were gorgeous—big and heavy with wide pink nipples. I could literally weigh them in my hands. I ran my hand down her back and slid it underneath the elastic of her thong, which I slowly pulled out of the cheeks of her ass. At the same time I ran my middle finger deep between her cheeks so that I touched her asshole and her pussy. She was warm and wet and slippery already . . . and

I had a hard-on that was almost bursting out of my shorts.

"I picked her up and carried her through to the bedroom, and laid her on the bed. Then I stripped off my pants and my shorts. I made sure I took my socks off with my pants . . . I remember what you wrote about what guys look like when they're naked except for their socks! Then I climbed onto the bed with her.

"Like I say, she was a very clever lover because she gave the impression of being all girly and inexperienced, but when I thought about it afterward she made sure that I gave her all the arousal she needed and that I plunged right in there, which it was my natural urge to do.

"When I lay next to her and started kissing her and fondling her breasts she took hold of my cock in her hand and very slowly massaged it up and down. The feeling was sensational but it also meant that she was in control of my cock!

"I kissed her lips and she opened her mouth to me so that I could slide my tongue inside it. A very submissive way of kissing, very arousing. All the time she was still slowly massaging my cock and gently fondling my balls. She had very long fingernails so the sensation was prickly as well as tickly! As I say, she knew exactly what she was doing and what she wanted and yet she gave me the impression that she was so sweet and inexperienced. I mean, a guy likes to think that he's in charge, right?

"She held up one of her breasts in her hand and I licked and sucked at her nipple. She let out a little gasp when I did that, and of course that encouraged me to do it more. I kissed and licked her other breast and she made this very sexy murmuring sound and moved her hips and gripped my cock even tighter. There was no question about it, she was one of the most responsive girls I've ever been to bed with. She reacted to everything I did, so that I knew if she liked it or not. It was like when I ran my tongue down her stomach and stuck the tip of it into her navel, she obviously didn't like that, because she kind of twisted herself away. I had a girl-friend once who only told me after six months that she didn't like me touching her anus, especially when I put my finger up it . . . it made me feel so bad to think that every time we made love she'd been hating it. But with Cindy I knew immediately when I was doing the right thing and when I was doing the wrong thing. How can you be a better lover if the girl never gives you any idea of how you're making her feel?

"Cindy wriggled underneath me and used my cock to massage her own breasts. She pressed her nipples against the head of my cock and then she took hold of my balls and squeezed them in her cleavage. All the time she was moan-

ing and panting like I was doing something incredibly sexy, but it was only later that I realized that she was doing something incredibly
sexy to *herself*. She was using me to turn herself
on . . . not that I minded, because she was turning me on, too. She was one of the first girls I
ever met who didn't leave everything up to me,
when it came to lovemaking. It was a revelation, believe me.

"She licked the end of my cock and then she
sucked it. It's hard to describe, but she sucked
it like she'd never sucked a man's cock before,
but had always wanted to try it. Very tentative
at first, little experimental pokes with her
tongue, then a long swirl all around the head,
and a long, deep suck; and all the time she was
doing it she never took her eyes off me, not once;
and if there's a sexier sight than a woman sucking your cock while she's looking up at you with
big, big eyes, then I don't know what it is.

"While she was sucking me I reached down
and touched her cunt, playing with her clitoris
and pushing my middle finger into her vagina.
She was incredibly wet. I'd never felt a girl so
wet. The insides of her thighs were really slick
and her juice was dripping down between the
cheeks of her ass. It turned me on even more
because I felt that I had managed to excite her
more than any girl I'd ever slept with before. It

was like a real sense of, wow, I'm really good in bed.

"I kissed her stomach and her hips and I then I licked her between her legs. She was so juicy and I loved the taste of it. I opened her cunt wide with my fingers and licked her clitoris and stuck my tongue into her vagina, and I even managed to push the tip of my tongue into her pee-hole. My cock was so hard, it was like an iron bar, and I was literally dripping juice out of the end of it, almost as wet as she was. I think if she'd started to massage my cock again, or suck it, I would have climaxed there and then.

"I buried my face in her cunt so that her juice was all over me, my cheeks, my eyelashes, my chin. I was tasting it and smelling it and breathing it. Then I sat up and pushed my cock into her. It was such a feeling . . . she was hot and slippery and her cunt-muscles squeezed me with this incredible rippling motion, almost like she was sucking me, trying to draw me in deeper.

"She held on to me tight, and she kissed me and licked all of her own juice off my face, and that seemed to excite her even more. I was close to climaxing. I could feel this gripping sensation between my legs and I knew that I wouldn't be able to hold on very much longer. But then she suddenly sank her teeth into my shoulder, I mean really bit me, and she started to shake and shudder and dig her fingernails deep into my ass. She seemed to go on and on, one orgasm after another, with her teeth still sunk into my shoulder, and her fingernails still clawing my butt. I didn't know if she was drawing blood or not, but it sure felt as if she was.

"If I hadn't been so turned on, I wouldn't have been able to stand it. Especially when she dragged the checks of my ass wide apart and stabbed one of her fingers into my asshole. Boy, her nails were sharp! But then she stabbed another finger in, and stretched my asshole wide open while I was fucking her.

"It was sheer pain and sheer pleasure. I tried to stop myself from climaxing so soon, but when she started digging her fingernails even deeper into my ass, that was it, that finished me. I pumped up sperm and kept on pumping, and then I dropped on top of her, totally exhausted.

"She was one of the most exciting girls I'd ever met; but the next day I still wasn't sure if I was ever going to see her again. But just before I left, she said, 'I took some pictures of you last night, while you were sleeping. Why don't you come around later when I've developed them?'

"So what was I going to say? No?"

Cindy was comparatively inexperienced with men—Chris was only her third lover. There had been some juvenile fumblings with a second cousin when she was 15, and her second lover had been a domineering character who had never been faithful to her, and—worse than that—had never been able to satisfy her sexually, although she had never dared to tell him.

Because of the nature of that relationship, Cindy had taken a lot of the blame for it herself, and that was why she had sought help by reading some of my books and other sex instruction books by women authors.

"The greatest revelation was finding out that I could take control of my own sex life... that I didn't have to wait for the guy to turn me on. I could teach him how to do it as we went along. I think that controlling the way that your lover makes love to you is the single most empowering thing that I've ever learned. It means that I'm almost always satisfied."

Cindy didn't only take charge of the physical aspects of making love, she also made sure that she controlled the pace and the development of her relationship with Chris. She was particularly lucky to be a skillful photographer, which gave her a "hook" she could use to catch and hold Chris's interest and attention, and also gave her a way of making sure that he would want to see her again.

Developing a new sexual relationship isn't all about sex. It's about showing your new lover that you have depth and character and maybe a little mystery about you, too. What makes a sexual relationship especially erotic is *personality,* just as much as passion. Otherwise your lover might as well pick up a hooker and use her for sexual relief. Once his initial sexual tension is spent, your lover ought to be able to look at you and think of the promise of what's going to come next.

Here's David, a 32-year-old builder from Peoria, Illinois. David met 28-year-old Anna at a party to celebrate the completion of her parents' new house. Anna lives in Peoria, too, and works in a restaurant.

"You know how you see somebody and you know—you just *know*—that you're going to like them? That was the way I felt when I first saw Anna. She was standing on the other side of the room, laughing at something that somebody had said, and that was it. I was smitten. She has long dark shiny hair and big dark eyes and a slightly Greek-looking face. You know, exotic. And she was so slim I could have clasped her around the waist with both hands—which, as it turned out, I eventually did.

"I went across to her and introduced myself and asked her how she liked her parents' new home. She said it was all well and fine but she wouldn't live in it herself. Now that, of course, intrigued me. She said the rooms were spacious enough, and there was plenty of light, but it was never going to be a calm house, because the front door faced east and the study faced south.

"You see how she caught my attention right away without openly flirting? This was a girl who had an interesting point of view, and the fact that she happened to be gorgeous to look at was more than an added bonus. Mind you, she *did* flirt, subtly. She had a way of looking you right in the eye, like she was staring right into your soul, and then suddenly dropping her eyelids, so that you felt that she's seen something inside of you that was deeply personal, and she wasn't going to embarrass you by prying.

I asked her if she was some kind of expert on feng shui, but she said that she wasn't. She had learned all she needed to know about the auspicious positioning of houses from a Native American friend. You should never build a house with its door facing due east because that was where the evil spirits came from. And you should never build a workroom facing due south because that was the place for relaxing and restoring yourself. I said that I ought to employ her as a consultant for my building company, and she said why not?

"She asked me all about what houses I built, and she seemed real interested when I told her how hard I worked to give my customers genuine old-fashioned quality. She said she could tell my fortune by palm-reading. She took hold of my hand and traced the lines on it with her fingertip—and I swear that was one of the sexiest things that a strange woman has ever done for me. I didn't realize then how much she liked me, and how hard she was working to arouse my interest in her. Well, all I can say is that she didn't have to work *too* hard.

"She said that today was going to change my life, even if I didn't know it yet. I was going to live until I was eighty, but I was soon going to be faced with two major opportunities in my life—one for love and one for work—and if I made the wrong decision about either of those two opportunities, that was it, I was doomed to a life of disappointment and failure.

"I asked her if she could go into more detail, and this was the really clever bit. She said that she owned a set of Native American medicine-sticks, which could tell my future practically down to the last day. I said why don't I cook her dinner that evening, and she could bring her sticks along and tell me everything I needed to know.

"We both knew that we were attracted to each other; and we both knew what we were really talking about, and it wasn't fortunes. But that's the great thing about a girl who really knows how to flirt. If she likes the look of you, she sets up the situation so that you have a perfectly reasonable excuse for asking her out, but if you're busy or you're married or you don't really like the idea of starting a new relationship, you can bow out without any embarrassment on either side.

"I picked Anna up later that evening, and she brought along this old beaded bag. She told me how her friend had taught her all about Native American magic, and that it was still a whole lot more powerful than people believed. 'It's right here, in the soil, in the water, in the sky.'

"I cooked a meal, chicken and red pepper sauce if I remember rightly, and afterward we sat by the fire with a bottle of wine and she showed me how to read the medicine-sticks. She got the mixture just right: the magic, the fortune-telling, the firelight. She used the medicine-sticks to flatter me. She said the sticks said that I was passionate and headstrong and that I liked to make instant decisions. You see how she was able to pay me all these compliments without having to do it directly? She said that the sticks revealed that I was very attractive to women.

"I said, 'How about you?' and she smiled and said, 'Try me,' and that was the moment.

"I moved closer to her and kissed her; and it wasn't long before we were locked into a really passionate kiss. She was a terrific kisser, she had a way of running the tip of her tongue around my lips that really tingled. I ran my fingers through her hair and it felt like silk. There's nothing sexier than a woman who keeps her hair really clean and shining.

"I felt her breasts through this soft red cardigan she was wearing. She closed her eyes and tilted her head back and she had a look on her face, like, that feels so erotic. I unbuttoned her cardigan and slipped my hand inside her bra. Her nipples were tiny but sticking up real hard. I kissed her again and took off her cardigan and unfastened her bra. Her breasts were beautiful, small and rounded, and her nipples were as pink and sweet as jelly beans. Something else turned me on, too. It was the way she breathed. You wouldn't think that just *breathing* was so arousing, but Anna was breathing like she was gradually growing more and more excited. And it made me harder and harder, like we were having sex already.

"We kissed so much that my mouth was sore. I pulled down the zipper of her skirt, and wrestled it out from underneath her butt. She was wearing pantyhose underneath, that was all, no panties, and I could see the pink lips of her cunt spread open, all juicy and moist. You never saw anything so sexy in your whole life . . . well, I never had!

"She opened my shirt and stripped it right off me, kissing my shoulders and my chest and my every place else. Then she pulled open my pants and wrenched them right down my hips, and took off my Calvin Kleins, too.

"So many girls lie back and wait for you to make love to them. They do. They just lie back, and expect you to kiss them and have sex with them, and that's it. They don't do anything, they don't even participate, if you know what I mean. But Anna kissed me and bit me all over, she was like a mad dog. She bit my nipples and she bit my muscles, and then she wriggled underneath me and bit the checks of my ass.

"I rolled over onto my stomach, laughing, but when I did she ran her tongue all the way down between the cheeks of my ass and licked all around my anus. If that's not the most intimate thing you can do to somebody you've only just met, then I don't know what is.

"I lay back on the bed, and she started to suck my balls and tickle my cock, little, skittering movements, all the way up and all the way down. Before I knew it, she had taken my cock into her mouth, and was sucking it and rubbing it so hard that there were two or three times when I thought that I was going to climax, right into her mouth.

"I rolled her over onto her back and I kissed her and fondled her breasts. I tried to slide my hand down between her legs but she kept her thighs tightly clenched together. She was teasing me, and she couldn't stop laughing. You never heard such a sexy laugh. I turned around and opened up her thighs with both hands, until they were wide apart. Her cunt was beautiful, just a little tuft of dark hair at the top and the rest of it shaved bare. Lips like rose petals, and brimming with juice. I put my head down and licked her clitoris and all around her cunt-hole. She was so wet that I could literally drink it.

"At first she kept trying to close her legs. But then she stopped struggling and started to do that deep breathing again. While I was licking her, she reached between my legs and took hold of my cock and my balls and started to pull on them, real slow and rhythmic, in time with her breathing.

"I licked faster and faster. I wanted to fuck her, but she tasted so good and she was getting so worked up that I didn't want to stop licking her. She stopped playing with my cock and reached down with both hands and pulled the lips of her cunt as wide apart as she could. I'd never had a girl do that before, and it was incredibly exciting. It was like she wanted to expose herself as much as possible, show me everything, and let me lick everything.

"I couldn't have been licking her for more than four or five minutes when her breathing went real slow. She started to lift her hips up and draw her thighs together tighter and tighter. She kept her hands between her legs, though, spreading herself wide. Then she had an orgasm, a real bed-quaking orgasm. She shuddered and shook but I didn't stop licking her; and even when she'd finished, and she started to relax, I opened her thighs and gave her cunt a long, slow tongue-bath, until I'd licked up every last drop of juice. Then I climbed on top of her and slowly slid my cock in. It was amazing. She was so slippery inside; it was like putting my cock into warm syrup.

"I fucked her good and slow, and all the time she looked up at me with this dreamy expression in her eyes, which was very flattering, and she trailed her fingers all the way down my back and between my legs, and played with my balls, and caressed her own cunt-lips. I didn't realize it until I read one of your books, but that's a good technique for a woman to use to make a man vary his strokes during sex. Obviously it's a turn-on, a woman fondling her own cunt while she's making love, but it means she can make sure that the guy doesn't go on banging his cock into her at the same old angle and the same old speed. So whether she was doing it on purpose or not, Anna sure used all the right moves.

"When I was just about to climax, she started to breathe deeply again. Her eyes closed and her face was all flushed. I pushed my cock into her harder and quicker, and she started to pant. I could feel the sperm building up between my legs, and I was right on the edge of coming when she came first. She bit my shoulder and held me so tight that I didn't think she was ever going to let me go, and I could feel her cunt going into spasm. That was it. I filled her up with sperm, four huge spurts that made me feel as if my whole soul was shooting out of my cock.

"We made love again twice that night. I was hooked, no doubt about it, because she was such a good lover. But she made sure that she saw me again. After she had left the next morning, I found one of her medicine-sticks under the pillows. I called her at work that morning and told her that I'd bring it to her. She asked me which stick it was, and when I described it, she said that it represented physical pleasure; and that when I brought it back she would be able to predict how much sexual delight I was going to have in the next six moons. Granted, it was a pretty obvious line, but how could I resist it?"

Anna, remarkably, had only had two lovers before David, and the first of those relationships had been, in her own words, "catastrophic. I was so awkward and so ignorant. I had no idea what a man wanted from a woman in bed, or how to give it to him, and most of all I didn't realize that most men are just as awkward and ignorant as women.

"The one thing I learned about being a good lover is that you have to stop thinking about yourself. Once you forget about your own pleasure and concentrate all of your attention on your partner, then you find that you get all the satisfaction you want."

Anna read an article of mine in *Woman's Own* in which I listed oral sex as the most popular way in which a woman can turn her man on. "I thought to myself, if that's what men really like, then I'll try it, and I'll try to be real good at it, too. I tried it with my second lover and he went wild for it, but for all kinds of other reasons our relationship broke up. He had problems at work and he was drinking a whole lot, which doesn't make for a very successful sex life.

"I guess Dave was the first guy who really enjoyed the benefit of my new sex techniques. I don't think he could believe his luck when I went down on him and started to give him head. He told me afterward that it was like Christmas and his birthday all rolled into one."

Anna was also pleased with the effectiveness of the simple technique of fondling her own vulva while David was having intercourse with her. Some women don't like the idea of touching themselves during sex, but men find it highly arousing, and of course it has the benefit of allowing you to control how deep his penis penetrates you, and at what angle, and at what rhythm and speed. As magazine writer Sarah

Lewis says, "Real men know that the best way to get a girl to come is to vary the strokes of penetration, and don't keep rubbing the same spot over and over again.

"Penetration is an art in itself. I like a man to rub the shaft of his dick in a circular motion hitting the inside entrance of my pussy, then push it up against the upper walls and rub them up and down. This hits the root of my clitoris and always makes me come over and over again."

With your hand down between your legs during intercourse you can circle your lover's penis with finger and thumb to prevent him from penetrating too deeply; or you can manipulate his erection as you would a dildo. Kelley, a 27-year-old manicurist from Boston, Massachusetts, said that she loves to take her lover's penis out of her vagina during intercourse and use it to massage her clitoris. "I rub it up and down in between my pussy-lips and Larry absolutely loves it. He says it feels great while I'm doing it, and when I let him put his cock back into my pussy, it feels even better than it did before. And of course it means that I'm even more aroused than ever."

If you're usually slow to reach orgasm, you can always masturbate yourself during intercourse, although some men find it off-putting if you're furiously rubbing your clitoris while they're making love to you. Your flying knuckles can be uncomfortable for them, and it tends to make them feel as if you don't think that they're doing much of a job of turning you on. So a slow, lascivious self-stroking would be more involving.

Incidentally, men are highly excited by the sight of a woman masturbating. If you want a guaranteed way of getting your lover and/or husband into bed, simply lie back, open your legs and play with yourself. You will not only stimulate him, you will be giving him a very explicit show-and-tell of the way you like to have your clitoris fondled.

Rita, a 24-year-old librarian from Port Charlotte, Florida, said, "I was always brought up to believe that there was something shameful about a woman touching herself. My mother was very old-fashioned about sex and never told me anything about sex technique. It was only when I went to summer camp when I was sixteen that I found out how to give myself an orgasm by masturbating. I met two girls there, Sally and Beth, who were very sexually forward. They spent the whole time talking about boys and what it would be like to have a penis up inside them, and whether they would swallow if a boy climaxed in their mouth. I didn't even know that women actually sucked men's penises, let alone swallowed their semen! I was shocked, you

know, but at the same time I was totally fasci-
nated, too.

"One evening Sally and Beth went walking
off into the woods. I asked them if I could come
with them, but at first they didn't want me to.
They said they were going to do something private, and I'd only tell. But I kept on saying please
and pretty-please and in the end they let me.
They went to a clearing which was hidden away
from the main trail. They spread out a blanket
and then without any kind of hesitation Beth
took off all of her clothes and Sally took off her
shorts and her panties. Beth lay on the ground.
She had huge breasts, much bigger than mine.
She opened up her legs and when I saw her
dark hairy pussy I didn't know where to look.
But Sally knelt beside her and started to play
with her, opening up her pussy-lips with her
fingers and stroking her clitoris. She said, 'This
is how you get the most fantastic feelings in the
world.' Then she slid a finger right up inside
her pussy, and then another, and then another.
I'd never touched *myself* like that. I can remember sitting there beside them, watching
Sally's fingers with their bright red nails disap-
pearing right up inside Beth's pussy. I was
stunned but incredibly turned-on, too.

"Sally masturbated Beth right up to an orgasm. Beth lay back, with her eyes tight shut,
clutching and squeezing her breasts, and when

she came she let out this high-pitched scream.
It was a good thing we were too far away from
camp for anybody to hear us. Then they changed
places. Sally lay on the blanket and Beth started
to masturbate *her*. I couldn't keep my eyes off
Sally's pussy. I'd never seen a girl completely
shaved before. I mean, I used to shave at the
side of my legs so that I wouldn't have any hairs
peeking out of my swimsuit, but I didn't realize that girls shaved everything off so that their
pussies were completely bare. I thought it was
amazingly daring. Supposing you were in the
bath and your mother walked in and saw you?

"Beth stroked Sally's clitoris and then she
leaned forward and actually started licking it.
Sally kept saying, 'That's beautiful, that's beautiful . . .' and opened her legs even wider. Then
Beth worked two fingers up inside Sally's pussy,
and then a third, and then a fourth. She kept on
licking her clitoris at the same time, and that
was the first time I had ever seen a clitoris stand
up really stiff. After a while, Beth folded her
thumb into the palm of her hand and slowly
pushed her whole hand into Sally's pussy, right
up to the wrist, almost as far as her charm
bracelet. Sally was going, 'Oh, oh, oh . . .' and I
could see that Beth was kind of churning her
hand around inside her. That was something else
I never knew that you could do . . . push your
whole hand right up somebody's pussy. Her

pussy was swollen and red and shiny with juice and she was so turned on that she was bumping her butt up and down on the blanket and going 'Oh, oh, oh . . .' and thrashing her head from side to side.

"Then, without any warning, while Beth was still licking her, she peed. It came spurting out of her pee-hole like a bright sparkling fountain, all over Beth's chin, and running down the cheeks of her ass. But Beth kept on licking her, didn't stop for a second, and even stuck her tongue out so that Sally peed on her tongue.

"A few seconds after that, Sally had an orgasm, too, and she clung onto Beth and shook and shook like we were going through an earthquake. Beth took her hand out slow and careful, but Sally's pussy was still red and wet and wide open. They sat side by side on the blanket, all hot and sweaty but with smiles on their faces. Sally said, 'If you haven't tried it, you haven't lived. Do you want to try it?'

"I think I hesitated for about two seconds. I was so turned-on by what they had shown me that I knew I had to find out what it was like. It seemed forbidden and dirty and disgusting, but that was what made it all the more exciting.

"I took off my shorts and my blouse but I left my socks and my bra on. I lay down on the blanket and Sally opened up my legs. I was shivering, and it wasn't just the breeze. But then Sally started to stroke my pussy with her fingertips, very lightly, so that I could hardly feel it, but the sensation was wonderful. She gently played with my clitoris, and then she opened my pussy-lips wider and pushed a finger inside me. I suddenly panicked and said, 'Not your whole hand!' but she smiled and said, 'Not this time . . . that's for later.' She kept on playing with my clitoris, rubbing it very light and quick, and it wasn't long before I began to have a feeling between my legs that was just like having warm honey poured all over me. Now Beth pushed a finger into my pussy, too, and circled it around and around and around. I closed my eyes. I thought that I had just discovered paradise. Beth took her finger out and circled it around my asshole, making sure that it was wet and slippery. If somebody had told me that morning that I would let another girl push her finger into my ass, I never would have believed them, not in a million years. But now it was actually happening, and I loved it, and I wanted it. I could feel the tip of her finger worming its way inside, and then I relaxed, and she pushed it further and further, right up to the knuckle, and then slowly rotated it around and around.

"At the same time, Sally was flicking my clitoris quicker and quicker. She slid her finger back into my pussy, and started to play with

Beth's finger, right through the wall of my pussy. That was when I suddenly felt as if I was blacking out. I had my first orgasm. It hit me just like that, and washed me away. The next thing I knew I was opening my eyes and looking up at the trees and feeling like every problem in my whole life had vanished.

"After that day, I masturbated almost every day, sometimes twice a day. I still masturbate a couple of times a week, because I enjoy it, even when I'm involved in a relationship. I think it's one of the best ways to keep in touch with your sensuality and to case all of your tensions.

"Most of all, though, it can really improve your sex life. While you're making love, you can give yourself just enough extra fondling to make sure that you're satisfied. And my boyfriends love to watch me masturbate. By the time they put their cock inside me, they know that I'm well turned-on, and they're turned-on, too."

Rita is the kind of girl who has her lovers coming back for more. Her Sex Hook is her openness about her sexual appetite and the way she helps the men in her life to satisfy it. But if you're a little more reticent than Rita, here are six ways in which real women have made sure that their first-night lovers call them back for a return engagement.

1) Jane, 26, from Spokane, Washington: "I left my panties in his bed, so he had to call me later to give them back to me. And I think the idea that I had gone home without any panties really turned him on."

2) Beatrice, 22, from Long Island City, New York: "I woke him up in the morning by giving him oral sex. Then before we were finished, I suddenly looked at the clock beside the bed and told him I had to go to an urgent meeting. I dressed in a mad hurry and rushed out of his apartment with a promise to see him later and finish off what I had started! He followed me to the door, his cock still sticking up, so frustrated that he was almost having a panic attack."

3) Linda, 31, from Fort Lee, North Carolina: "I took a shower in the morning and asked him if he'd mind if I borrowed his razor. I said there was something that I'd been meaning to do for a long time. That was all. I said that he could see what it was when I met him again. He called me three times that day!"

4) Fran, 28, from Marina del Rey, California: "He was a very serious jazz lover. I called him the day after we first met and told him that a friend of mine had given me two free tickets to a jazz concert. Actually,

I'd paid for them myself, but they turned out to be a great investment. He said it was great to meet a girl with personality as well as looks."

5) Jessica, 35, from Chicago, Illinois: "I cooked him breakfast in the nude. Nothing too fancy, just pancakes and eggs. He asked me if I wanted to borrow a robe but I told him I always did my household chores naked. That really got him going. He told me later that every time he thought of me, he imagined me vacuum-cleaning in the nude, and it gave him an instant hard-on!"

6) Sara, 23, from Scranton, Pennsylvania: "The day after we first slept together, I had my hair done, and I put on my shortest, sexiest dress, and I made a visit to his office when I knew that he was going to be out. I made sure that I flirted with his colleagues, left him a message that I had just stopped by to say hello and then I left. He called me about an hour later, to make another date. Everybody in his office had been so impressed by what a sexy girl-friend he had that his ego had been boosted to the skies."

A last word about the morning after, and how to be sure that you've hooked your man: remember that dressing is just as much of an erotic art as stripping. How many women who slipped so seductively out of their underwear the night before sit down on the end of the bed and drag on their pantyhose as if they're filling up bags of coal? I've even seen women pull their pantyhose halfway up their thighs and then give a little jump in the air to pull them up the rest of the way. Very alluring . . . not.

And bras. I know it's easier to fasten them up by putting them on back to front and then twisting them around, but the sight of two empty cups hanging from your back isn't exactly guaranteed to raise an instant erection. Similarly, wrestling your way into your discarded sweater and appearing hot and flushed out of the neckhole isn't the sexiest sight ever.

To look your sexiest, put on your bra first (right way 'round), and then your sweater or blouse. Brush your hair before you put on anything else. If you're wearing pantyhose, sit on a chair facing him so that as you lift your knees he will get a quick, tantalizing glimpse between your legs. Make sure that you've rolled your pantyhose right down to the toes so that you can insert your feet and then smooth them all the way up to your thighs. Then stand, and draw them right up to your waist, facing him for just an instant longer, and then turning away. It's not necessary to wear pantyhose *and* panties, and they certainly don't look very elegant to-gether.

Remember that when you're gone, your new lover will think of you the way you were when he last saw you, and if you tugged on your clothes any which way, and half-brushed your hair, and yawned, and couldn't be bothered to put on any make-up, that's what he'll see in his mind's eye—no matter how dishy you looked the night before. So don't be too sure that he'll call you again.

It takes confidence and a little experience to be good at hooking a man. But what do you do if you've never had a man before? What do you do if you're still a virgin, and your experience of sex is confined to kissing and fumbling and not much else? How can you control your sex-ual arousal with any kind of expertise if you've never touched a man's penis before, and you have very little idea of what it's like to have one inside you?

Let's take a look now at very first loves, and how to make sure that they're thrilling and re-warding instead of leaving you thinking that sex is a terrible disappointment, and wishing you'd never done it.

5

Very First Love

It's always fascinating to ask women about the very first time they made love. Every experience is different. Some of them are characterized by youthful awkwardness, like trying to have intercourse on the backseat of a Volkswagen Beetle. Some of them are tense and uneasy, like waiting until your parents are away for the weekend and then guiltily making love in their bed. Some of them are romantic: sex on the seashore, among the dunes, with the breeze blowing on your bare skin. Some of them are funny, like the couple who tried to make love in an armoire during an 18th birthday party. The closet fell over, trapping them both inside. True story!

But almost every woman I've ever spoken to about her first sexual experience—no matter how pleasurable or happy it was—says, "I wish I'd known much, much more about men."

They felt that if they had been more knowledgeable about male sexuality, they could have derived much more pleasure and satisfaction not just from their first experience but from all their subsequent experiences. The first time you make love sets a pattern. It can permanently affect your attitude toward sex for the rest of your life, in spite of the fact that you are completely inexperienced and have no way of judging whether the lovemaking was the best you're ever going to get, or moderately good, or simply ho-hum.

Women also often express regret that the man they first slept with didn't know more about women. Quite frequently, they entered into a sexual relationship that lasted for months or years or even blossomed into marriage, unaware that their lovers were not very good at sex at all.

Philippa, 32, a florist from Portland, Maine, said: "The greatest regret in the whole of my life is that I was so innocent when I first had sex. I knew all of the technical details they teach you at school, but what they don't teach you is how to know if you're having a great sex life or not. How can you judge, unless you sleep with dozens and dozens of men, and I'm not the kind of person who likes the idea of sleeping around. I'm monogamous. I'm loyal. Unfortunately I was monogamous and loyal to a guy who had no idea how to satisfy me in bed. We were married for seven years and he never once gave me an orgasm. Not once. And it wasn't just orgasms. He never made love to me as if he really cared about me sexually. He just used me for his own satisfaction.

"I was unfaithful with my neighbor's husband. We only did it once and we were both ashamed of it afterward, but it was a revelation. I cried all night because I suddenly knew what I'd been missing."

Philippa's experience is not at all uncommon, and it's the fundamental reason why I always tell women that they need to take control of their own sex lives, regardless of whether they believe that their lover is a grunt'n'groan'n'go-to-sleep merchant or the hottest lover since Casanova. Because, quite honestly, too many men regard their own sexual release as their highest priority, and ignore the needs and feelings of the women they're supposed to be making love to. Even men who are technically quite good in bed, and give their partners regular orgasms, can be guilty of doing it only because it gives them greater pleasure. It may not be deliberate, most of the time, but out of plain old-fashioned ignorance.

Greg, 36, a computer programmer from Los Angeles, California, said, "I love the feeling when a woman comes. I love it. It sends ripples all the way up and down your cock." When I asked him what he thought orgasm felt like for a woman, he didn't have an answer. It hadn't even occurred to him to think about it. Did he think women experienced different kinds of orgasms? "I don't know. Maybe. Sometimes they scream and sometimes they don't."

Arnold, 24, a realtor trainee from San Diego, California, said, "Women can have a climax, for sure, but it's not a climax in the same way that a guy has a climax. Like, a guy *needs* to have a climax, otherwise he feels bad—you know, psychologically as well as physically. It's actually harmful for a guy to get aroused and then not come. But with a woman, a climax is like a bonus you know, because it's not essential, is it, for having kids or anything. But if a man didn't climax he'd never have any kids, would he?"

This kind of thinking is so misguided that it is almost hilarious. But there is nothing hilarious about a sexual relationship in which a woman is never given the full pleasure she deserves. It's a constant feeling that there *must* be more to sex than a few minutes of silent coupling twice a week that leads so many women to seek excitement in the arms of other men.

So if you're thinking of having sex for the very first time—or if you suspect that it might very well happen to you soon—make sure that you have a clear idea of your own sexual needs and entitlements, and that you have a reasonable idea how to guide your lover-to-be into satisfying them for you.

Although your needs and entitlements may vary from those of others, consider the possible benefits of a healthy and fulfilling sexual relationship:

(a) compliments, affectionate kisses and caresses.
(b) comprehensive and pleasurable stimulation, leading to
(c) an overwhelming feeling of erotic excitement, and
(d) a discovery of the intimacy that complete physical bonding can bring you. Good sex is a journey of the mind as well as the body.

After (a),(b),(c) and (d) you may have

(e) one or more orgasms, but you should certainly have
(f) a feeling of satisfaction, mental and physical well-being, and a very special closeness to the man with whom you have just made love.

If you feel that you haven't had these needs and entitlements fulfilled, if you feel in any way disappointed or confused, and especially if you feel that you haven't achieved that very special closeness, then you should be thinking twice about your first-time lover. He may not be as good in bed as he thinks he is. That's not to say that you should dismiss him out of hand, especially if it's *his* first time, too. First sexual encounters are invariably hurried, flurried, and less than technically perfect. But your first partner should show that his primary concern is to make you feel good, and to show less interest in his own satisfaction than he does in yours. If he doesn't, then he's going to need some serious guidance, and it's up to you whether you want to be the woman who's going to give it to him.

Your first sexual experience doesn't have to be stylish or complicated. Making love and feeling good about it is all that you need to do. Enthusiasm will more than make up for elegance, and besides, I've never been a subscriber to the idea that you ought to know scores of complicated sexual positions.

There are only a handful of positions that are comfortable and effective for really good lovemaking. Of course they *look* highly erotic, but all of those Indian temple sculptures and Japanese pillow-books showing women tying themselves into knots so that they can expose their genitalia to their rampant lovers in ever more extravagant ways were all produced as erotica rather than practical guides. I can't believe that many couples were ever capable of doing "Diving Cormorant Scoops An Oyster Out Of Woven Basket" without both of them putting their backs out.

Practically all the repertoire you need is:

1: Him on top of you
2: You on top of him
3: Both of you side-by-side
4: Him behind you while you're on your hands and knees—the so-called "doggy style."

If you're athletic, you might be able to make love standing up; and there are plenty of minor variations that can give you deeper penetration, such as draping your legs over his shoulders. I've seen some girls who are so supple that they can hook their ankles behind their own heads, which opens their vulva wide and probably allows the maximum penetration possible (in addition to looking amazingly sexy). Similarly, a few men can fold themselves up so that they can suck their own penises. But don't worry if you can't manage anything so gymnastic. You'll still have a terrific time in bed.

I said that orgasm was one of your sexual entitlements. But the very first time you make love you may not find that you're capable of achieving it, and you shouldn't necessarily regard it as an essential goal. You should enjoy the sheer pleasure of losing your virginity without worrying about reaching a climax, although there are several ways in which you can increase the likelihood of reaching an orgasm either before or after intercourse. Your very first urge will be for penetration, to feel your lover's penis inside you. Once you've savored that experience, you can start thinking about full sexual release.

Katherine, 25, a fitness trainer from Atlanta, Georgia, said, "I've had three sexual relationships and I have never once had an orgasm from intercourse alone. The very first time I made love I expected to feel something like an atomic explosion inside me—or fireworks at least, or crashing waves, like you see in the movies. And my first lover wasn't too bad—he had an enormous cock and he was fit: he could keep going for fifteen minutes without even breathing any harder. Sometimes I was nearly there, but I never quite made it. You can imagine how disappointed I was. I seriously thought there was something wrong with me. Maybe I wasn't sexy enough. But then I talked to a friend of mine and she said that *she* never reached orgasm either—not through intercourse alone, anyhow. She and her husband had tried one of those rubber rings that a man fits around the base of his cock, with a clitoral stimulator attached to it.

She said that worked a couple of times, but after a while it made her sore and it didn't really have the right sensitive touch that she was looking for. In the end, she insisted that her husband finger her clitoris or go down on her and lick her before they had intercourse, so that she had a guaranteed orgasm. I tried that with my boyfriend, and he liked it and I liked it—especially when I had my very first orgasm."

Very few women are regularly brought to orgasm by intercourse alone, regardless of what you read in romantic novels or see in the movies. You may have one from the sheer excitement of making love for the first time, but, as I say, don't be disappointed if you don't. The great advantage of having your lover bring you to orgasm before penetration is that you will be guaranteed 100 percent sexual satisfaction, and your lovemaking will also be prolonged. If you make sure that you respond to his caresses with plenty of obvious pleasure (moaning is good, so is gasping) then you will greatly increase his arousal, too, and make him feel much more virile.

When your lover penetrates you immediately after your orgasm, there is always a much greater chance of your experiencing yet another orgasm, or even more. Julia, 27, from Pittsburgh, Pennsylvania, told me that she once had so many orgasms "I had to beg my partner to stop." If you're going to encourage your lover to give you a pre-penetrative climax, it's important that you're happy and comfortable with the idea of him fondling you with his fingers or giving you oral stimulation with his tongue.

Maggie, 26, an accountant from White Plains, New York, said, "Right from the start, I was shy about showing my pussy to my boyfriend. I was one of those girls who prefers to make love in the dark, right under the blankets. I couldn't understand how a boy could possibly think that anything so wet and hairy was attractive. I knew about men going down on women but I thought it sounded yukky. How could a man actually want to lick your pussy? I guess you could say that I had a very poor sexual self-image. Then one day I was talking to my friend Janice and she said that her boyfriend couldn't get enough of going down on her, and he was fantastic. She said that she'd had fifteen orgasms in one weekend. Fifteen! And I had only ever had one, and that was more like a sneeze than an orgasm. I told her I didn't like the idea of John licking my pussy but she said that I didn't know what I was missing."

Many young women feel the same way about oral sex as Maggie. Because *they* don't relish the idea of kissing and licking a well-lubricated vulva, they don't realize that almost all men find it a highly arousing and overwhelmingly intimate experience. Many men not only relish the flavor of woman's sexual juices, they like to "wash" their faces between their lovers' legs while they're giving them cunnilingus. Jeff, a 33-year-old journalist from Minneapolis, Minnesota, said that he never cleaned his face after going down on his girlfriend because "I love to sit at work and breathe in the smell of her cunt. It reminds me of the last time we fucked and it makes me even more eager for the next time."

Like Maggie, many women find the sight of their lover lying between their legs and licking their vulva to be embarrassing or even disturbing. Jenny Fabian, author of a notorious 1960s memoir called *Groupie*, confessed to having oral sex with so many men that she could taste sperm in her mouth day and night. But when I asked her what she thought about a man giving *her* oral sex, she said that she didn't like the idea of it at all. "I can't stand the thought of a man's *face* down there. I would really put me off." Other women find the sight of their lover with a pubic hair moustache to be frankly ridiculous, and what should have been an intensely arousing sexual act is ruined by fits of giggles (hers) and annoyance (his).

So if you do find the idea of your lover going down on you to be either unsettling or amusing, close your eyes and pretend that you're doing it out of sheer ecstasy. After a while, don't worry, your ecstasy will be genuine.

I advised Maggie to overcome her shyness not by switching off the light and hiding under the comforter but by the simple expedient of closing her eyes, and (for the first few times at least) concentrating on nothing but the pleasure that her lover was giving her.

Another way of dealing with any reservations that you may have about your lover giving you oral sex is to give *him* oral sex in return. You can turn yourself around in bed so that your mouth is close to his penis, and divert all your attention to kissing and licking it, rolling it against your cheeks and tangling it in your hair. This is the famous position known as "69" because of the shape that you and your lover's bodies form together. However, while it will distract your attention from what your lover is doing to you, it will be more difficult for you to achieve orgasm in the 69 position than it would be if you were simply lying back and letting him concentrate all his oral attention on your clitoris. Sixty-nine is very arousing as part of your love play, but the real satisfaction of giving oral sex is gained from concentrating on making your lover feel as pampered and aroused as possible, and it isn't easy to keep your mind on what you're doing while you are being orally stimulated in return.

Jack, 29, an electrical engineer from Milwaukee, Wisconsin, said, "I love going down on my partner. I could do it all night and all the next day. But as soon as I start doing it she twists around and starts sucking me out, too. I like it. I mean, it's kind of hard to complain about your girl sucking your cock and licking your balls. But I always find it frustrating, because I start to think about how *I'm* feeling, and I lose my rhythm. I start to think things like, what am I going to do if I come? Am I going to come in her mouth or am I going to take my cock out? What would she think if I didn't tell her that I was coming and just shot my load right down her throat? I can't keep my mind on licking her and in the end neither of us end up coming. Which is a pity, because there's nothing I like better in the world than having my face between her legs while she's having an orgasm. You can keep Magic Mountain, that's the ride for me."

I was interested to learn why Jack hadn't ever told his partner how he felt; and why he hadn't asked her if she would like him to ejaculate into her mouth or not. He said that he "couldn't find the words," and I wasn't altogether surprised. Many couples find it difficult to discuss sex frankly—even couples who have lived together and had sex together for years. Many women would take a question like "Would you mind if I came in your mouth?" as an expression of their lover's desire for them to swallow their semen, rather than a simple request to find out if they would enjoy it or not. Then there's the problem of *when* to ask such a question. A woman who might relish the idea of drinking her lover's ejaculate while she is sexually aroused may find the idea repulsive when she isn't.

This is why it's important to start talking about sex from the moment you start your first intimate relationship. If you do it from the very beginning, you'll find it much easier as your relationship develops. Try a few words like "I really love it when you do that . . ." or "the way you kiss me . . . it really turns me on." Or try a sexy idea like "When you play with my nipples like that . . . I think I could almost have an orgasm without you touching me anyplace else."

From the very first time you make love, keep up a sexual dialogue with your lover, letting him know what you enjoy and what you don't. And don't be afraid of using "dirty" words that you wouldn't normally dream of using with anybody else. Some couples get around the problem by using pet names for their sexual parts, such as "Petey" and "Mary." Others use any one of the infinite variety of slang expressions such as "pecker" and "muff." I have even heard a man (quite straight-faced) refer to his wife's anus as her "dishcloth holder." But personally I think that the good old Anglo-Saxon words like "cock" and "cunt" and "fuck" are the best way in which lovers can express themselves. Spoken with affection and passion, they're arousing, direct, and loving.

Going back to Maggie's problem with oral sex, I told her that it was vital that she learn physical self-love. She needed to be proud of her nakedness, and to understand in particular that her vulva was beautiful and highly desirable, and that far from being off-putting, its wetness gave her lover proof that she found him sexually exciting, and would excite him in return.

I told her to remember that sex escalates. If your lover knows that you are stimulated by what he is doing to you, he will be stimulated by your response, which in turn will stimulate you even more. That is why I always place such emphasis on showing your partner that he is making you feel good, even if you have to act a little.

Learn to love your genitalia as much as your lovers will. One of my most successful self-training programs was "The Sex Glow"—giving yourself a quiet, undisturbed time during the day when you sit in front of a mirror with soft music playing and examine yourself sexually, as well as gradually stimulating yourself so that you can see how your vulva changes when you become erotically excited. I have had countless comments from women who found these sessions helped them to become familiar with the attractiveness of their own sexual organs and to lose their inhibitions about displaying them to their lovers. And when I say "displaying," I don't just mean letting them catch an occasional glimpse. Your lover would love the opportunity to examine you closely and slowly and in great detail. He loves the look of you and the feel of you, and like all men he has an overwhelming sexual curiosity. In Japan, strippers squat on stage shining a powerful flashlight into their vaginas so that their audience can have a good long stare at "the holy of holies." And there is a widespread sexual fetish in which men use surgical speculums (stainless-steel spreaders) to examine women's vaginas. These are obviously extreme examples, but don't forget that no matter what *you* think your genitalia look like, *he* will adore them.

"I have unusually long vaginal lips," wrote Sandra, from Gainesville, Florida. "So much so that I don't like the idea of a man seeing me naked." Jill, from Cincinnati, Ohio, wrote, "My pubic hair is very thick and dark. I tried to shave it but I ended up with a dark shadow which looked worse." Naomi, from Boston, Massachusetts, wrote, "Whenever I kiss my boyfriend I get so wet between my legs that I don't want him to touch me there. Is there something I can do to stop myself from getting so wet? I'm too embarrassed to talk to my doctor."

If you have any doubts about the appearance of your genitalia, the best thing that you can do is to buy or borrow a man's magazine such as *Playboy* or *Hustler*, or, better yet, a naturist magazine that shows ordinary everyday women without their clothes on. Or rent a porno video. You will then immediately see that women's vulvas are as infinitely varied in appearance as their faces. You will see long lips, fleshy lips, narrow lips, wavy lips, and straight lips. You will see clitorises that stand proud and some that are tucked away almost invisibly. You will see darkly pigmented vulvas and crimson vulvas and pink vulvas. You will see pubic hair that looks like a briar patch, pubic hair that looks like corn silk, and no pubic hair at all. They're *all* "normal."

Once Maggie was convinced that there was nothing at all distasteful about her genitalia, she became much more confident about allowing her lover to give her oral sex, and about displaying herself naked. She said that the "eyes-closed" trick worked extremely well. Not only did it give her the nerve to lie on the bed naked, with the lights on, but it actually encouraged her lover to go down on her. "I pretended to be sleeping. I lay on my back with my legs slightly apart. I was nervous but pretending that I was asleep made it much easier. Rick came into the bedroom talking, but then he hushed up as soon as he saw me. He took off his clothes, creeping around on tippytoe. Then he sat on the bed beside me. He stroked my forehead and kissed me. I murmured a little, like I was talking in my sleep, but I kept my eyes closed. The next thing I knew he was kissing my breasts. He licked my nipples, and fondled my breasts more than he ever did when I was awake. It felt gorgeous, because he was really taking his time, rolling my nipples in between his fingers and gently squeezing my breasts.

"He ran the tip of his tongue right down my stomach. He licked around my tummy-button and that was so sexy that it was everything I could do to pretend that I was still asleep. It always gives me this weird feeling that's part sexy and part shivery.

"I was quite tense by now, because he was kissing all around my thighs and licking me close to my pussy. But I tried to relax, the way you told me, and tried not to think about anything at all except how good it felt. It really helped, having my eyes closed. I think if I'd been watching him kissing my pussy I would have been so embarrassed. He opened up my thighs a little, and then I felt his tongue on my clitoris. He licked it very, very gently, scarcely touching it at all, and the feeling was sensational. In fact it was like nothing that I'd ever felt before. I used to masturbate sometimes but you can't lick yourself, can you? And the tip of his tongue was flicking me so quick and so light that I thought I was going to pass out for real! Then I felt his tongue slide down between my pussy-lips, and dip right into my pussy-hole. He swirled it round and then he pushed it right inside. I was very wet, it was dripping down between my butt-cheeks, and I could feel myself blushing. But kept telling myself that he wouldn't be doing it if he didn't like it . . . and if it was yukky and horrible, how come it felt so good?

"He went back to licking my clitoris. He was holding my pussy open with his fingers and licking me incredibly fast. The feeling that he was giving me was just amazing, and it was then that I knew that I wasn't ever going to be shy of letting him see my pussy anymore, no matter how wet it was. I wanted him to hold me open wider and wider. I wanted to be so wet that my juice was everywhere all over my legs, all over my butt, all over his fingers, all over his face.

"I 'woke up' then, and opened my eyes. I looked down and he was lying between my thighs, and I could see his tongue dancing on my clitoris. He glanced up at me and there was a sparkle in his eyes which I can't describe. All I could say was 'ohhhh . . .' because that was the way I was feeling. I don't know whether he knew that I had been pretending to sleep, but right now it didn't matter. All I could think about was his tongue between my legs, and it was heaven.

"He pushed both his hands under my butt and lifted my hips up a little bit. Then he ran his tongue down into my pussy-hole again, but this time he went further. He used his thumbs to hold my butt-cheeks apart, and he licked my asshole. I remember thinking that it was like being in some kind of erotic dream where you can do absolutely anything. His tongue circled around my asshole and then he actually pushed the tip of it inside. It was the dirtiest thing that anybody had ever done to me and I loved it. I reached down and buried my fingers in his hair and held his head while he licked my asshole like it was the most delicious thing that he'd ever tasted.

"He went back to my clitoris again, and this time I wasn't ready for what happened. As soon as his tongue touched it, I started to come. I gripped his hair tight and held him so that he wouldn't take his tongue away, but at the same time the feeling was so much that I couldn't bear him to go on licking me, either. I was gasping for breath and my hips were jerking up and down like I was being electrocuted.

"He knelt up between my legs with his cock in his hand. It was enormous, and the head was dark purple, like a huge purple mushroom. A

long drip of juice was actually swinging from
the end of it. I was still shaking from my orgasm when he pushed his cock inside me, all
the way up. I started to jerk up and down again,
I couldn't stop myself. He fucked me very, very
slowly, so that I began to calm down. He kissed
me and I licked his face and his face tasted like
my pussy . . . the first time I'd ever tasted myself and it wasn't yukky at all, it was salty-sweet,
that's all. His cock kept sliding in and out of me
and I put my hand down and played with his
balls, which were tight and hard and slippery
with juice.

"He started to fuck me faster, and I began to
think that I might have another orgasm. It was
such a wild ride, all I could feel was his cock
slamming in and out of me, and his hands gripping my breasts. I nearly came, but not quite,
but I could feel his cock spasm, right deep inside me, and I knew that he was filling me up
with his come.

"Afterward we lay together on the bed. Yes,
naked. Yes, with the lights on! He kissed me and
kept fondling me like he'd discovered me for
the first time, and I guess in a way, he had. That
evening was more like losing my virginity than
actually having sex for the first time, because
that evening I gave him my body to look at, and
caress, and really enjoy.

"He never asked me if I had really been

asleep. I'm glad he didn't because it didn't matter. When he went to the bathroom I took the mirror off my nightstand and looked down between my legs. My pussy was still red from fucking, and my pussy-hole was still open. A thick drip of white sperm was dribbling out of me, and that was such a turn-on to see. I couldn't understand why I'd been so shy about myself . . . if men thought my pussy was beautiful, then it was beautiful. It was a flower, it was a pink seashell. It was me, and I wanted to show myself off to the man who loved me."

Showing yourself off to the man in your life is a very important part of your sexual technique. Women who not only attract men but keep them interested are women who understand that men like to be visually aroused—not just on the very first night, but the morning after, and the day after that, and whenever they get the chance.

Psychologists say that men are excited by the sexual vulnerability of naked or partially naked women, especially in unusual situations. You can play on that. One of the most surefire ways of arousing your lover's interest is to walk around wearing nothing but one of his shirts. Or you can make breakfast wearing nothing but shorts (or have him make breakfast while you sit up, bare-breasted, in bed.) Too many women are overly modest about their looks, and underestimate the sexual effect they have on their partners. You should think about flirting any time of the day or night.

After talking to Karen, who works for an advertising agency in San Francisco, I managed to contact her first-ever lover Ken. Ken is a 26-year-old session musician from Los Angeles, California, who met her when she was an 18-year-old media student, at a party to celebrate the completion of his latest motion picture soundtrack. "Karen came with a friend and she was obviously very shy. But she had a quality about her that I couldn't resist. She had long blond hair and the biggest blue eyes and she was skinny like a fashion model. You couldn't say that she was pretty but she had a look about her that I couldn't take my eyes off. And she wore this little pale-blue dress that looked as if it might have been see-through but maybe it wasn't. More than anything, she had this coy way of looking at you with her head lowered and her eyes peeking out from under her fringe.

"I'll tell you what she had. I'll tell you exactly what she had. She made you think that she wasn't wearing any panties. Don't ask me how she did it. She didn't look like a slut. She looked completely innocent. But she made you think that, underneath that little slip of a dress, she was naked. It was that vulnerability that caught my attention. It turned me on; but it also made me want to go over to her and protect her from all the other Hollywood scumbags in the room who might be feeling the same way about her.

"I started talking to her, and yes, she was shy, but she asked me a whole lot of questions about what I did, and what movie soundtracks I'd played for, and she made me feel good. I didn't know then that she was still a virgin, and I wouldn't have guessed it, because she was so self-possessed. But when I got to know her, I realized that it was that same self-possession that had stopped her from losing her virginity to a man she didn't particularly like or trust. She was innocent, for sure, but only in terms of sexual experience. Actual fucking. She wasn't innocent when it came to making up her mind who she wanted to fuck, and when. She had a strength about her that I really admired, and I can tell you that I still do. It takes a lot these days for a girl to hold out against all of the schmucks and lecherous a-holes you find in Hollywood, especially when they're offering you parts in movies and dinner at the best restaurants and how about a little snort, darling?

"I'm impressed by girls with integrity, and clear-sightedness about what they are, and who they are, and what they want out of life, and Karen had that. Self-control, in a girl, I think that's erotic. I'd rather go out with a girl who said, no, I'm not going to bed with you, so I have to go home and jerk myself off to relieve my frustration, and fantasize about her, than a girl who says okay, and that's it, we fuck, and it doesn't have any real meaning to it.

"In this business, I meet dozens of girls, but you very rarely meet a girl who makes your hair stand on end, like Karen did. And she did it by looking vulnerable, you know, but difficult. I like difficult girls. I like girls with personality, with opinions, with points of view. I like girls who expect something out of me, apart from a vegetarian lasagne and a bottle of sparkling wine and a fuck on my waterbed. Did I tell you how much I hate thongs? I hate thongs. I like girls who don't wear any panties at all. That's sexy. That's innocent and risky, both at the same time.

"Anyhow, I talked to Karen and she reeled me in. She was a virgin, but she reeled me in, because she liked me, and I was demanding. I hate it when girls are so impressed by the fact that you work in movies that you know they're not at all interested in who you really are—only in *what* you are. Can you imagine what a pain it must be to be really famous? You'd never know if girls wanted to fuck you because you were interesting and good looking, or if they couldn't wait to rush back to their friends and say 'Guess what! I just fucked X!'

"Karen was different. I could sense it. I asked her if she wanted to come to dinner after the party and she said she'd think about it. I said, 'Please think hard, because you're very unusual and I'd really like to talk to you.' She said, 'You're unusual, too. But do you think that's enough?' What a girl! She was eighteen, and she was keeping me right on the edge. And I still didn't think that she was wearing any panties.

"We went for dinner. No place special. Just a Tex-Mex joint that does great burritos. I asked her all about herself—what she wanted to be, what she wanted to do. She said she wanted to get into investigative journalism, hunting down the big story. We laughed a whole lot. She was very funny. Behind all of that shyness, she was such a character. I came out with it straight and told her that I thought she was a girl in a million. I said that I didn't know why, she just had it. The look, the appeal, everything. She put her hand on top of mine and said, 'The minute you walked through that door, I knew that you were the man I wanted to take my virginity.'

"Well, you can imagine that coldcocked me on the spot. But she meant it. She'd been looking for so long for a guy who respected her for what she said, and what she wanted to be; and I guess that I'd been looking for exactly the same thing in a girl. There's a whole lot more to being sexy than the physical side of things. I'm not saying that I wasn't attracted by Karen's aura . . . this feeling she gave off that she was naked under her clothes. But what really turned me on was the way in which she talked to me as if I was somebody she was interested in mentally as well as sexually, because as far as I'm concerned sex doesn't mean anything unless you're doing it with somebody you like and respect. You might as well pay for a hooker, no disrespect to hookers.

"We went back to my place. It isn't the Bel Air, but it has a balcony, and a great view of the city and it was one of those soft warm nights. I opened a bottle of sparkling wine and we kissed on the balcony and toasted each other. She lay back on the sunbed and the hem of her dress was only covered her cunt by about an inch. She had such long, long legs, but still I couldn't see if she was wearing any panties or not. So in the end I asked her. Like, 'Are you wearing any panties under that dress?'

"She was a virgin, remember. Never been to bed with a man before. Kissed, petted, messed around, sure, but never had real penetrative sex. She didn't do anything for a while, but then she tugged her dress up a half-inch, and then another half-inch, and then I saw it. Her cunt, completely waxed, perfect, like a peach. That was absolutely the sexiest thing that ever happened to me in my whole life. I'll tell you, I could hardly breathe.

"I leaned over the sunbed and kissed her and

she opened her mouth and accepted my tongue like it was something that she had been waiting for all of her life. I swear to God that I had such a hard-on that my pants were almost on the point of bursting open. She had such an incredible mixture of innocence and sensuality, but she knew what she wanted from her first sexual relationship. She didn't want to be used or abused; she wanted a relationship that was based on respect. Very rare. And even more erotic, because of that. It meant that I couldn't just fuck her and light a joint and think, 'That's it, I'm satisfied.'

"We went to bed and she was sweet and charming and shy, but at the same time she was enthusiastic, too. This was going to be her first time and you could tell that she wanted to enjoy it. She let me take off her dress and all she was wearing underneath was this tiny lacy bra. She had breasts like a fairy, with little pink nipples. She knelt on the bed and helped me to take off my polo shirt. Then she opened my zipper and slid her hand into my pants. She felt my cock through my shorts and she took hold of it real tight, like she wasn't afraid of it or anything. I unbuttoned my pants and pulled them down, and she took my cock out of my shorts. She held my balls in one hand and rubbed my cock with the other, real slow strokes, up and down, and she said, 'It's wonderful.' Don't you think that's

an incredible thing for a girl to say? 'It's wonderful.' I think those two word turned me on
more than anything else she could have said.

"I took a condom out of the nightstand and
rolled it on, while she watched me. I loved that
innocent curiosity. We lay back on the bed and
I kissed her and fondled her. She may have had
tiny little breasts, but you should have seen her
nipples stick out. She was totally inexperienced,
but she didn't leave everything to me. She kissed
me and stroked my hair and ran her fingers
down my back. And she kept on slipping her
hand down between my legs so that she could
play with my balls. Most girls are worried about
touching your balls, they think they're going to
hurt you or something, but Karen had an in-
stinctive way of fondling them just right. She
pulled the skin of my ball-sac quite hard, so that
it gave me this incredible tugging sensation between my legs, but when it came to the balls
themselves she was real gentle. Not *too* gentle,
but she didn't bring tears to my eyes, like my
first girlfriend did!

"And she kept on slowly rubbing my cock,
too. She rubbed it against her stomach and then
she rubbed the head of it up and down between
the lips of her cunt, nearly letting me into her
but not quite, and that was so tantalizing. At
last I couldn't hold out any longer and I pushed
myself into her. She was very juicy, but she was

so tight that it took me two or three pushes before I got my cock completely inside her. All the
time I was forcing my way into her cunt, she
was looking up at me with this misty, magical
kind of expression, like this was something that
she'd been dreaming about for years, and at last
it had come true, and she loved it. I asked her
if she was okay, and she smiled and nodded and
said, 'I never knew it was going to feel as good
as this.'

"I made love to her very slowly. Apart from
the fact that she was so tight, I wanted to savor
every second of it, and I wanted *her* to know
just how fantastic sex can be. I turned over onto
my back and she sat on top of me, guiding my
cock into her cunt and then easing herself down
very gently. She gave a little jump because she
was so small and my cock was so big that it had
touched her womb. She leaned forward on me
so that my cock wouldn't go up quite so far,
and she rode up and down with her eyes half-
closed and her hair trailing all over me and her
cunt making this soft kind of kissing sound
every time she went up and down.

"Next she lay on her back and I lifted her leg
and pushed my cock into her from the side. I
stroked her clitoris while I fucked her because
I thought it would be great if I could give her
an orgasm the very first time she made love. But
I couldn't hold myself back any longer. That

sperm was building up between my legs and even when I stopped pushing myself into her, and waited for a moment to calm myself down, her cunt was so tight and she kept twitching it and there was nothing I could do to stop myself from coming. And did I come. I felt like I was being shaken around by a WWF wrestler.

"I took my cock out but I kept on stroking Karen's clitoris. She thought it was all over, but I didn't stop. She was such a great natural lover that I wanted her to be satisfied, too. I kissed her and stroked her tender and quick, and in return she rubbed my half-hard cock, until the condom slipped off. Then she massaged my cock and my balls with my own sperm, and smeared it on my stomach. Like I say, she seemed like a natural lover. She used her imagination to think of really sexy things to do to you. I kept on stroking her and I reached down and slipped two fingers inside her cunt, so that I could massage her G-spot. She was panting like she was running a relay race and her cheeks were all red. One thing about massaging a girl's G-spot, it always makes her extra juicy, and Karen was pouring it out like she'd wet the bed. She didn't make a sound when she came. She just arched her head back and bit her lip and *trembled*, you know?

"I hope that was just about the best initiation to sex she could have had. I tried to treat her with respect but give her a good time, too. We made love twice more that night, and once again in the morning, before she left. She was so sexy that I didn't know why she hadn't slept with a man before, and when I tried to talk to her about it, all she said was that until she met me, she hadn't found Mr. Right. I never really knew why I was Mr. Right and nobody else was, but that's the way it goes, isn't it? Somebody had to be her first lover and it happened to be me.

"We stayed together quite a long time—seven or eight months. Then she went off to college in San Francisco and we didn't see too much of each other after that. But I'll never forget her, and I'll never forget that first night. She didn't have any experience but she knew what she wanted out of a sexual relationship and she made sure that she got it. Sometimes, looking back on it, I think that I was the one who lost their virginity that night, not her."

Sexual confidence of the kind that Karen displayed with Ken will help you to enjoy your first-ever act of sexual intercourse and ensure that you don't wake up the next morning feel cheated or disappointed. Taking charge of your lover's penis by holding it and massaging it is one important way to make sure that your lovemaking proceeds at a pace that suits *you*, rather than him. It's a physiological fact that women are much slower to reach a high state of sexual arousal than men, but once you're in control of his penis you're in control of the entire situation—in a way your lover certainly won't object to.

Even if you've never touched a man's penis before, try to be firm and assertive and grab it tight. No matter how hard you squeeze his shaft, you won't be able to hurt him. You can fine-tune how much you stimulate him. If you rub the shaft of his penis, where there are comparatively few nerve endings, you can give him a very pleasant sensation without unduly hurrying him toward a climax. If, however, you massage the head of his penis, where most of his sensitive nerve-endings are concentrated, you will soon find that you have brought him to the point of no return—especially if you gently tickle the thin web of skin immediately behind the opening of his penis, known as the frenum.

Karen greatly increased her own arousal by taking hold of Ken's penis and massaging it up and down against her clitoris. This is an excellent technique for turning yourself on while delaying penetration. Your lover may be impatient to put his penis into you, but he is very unlikely to complain, since he will enjoy both the feeling of what you are doing, as well as the visual stimulation of seeing the head of his penis sliding up and down between the lips of your vulva. An added bonus is that this technique encourages and spreads vaginal lubrication.

Karen says she didn't learn this technique from a book or a video. "It was what I felt like, that's all. His cock was beautiful and I wanted to rub it up against me." Other women have said that if they hold their lover's penis tight (so that he has no control over when he is actually going to penetrate them) they can use it like a living dildo, to stimulate their clitoris, their vaginal lips, and their anus.

So one of the first lessons in making love for the first time, is no matter how swept away you are, no matter how much he makes you tingle, take control of your lovemaking and don't let him fuck you like a jackrabbit and leave you feeling unfulfilled and disenchanted.

If you don't manage to achieve orgasm the first time you make love, remember that sex isn't over until the sexy lady sings. In other words, your lovemaking doesn't finish with *his* climax, even if his penis is going soft. Your lovemaking finishes when *you're* satisfied, too. That means that if he hasn't given you an orgasm prior to penetration, or during penetration, then he should make sure that he does it *after* penetration, even if he doesn't immediately feel like it.

It's true that, after ejaculation, men almost instantly lose interest in sex: *That's it, I've climaxed, what's on TV?* One of the most critical things that you have to teach your new lover is that he can't just turn over and go to sleep, or light up a cigarette, or go to the kitchen and make himself a Dagwood sandwich. He has to make sure that your sexual needs have been completely cared for.

How do you do this? Well, strong physical stimulation isn't a great idea. Immediately after intercourse, men find forceful cock-rubbing to be irritating rather than arousing. You know what it's like after you've reached orgasm, and your lover keeps on fondling you and fondling you and you wish he'd stop.

But don't let him go. Don't let him leave the bed, or couch, or wherever you've been making love. Keep up close physical contact and encourage him to carry on making love to you at a level that is less intense, but that will eventually bring you far greater sexual fulfillment. You may not reach orgasm, but at least you should achieve a feeling that you've had your money's worth: peace, repose, totally shagged out, as they say in England.

Barbara, 21, a dressmaker from Richmond, Virginia, said that "once we'd made love for the first time, I didn't want to let Pryce go. I felt that he and me, we'd both become one. It's so hard to describe but it changed my perspective on the whole world. He came, and lay there for a while, until he got his breath back. Then without even kissing me or saying anything he climbed out of bed. I said, 'Where are you going?' and he said,

'I have to go to the john.' I said, 'You can't leave me, not now.' I didn't even feel that I was finished. I wanted more, I wanted so much more. So I followed him into the john and he was standing there naked. He took off his condom and all of his sperm dripped into the john. I took hold of his cock and it felt so good, warm and slippery and soft. He said 'I have to piss,' so I said, 'I'll help you.' I don't know how I found the nerve, but I was still very turned on. He said, 'Let go of my cock,' but I wouldn't, and in the end I suddenly felt his cock bulge and he started to piss. I'd never seen a man doing it before, not close up like that, and it was so sexy. I held his cock and waved it up and down so that he was pissing all over the bathroom. Then I put my fingers into it so that it splashed all over my hand. By the time he was finished his cock was sticking up again, and we went right back into the bedroom. We didn't say a word, but we had such a hunger for each other. He went down on me, licking my pussy, and I absolutely swear that was the first time that a man had ever licked me. I sucked his cock at the same time, and it was delicious because it tasted of fresh piss. It was only a few seconds before I started to come. I didn't realize I was coming, because it didn't feel like any orgasm that I'd ever had before, when I was masturbating myself. But I grabbed hold of Pryce's cock and forced it hard down my throat because I wanted to feel that he was filling me up completely.

"I had an orgasm like an earthquake. I couldn't breathe, because my mouth was full of cock. I had always thought that making love was going to be romantic and gentle, but this was something different. I wanted to be taken. I wanted to be opened up. I wanted to be fucked and licked and choked with cock. Right at the last moment Pryce pushed one of his fingers into my asshole and that did it for me. I didn't make a sound but I felt like I was screaming. It was so nice, it was such a fantastic feeling. After it was over I lay on the bed and Pryce put his arm around me and both of us were totally exhausted. But I never felt so good in my life, ever."

Barbara enjoyed losing her virginity because she didn't feel that Pryce was taking anything away from her, or using her. She wasn't sexually skilled, but she was confident enough to pursue Pryce into the bathroom when she didn't feel completely satisfied, and to play with his penis while he urinated. The first time you make love, remember that you've decided to commit yourself sexually, and that means that anything goes. You can do whatever you like, and if you feel like fondling your new lover while he goes to the john, then do it. He may feel like doing the same to you.

The most important thing about making love to a man for the first time is to remember that it's your decision, not his. Even if you reach the point where you're both lying naked in bed and his erection is the size of the Lincoln Memorial, and you change your mind, then that's it. You don't have to go through with it. It's your vagina and if you don't want his penis inside it, that's your choice. I will say, though, that if you think you're going to have any reservations about making love, you should say so long before you take your clothes off. It's better for men to think that you're picky about your partners rather than that you're a cock-teaser. You shouldn't play with men's feelings if you don't really want them, any more than you should play with their penises. Men, like women, are not toys.

Barbara was clever because she aroused her lover after he had climaxed—perhaps not to the point of being able to penetrate her again, but he felt sufficiently aroused to want to bring her to orgasm. This was her reward—a period of gentle stimulation that I call the Post-Climax Pay-Off. Pryce had ejaculated, and didn't really feel like any more sex. But Barbara gradually coaxed him into giving her oral arousal, which eventually led to a very dynamic orgasm. You'll have noticed that Barbara momentarily restricted her breathing before she climaxed, by deliberately forcing Pryce's erect penis deep into her mouth. Breathing restriction is a recognized way of intensifying orgasm, but I must emphasize that any

form of self-strangulation is extremely dangerous. I personally know of five people who have
died from sexual self-strangulation, two of them
very young, and I am very strongly opposed to
any form of erotic stimulation that puts its practitioners at physical risk. There are so many ways
to get yourself sexually excited without endan-
gering your life.

If you've never had intercourse with a man
before, but you suspect (or hope) that it might
happen very soon, there are several important
aspects of sex that are really worth thinking
about. The very first unshakable rule is this:
never, *ever*, have unprotected sex with a man
whose sexual history you're not 110 percent sure
of. And that means a proper blood test.

There are no exceptions to this rule whatsoever. He forgot to bring condoms? Then he's out
of luck. He's been sterilized? Too bad, he could
still be HIV positive, or suffer from any number
of venereal diseases. Just because AIDS has arrived, that doesn't mean that gonorrhea and non-
specific urethritis have magically disappeared.
You think he must be clean because he's married with three children? Sorry, his wife may be
infected, too.

No matter how aroused you are, no matter
how your groin is tingling, no matter how much
you desperately want to have this man make
love to you, the answer to unprotected sex is no.

If you have any inkling that you're going to find yourself in this situation, buy a pack of condoms and carry them around in your purse. Or like one lady sex writer I met, have a large glass bowl full of different colored and flavored condoms beside the bed for your lovers to dip into.

The same goes for oral sex. Use a flavored condom to make his rubber-coated penis more palatable, but don't suck him without one, and don't lick or swallow any of his semen. Condoms come in almost every imaginable flavor these days, from peppermint to raspberry ripple. If you can't find any, improvize your own. Boysenberry jelly is good. So is honey.

And one last caution: the success of your love life will depend very much on your first sexual experience. Don't throw that experience away. Don't do it because your friends have all done it. Don't do it because you're drunk, or high, or simply feeling lonely. Do it with a good man; and use your creativity and your confidence to make that good man make love to you even better. And never lose sight of the fact that it's your body, and that you want all the pleasure out of it that it's possible to get.

6

The Learning Curve of Making Love

Like all relationships, sexual affairs have to develop and progress if they are going to flourish. This is one of the reasons why I place such a strong emphasis on dialogue—talking to your partner about how you feel and what you want, and listening carefully in return to what *his* needs are.

Once they begin an affair, it's extraordinary how many couples almost immediately settle into a pattern, always making love in a similar way in similar surroundings, and very rarely venturing to try anything different. This is partly because it doesn't occur to them that their physical relationship needs to be expanded and explored just to maintain the same level of erotic excitement that they experienced on their first night together, and that if they want to discover even more intense sexual pleasures, they're going to have to learn all kinds of new ways of stimulating each other.

Erotic pleasure is greatly intensified by novelty and surprise. If you look at the same sex video over and over, it rapidly loses its ability to arouse you. When I was editing *Penthouse* magazine, we were constantly trying to create pictures that would stop our readers in their tracks, and this had to be done by placing our models in unusual situations, in unusual clothing, in unusual poses. And each month, to keep up our readers' erotic interest, we had to push the envelope a little further.

Early in the life of the magazine, we would have been risking prosecution for obscenity if we showed even the faintest wisp of pubic hair. These days, mass-circulation sex magazines are free to show women's sexual parts and men's too, provided they're not completely erect. Two years ago, it was considered too legally risky to show close-up photographs of women's anuses, and to discus anal sex between men and women, since in many countries it remains an offense (despite, paradoxically, being legal between men). But, again, the boundaries of acceptability have edged a little further forward, and yesterday's obscene photograph has become today's quite unremarkable pin-up, with models deliberately posed so that they are displaying their anuses, and anal sex experiences being recounted in lascivious detail.

In personal relationships, too, time and familiarity have the effect of taking the edge off our sexual excitement. "Did he ever make me tingle?" said 33-year-old Tina, from St. Louis, Missouri. "Once he only had to take off his shorts so that I could see his big stiff cock sticking out. Now, well . . . I find myself thinking about what it would be like to have two men, or even more." Regrettably it can often be too late before a couple realize that not only have they lost sexual interest in each other, but they have fallen out of love, too. It's not easy to keep up that special intimacy without regular, exciting sex. This is why so many men and women go looking for extramarital affairs, in the belief that they will "spice up" their relationship with their partners.

In a very few cases, sweet cheating *can* work. But it usually only helps those couples who have never been especially close to start with, and who can accept their spouse sleeping with other men or women without feeling jealous and hurt. I've talked to many sweet cheaters who say that having affairs saved them from splitting up. But right from the very beginning, hardly any of them had a relationship that you could describe as possessive or emotionally intense, and they had rarely invested very much effort into developing their love life and trying to make sure that their partner was always surprised, aroused, and satisfied. They were always much more concerned with their *own* excitement.

Time and time again, cheating women say that "my husband has really improved as a lover . . . he can't get enough of me now . . . he gives me thrills that he never gave me before." Here's a typical letter from the correspondence page of *Woman's Own*: "I've noticed lots of letters from wives who have their husband's permission to cheat, and I just love them! Many women reading them may feel as I once did—'No way! That would never work in our marriage.' Over the past year, I've learned that it does, and very, very nicely. A woman named Melissa wrote you as she and her husband were just getting ready to start. It would certainly be good hearing from her a year from now. If her husband is like mine, she'll have no problems with him except for getting him back down to earth."

Almost every cheating woman talks with rapture about the way that *she* feels, and how much more attentive her husband has become, and how he gives her so much more pleasure. Not a single word about what she's done for him (apart from enjoying herself with some other man). Not a word to suggest that she's done absolutely everything she can to become a much better lover, too. The sexual selfishness of it is quite breathtaking.

What is especially revealing is that these women have been married, on average, only three or four years, and they're bored *already*. My wife and I have been married for 27 years and we haven't even begun to tire of each other, or run out of sexual excitement.

As we've seen from the previous chapter, a great sex life begins on the very first night, and from that moment on, you both need to nourish it. Communicate, take care, and most of all devote your attention and your imagination to giving your partner a really fantastic time in bed. You won't need to be selfish about your own pleasure, because the natural effect of exciting your partner is that you become excited, too. Acts of sexual love are like acts of kindness, they always bring their own reward.

I'd like you to meet Barbara, a 30-year-old salesperson and part-time model from Redondo Beach, California. Barbara is a very pretty blonde with an eye-catching figure. She married Chet, 32, an engineer, after a "whirlwind romance" when she was 26. In many ways, Barbara is a sweet and very considerate person—at least, she appeared so in the limited time that I had to talk to her. But sexually, she is completely self-absorbed, and has no interest in the needs of the men with whom she makes love—including her husband. Her sexual experiences may be a little more extreme and exhibitionistic than those of most women, but you will recognize much of Barbara's sexual vanity even in women who have had much more mundane love lives.

It's quite easy to see from Barbara's story why she was now feeling that her marriage to Chet was "very rocky" and that she was thinking of finding herself another lover—"the kind of man who can give me real sexual satisfaction. I'm entitled to it." Of course, every woman is entitled to sexual satisfaction. But then so is every man. And the price of sexual satisfaction is satisfying your partner in return.

Anyhow, listen to Barbara's story and judge for yourself.

"If I say it myself, I was always the girl who turned heads. I was a very early developer, so by the time I was fifteen I was wearing a C-cup bra and by my sixteenth birthday I was 36D, which is the same as I am now. I can still wear the dresses I used to wear when I was at high school. I used to love clothes and makeup and dancing and boys. I had so many boyfriends, and I was always winning beauty pageants. I knew this photographer called David who said I ought to send my pictures off to *Playboy*. He was the first man who ever made love to me. He was twenty-eight, I think, eleven years older than me. He took me to his studio and took a whole lot of pictures of me in swimsuits and lingerie, and then he said I should do some topless, and maybe some nudes.

"At first I wasn't too happy about it, but he said that a body like mine was too beautiful to cover up. If you were really beautiful it wasn't like pornography or anything, it was art. So he took some nudes on these red satin sheets, with candlelight, and he was the first man who made me feel really special. And he was a *man*, you know, not a boy. He didn't fumble around. He massaged my breasts and said that it was good for the blood flow, you know, and helped to keep them firm, especially with breasts as big as mine. He twisted my nipples around, too, because that stiffens them up and they always look better in photographs if they're standing up. Sometimes they touch them with ice cubes, or blow a cold electric fan on them.

"David gave me such amazing feelings. Like, I'd kissed boys before, and they'd touched my breasts, and once or twice my boyfriend had put his hand into my panties. But David made me feel like a goddess, he really did. He said that I was the kind of woman who was born for men to make love to, and that I'd always have a sex life that was out of this world.

"He took off his clothes. He had a great body, very muscular, with like a crucifix of black hair on his chest. He took my hand and wrapped my fingers around his cock. I'd felt my boyfriend's cock through his pants but I'd never held a naked cock before. I hadn't even *seen* one properly. David said, 'Do you know why my cock's so big? It's never as big as this with any other woman. It's you, it's the effect you have on me.' And it's true, I do have this kind of sexual magnetism that makes men's cocks bigger than they usually are with other women.

"He asked me if I'd ever had sex with a man before, and I told him no. He said that was almost criminal, with looks like mine. I didn't know what I'd been missing. He climbed on top of me an opened up my legs and pushed his cock into me. It felt so good. I never imagined it would feel anything like as good as it did. And all the time, David was stroking my hair and kissing me and fondling my breasts and telling me how beautiful I was, which was something that none of my boyfriends had ever done to me before. Maybe they hadn't been mature enough to recognize true beauty, and sexual magnetism. David said I was a world-class beauty. I'll never forget him saying that. World-class beauty. You can't have a man pay you a finer compliment than that, can you? He raised my consciousness about myself and my own sexuality. He made me understand that I *deserve* a truly exciting sex life.

"He took some pictures of us making love.

He said he was going to call them 'Homage to Beauty.' Before he came, he took his cock out of me, because he wasn't wearing a condom, that's how considerate he was. He showed me how to rub him, and he said that no woman had ever managed to rub him like that before. He said I have natural sex technique, which is very rare. Even after they practice and practice, very few women have sex technique as good as mine. David suddenly climaxed all over my breasts, all of this sperm. He said that he'd never shot out so much sperm in his life. I was the only woman who had ever made him climax so much. He massaged his sperm into my breasts because it's good for the skin and helps to enlarge them. In fact he said that, ideally, I should massage sperm into my breasts every day, because of its hormone content, and I do try to do that.

"It was David who showed me how much of a woman I was and recognized my true beauty. He took a whole portfolio of pictures of me, some in the studio and others on the beach. One weekend we went out to the beach and this time two guys came along with us. One was around twenty-four, Terry, I think his name was, I forget; but the other was older, maybe mid-thirties. They were both good looking, though. David said that if I was going to break into the big time, and be internationally famous, I had to do some sensitive love making scenes, so that movie directors and model agencies could see how truly sexual I was.

"We went to this beach that was totally deserted. The sand was white and soft and it was a beautiful warm day. The guys took their clothes off first. David did, too. He said it helped him to empathize. It was such a turn-on, having three handsome guys around me, all of them completely naked, and all of them with huge hard-ons, because of me. I undressed and lay on the sand, and David took a whole lot of pictures of me fondling my own breasts and licking my own nipples That's how big my breasts are, I can lick my own nipples. He took a whole lot more, with my legs open, and stretching my pussy open with my fingers. He always said that I had the most perfect pussy that he'd ever seen, and when he was taking pictures of me he said, 'imagine all the thousands of guys who are going to look at your pussy . . . like, right inside . . . and they're going to be desperate that they can't stick their cocks into it. They'll be masturbating like crazy, thousands of them, and coming all over your picture.' That gave me such a feeling of power, you know? I couldn't stop fingering myself and thinking of all of those guys. Even David was rubbing himself, and so were the two other guys. They were all standing there on the beach, masturbating themselves, because I was so sexy and such a turn-on.

"David said, 'Now I want some loving pictures. I want you to show the world what you've got.' He said I could do whatever I liked with these guys, they'd both had AIDS tests. You see how considerate he was? I knelt in the sand—you should see those pictures, my butt is all covered in sand!—and these two guys stood one on each side of me, and I took hold of their cocks and licked them and sucked them, one after the other, while David took pictures. You never saw guys with such enormous cocks. I really have that effect on men, I think the way that I look and my sexual aura increases their cock size by ten percent at least.

"I lay back on the sand and the older guy put his cock straight up my pussy and started to fuck me, while I kept on sucking the younger guy's cock. That was the day I found out how good I was at cock sucking. I love sucking men's cocks because they're so fat and hard it's like having a huge plum in your mouth, and it gives me the feeling that the guy really adores me. You should see me in some of those pictures. I have naturally full lips, and I was wearing this incredible scarlet lip gloss, and there's my lips around this young guy's cock. It's just enormous, you've never seen a cock so big in your life.

"The older guy was very toned. I guess he must have gone to the gym every day. I moved my hips up and down and he said he couldn't believe how strong my pussy-muscles were. He said it was like being masturbated by a woman's hand rather than a pussy, which was a real compliment to me. And the sensations his cock was giving me while he was pushing it in and out . . . I could feel the rim of it rubbing my insides. I could feel every one of his veins. These guys were giving me such pleasure that I thought I had to be dreaming. There was a warm breeze blowing from the sea and it blew right between my legs and I could feel my wet pussy totally filled up with cock. There were grains of sand in my pussy which made it a little sore but right then I was too turned on to worry about it.

"I was so excited that I bit the younger guy's scrotum, sank my teeth right into his skin, and do you know what he did? He instantly shot his sperm all over the side of my face, right into my eye, and then another load which dripped into my ear. David said something to the older guy and he took his cock out of me and knelt right down in the sand beside me. I said, 'What's going on?' but David said, 'This is it . . . this is the ultimate adoration.' And the older guy rubbed himself three or four times and climaxed all over my nose and my lips and all over the younger guy's cock, and the two of them rubbed their cocks all around my face. I stuck my tongue out and licked them, and they tasted so good. I was sucking big warm globs of the older guy's sperm right out of the young guy's pubic hair.

"David was standing right over me with his camera, taking pictures of everything. He kept saying, 'Beautiful, you're so fantastically beautiful,' and I think that was the first time that I really believed that I was. You can't make men's cocks grow so big unless you're very sexually attractive, and there's no way in the world that a man is going to want to climax over your face unless you're really special.

"The younger guy took hold of David's cock while he was photographing me, and started to masturbate him. He rubbed him quicker and quicker, and it only took about half a minute before David was shooting his sperm out, too. I stuck out my tongue and his sperm squirted all over it, and then the second squirt went right down my throat and made me cough.

"We spent the whole afternoon on the beach taking pictures. The most fantastic picture of all is the younger guy lying facedown on the sand, with his butt in the air. I'm kneeling behind him, holding his cock in one hand, while the older guy is standing over him, squirting sperm between the cheeks of his butt so that it drips down onto his asshole . . . and I've got my tongue right out, and I'm licking up the sperm, right from his tight crinkled asshole, and you should see me in that picture. It's the most erotic picture

I've ever seen, and a whole lot of people have said that it's so daring, yet it's so natural. I really look like I'm in ecstasy, and my hair's all blowing in the breeze. I have to tell you I look beautiful. That's what David said the whole meaning of the picture was. Every guy in the world is going to look at it and think, 'I wish a goddess like her would do something like that to *me.*' I think it raises men's self-esteem, you know, that they can please a woman like me.

"I did a few more magazine spreads for David, and two videos down in Cancún, in Mexico, but he kept on wanting me to appear with other girls and do this lesbian stuff, two girls kissing each other's pussies and things like that. It wasn't so much the sex I objected to. That first video we filmed in Mexico we were on this powerboat, and I was supposed to do a scene with this black girl. She had a completely shaved head and no body hair at all, and enormous breasts. They must have been solid silicone because they were even bigger than mine, but at least mine are natural. I had to lie back on a towel on the deck while this girl went down on me, and I have to confess that she gave me such pleasure. You don't know what a pussy-licking is like until a girl's done it to you. A girl knows exactly how to touch your most sensitive spots, and how quick to lick you, and you don't mind a girl sticking her finger up your ass or anything like that, so long as her nails aren't too sharp! I think that guys are probably better at sucking other guys' cocks than girls are, for the same reason. They really know what they like. I really get a kick out of watching a man sucking another man's cock. They were making a gay video in one of the studios that David took me to, and they were doing it there. The guy was licking it and sucking it and taking it so far down his throat that the other guy's balls were bouncing on his chin! It turned me on so much that I wanted David to take me straight home and fuck me.

"Anyhow, like I say, it wasn't the sex I minded, because sex is a natural thing, and I have a natural sexual aura. But I was so much better-looking than any of the other girls, it wasn't their fault, but they were taking all the attention away from me by laughing and fooling around, and when it came to the sex scenes they were doing more extreme things, you know, like ass-fucking and fist-fucking. They were bringing down the whole quality of the video because they weren't treating it like art, and they didn't have that radiance like I have. David and I had a nasty row about it and he said some mean things to me, like who did I think I was. I told him he was crazy. He was the one who recognized what I had. He was the one whose cock had gone ten percent bigger than normal when he first saw me naked. Personally I don't think he meant anything he said. He was under a whole lot of financial pressure and he couldn't make the videos he really wanted to make—you know, much more artistic, something to showcase my talent. Even today I don't blame him. I called him once or twice but he doesn't return my calls. If you ask me the whole situation humiliated him too much. He feels like he's let me down and doesn't know how to face me.

"I did one or two more modeling jobs but so many of those people in that business are such creeps. They don't have any eye for beauty or natural sexuality, all they want is for you to open your legs and show your pussy, or have sex with some stupid young waiter whose only asset is a cock the size of a horse.

"I guess that was why I had that whirlwind romance with Chet. I was selling cosmetics and perfume at this store and we had a promotional evening. He came along because he was friends with one of our managers. He started talking to me and I could tell right off that he could sense my natural sexuality. He kept bringing me glasses of champagne and he talked to me like I was special. He drove me home that night and I invited him to come on up for another drink, because he was the first man since David to treat me the way that I deserved.

"He told me that I was perfect, that I was

every man's dream. He's physically big, over six feet, three inches, and he's slow, in his way, but he's very handsome. I think that most women, when they first met him, would find him hard to resist.

"He picked me up bodily and carried me into the bedroom and laid me down on the bed. He knelt down by the end of the bed and took off my sandals, and kissed my feet, one after the other. Then he stripped off his shirt and his pants and stepped out of his shorts, so that he was completely naked. He climbed on the bed next to me and his cock was gigantic. I took hold of it and circled my thumb around the top of it, and said, 'I'll bet you something . . . I'll bet that your cock has never been as big as this before.' But he didn't say a word. It was like he couldn't understand what I was talking about. I guess I should have realized right then and there that he couldn't see how special I was. Alarm bells should have rung! But his cock was very, very big, and I had my hand closed around it, and there was juice coming out of his hole, which was an obvious sign that I was doing *something* to him, right? And I did feel like a really good fuck.

"I opened my thighs real wide, like I was doing splits, and I took hold of his cock and fitted it into my pussy. I looked him right in the eyes and said, 'Go on, now. Push it in. I dare you.' And he smiled back at me and pushed it in—this huge, huge cock. It was so big that I could hardly fit it all into me—well, you know how snug my pussy is. And then he fucked me and fucked me, like a fucking machine, his cock ramming in and out of me, his balls banging against my butt, just like the way that gay guy's balls banged against his lover's chin, and he was grunting just like an animal. In the end, he climaxed, right up inside me, even though he wasn't wearing a condom. It was incredibly sexy for a second and a half, but then I thought, this is crazy. David never would have fucked me without a condom. David cared about me. And in any case, David knew that I liked to see his sperm shooting out, and that I liked to massage it into my breasts.

"But, you know, in spite of everything, Chet always made me feel good. When I needed a fuck he was always there, with his cock sticking up. And he treated me like a lady. We got married, and for six months at least I was proud to be Chet's wife. But it all got too boring, after a while. I had to work, and then I had to come home and clean and cook his dinner, and then he expected me to lie underneath him while he shoved that huge cock of his up my pussy, grunt, grunt, grunt. No oral sex, ever. I would have loved to have sucked his cock and shown him what a goddess I was. No anal sex. I don't like anal sex very much, but at least he could have tried. It might have hurt, taking a cock as big as that up your asshole, but he never even attempted it, even when I took hold of his cock and rubbed it between the cheeks of my butt."

I asked Barbara if she had ever suggested anal sex. Out loud. In words.

"I told you. I don't like it. Besides, his cock was far too big. He wouldn't admit it, but I have that effect on men."

But you wouldn't have resisted if he'd tried to do it?

"Of course not. But it's a man's job to please a woman, isn't it?"

After only four years of marriage, Barbara was so disillusioned with her "whirlwind romance" that she was looking for another man—a man who would make her feel like the sex goddess that she believed herself to be.

The reality was that Chet was a very decent guy, and a very reasonable lover—physically well-endowed and very eager to please his wife if only she would reciprocate, and please him in return.

"I know that I couldn't be there for Barbara twenty-four hours a day," he told me. "I have a very demanding career, and if I don't jump when my boss says jump, then I'm not going to get that promotion, and I'm not going to get that raise—and who do you think will be the first person to complain if I don't? Yes, Barbara.

"She's a very, very attractive woman. All right, she's a very, very sexy woman. She walks into a bar and every man in the whole place swivels his head around one hundred and eighty degrees like Linda Blair in *The Exorcist*. That isn't always easy for a husband to deal with, particularly when his wife always plays up to it, and flaunts her breasts and her legs and flutters her eyelashes at every good-looking guy who walks past.

"I think I'm a reasonably good lover. I usually get it up, and I kiss her, and I fondle her. But I always feel that Barbara expects me to give her an orgasm but she doesn't care if I'm having a good time, too. She makes a whole lot of noise like she's really enjoying herself, and that used to be turn-on, but she never does anything in return. She gives me oral sex, for sure, but I always feel that she's doing it for her own excitement, not mine. She bites my neck and my cock and my scrotum, which hurts, and which I don't enjoy at all, but if I complain about it she turns sulky and says that I'm acting like a wimp and I don't really love her at all. She keeps saying that she's known men who love her so much that they'd do anything for her, and if I don't treat her right she's going to find another man who's going to give her what she wants.

Well, I can tell you, that doesn't do very much for my confidence, and once or twice I haven't been able to get it up because of the way she's been talking to me. Of course that always makes it worse because she says that I'm not much of a man.

"She's a great-looking girl, but I think she believes that she's a whole lot more stunning than she really is. I know she's done some model work, pornography, stuff like that. I knew that before I married her, but you can't get upset about anything that anybody did before you met them, can you? It wouldn't be reasonable. It's just that Barbara thinks she's some kind of star and she forgets that I need some loving, too."

As I said before, Barbara's case is quite an extreme example of a woman whose sexual vanity has progressively destroyed her sexual relationship with her husband. She was seriously led astray by David, her photographer, who fed her an endless line of flattery and lies. But any girl of average intelligence who wasn't so preoccupied with her own appearance and her own pleasures would have seen through David's compliments immediately. No matter how desirable she looks, no woman is capable of adding 10 percent to the size of a man's erection. And although its viscosity can make it seem more, the amount of semen that a man ejaculates is rarely more than a teaspoonful, however attractive his partner may be. Your lover's penis may feel "enormous," but this is invariably because you are feeling more sexually aroused than usual, and your vagina is much more sensitive.

Your perception of the size of your lover's erection can be affected by your hormones at different times of the month, just as your hormones can affect your perception of the world at large. Kristine, 50, a British engineer, said, "A couple of days before my period, I feel really sexual. If I don't have a man, it's like . . . oh, my God. I wish I did. It can put me in a frenzy. I always have the best sex ever during these days."

But Barbara's perception wasn't distorted by hormones. It was affected by her naïve acceptance of David's lies, and her readiness to believe that she was much more attractive than any other woman. It's important to have a strong belief in your own sexual attractiveness, and confidence in your self-image. No matter what size or shape you are, you're sexually attractive to the right partner, and a few of the wrong partners as well. But no matter how magnetic you are, your sexual relationships will still falter and come to a premature end if you don't behave selflessly, and devote all of your attention to giving your partner a good time.

I tried to explain to Barbara that she and Chet still had a good chance of reconstructing their marriage if she was willing to think about the way that *he* felt, and the sexual acts that turned *him* on. But I seriously doubt if I managed to penetrate the perfect varnish of her own vanity. She had no qualms about what men did to her— ejaculating on her face, having intercourse on the beach in front of the camera, giving her oral and anal stimulation—so long as *she* enjoyed it. When I asked her if she thought that her various partners had been satisfied, she stared at me in bewilderment and said, "Of course they were. Weren't they?" There was a strong likelihood that they *had* been satisfied, especially if they were paid well for having sex with her, but Barbara hadn't once considered whether she had given them as exciting a time as they had given her. Her belief was, "Men don't care, do they, so long as they climax?"

Unfortunately for Barbara, and for many of those women who find that their sexual relationships never seem to last very long for similar reasons, men *do* care. If they needed nothing more than a climax, then all they would have to do is buy a pornographic video and masturbate. But men need everything that you need: affection, stimulation, excitement, surprise, and satisfaction—as well as constant reassurance that they're good in bed.

I know, I know. *Poor little fellows. Why do I have to keep telling them that their cocks are the biggest and the hardest in the Western hemisphere?* Simply because men cannot achieve erections by willpower alone. A man can sit and stare at his penis for hours on end, trying to will it into a state of stiffness, but it will only rise up if he is mentally and physically stimulated, provided that he isn't suffering from all kinds of incidental problems like stress at work, alcoholic addiction, drug abuse, physical exhaustion, or waning testosterone in middle age.

They could be suffering from functional impotence, which can be brought on by all kinds of neurotic difficulties. One young man was unable to make love to his wife because he simply couldn't decide when it was appropriate to do so—she seemed to be too tired at night, and too busy in the morning. Another didn't resolve his impotence until he'd visited a psychiatrist, who discovered that when the patient was a very small boy he had seen his mother urinating, revealing her vulva and her pubic hair. His new bride was persuaded to remove her pubic hair, and the problem was almost immediately solved.

A man who is suffering from functional impotence should go talk to his doctor as soon as possible. It's one of those problems that it's almost impossible to sort out for yourself, and yet it doesn't take very long to regain full virility. If a man is suffering from any of the other five problems, then apart from removing the source of his problem, he's going to need plenty of TLC—and no recriminations that he doesn't find you sexy, or that he doesn't love you anymore. He wouldn't stay with you if he didn't love you, so don't make matters worse.

Even if the man in your life doesn't suffer from impotence, he is still going to need active sexual guidance and response in order to give you the kind of satisfaction you're looking for, so you can enjoy your sexual relationship to its utmost. You can't just lie back, like Melissa, thinking that you're the sexiest woman on God's good earth, and expect your lover to do all of the work.

Sexually, one of the most generous women I have ever met was 31-year-old Pauline, a publisher's assistant from New York. She was a vivacious brunette, not stunningly pretty, but full of humor and energy. When she met Michael, a very smooth, handsome publicity director, she was determined to win him—and, not only that, she was determined to make their relationship last.

"I don't think anybody in the office could believe that Michael had asked me out to dinner. He's the sort of guy who walks into a room and you can see all the girls going all weak at the knees. Tall, dark-haired, very good looking, and always immaculately dressed. Yet, you know, the one thing that I realized about him almost the first second I met him, he's seriously lacking in self-confidence. You wouldn't know it, if you were dealing with him professionally, because he puts on this incredible act. Smiling, glad-handing, back-slapping, you'd think he was selling you a previously enjoyed Oldsmobile.

"But when I first saw him at this trade fair, he was standing in a corner on his own and he looked so lost and vulnerable that I went up and asked him if he was okay. He just shrugged, and somebody came up to him and pumped his hand, and suddenly he was Jim Carrey, but I knew then that I had caught him at a genuine moment, when his guard was down, when he was being himself.

"And surprise, surprise, at the end of the trade fair, he came over and asked me out for dinner. So of course I said get the hell out of here, what kind of girl do you think I am? Not.

"He didn't take me anyplace particularly glamorous. Some Thai restaurant, on Seventh Avenue. But it was quiet, you know, apart from all this bingly-bongly Thai music, and it was obvious that he wanted somebody to talk to.

"I asked him all about his work, and he said that he was doing better than okay, and that he expected to be promoted to publicity director of the whole group. But he said that his career didn't really mean too much to him these days; by which I got the impression that he must have recently broken up with somebody who meant a lot to him. I was right. We hadn't even finished the soup before he told me that he was separated from his wife.

"He said she was a fantastic-looking woman, but she never seemed to be satisfied. She demanded compliments and gifts and constant attention, which he had been happy to give her, you know? But the more he gave her the less she gave back. In the end she started to say that she was bored in bed and only six or seven weeks after that she started an affair with a younger man she worked with. She said she needed the excitement and she used to come back and describe everything that she and this younger man had done together, in detail, while Michael was making love to her. It turned her on, and even Michael admitted that for a couple of weeks their sex life was better than ever.

"But in the end he couldn't take any more. He'd been pretending that he thought her affair was a turn-on, because he really loved her, and he couldn't bear to lose her. For a while he nearly managed to convince *himself* that her affair was good for the both of them. But then his wife started talking about having affairs with two or three men, and swapping partners, and he knew then that their marriage was finished . . . at least, the marriage that *he'd* always wanted to have.

"I listened, and I asked him questions, but I didn't sympathize. He wasn't the kind of man who needed sympathy. He was too strong for that. He was obviously loving and giving and he couldn't understand why his wife hadn't been loving and giving in return. Well, I think I knew the answer to that. I've known enough women who care about nobody else but themselves, and who love having men running after them. Flattery—it's like food and drink as far as they're concerned. They can't survive without it. Mind you, I think it's because they're desperately insecure. They need men to tell them that they're gorgeous and sexy because they don't truly believe that they are. And that's why they're so selfish in bed, and never give anything, because they don't have any confidence in themselves. That's my theory, anyhow.

"Michael was still hurting from his separation, so I didn't push him too hard. I didn't want to rush into anything, either, because I'd been living on my own for over a year and to tell you the truth I'd kind of gotten used to it. But after dinner, when he took me home, I thanked him, and gave him a kiss, and squeezed his hand, and I didn't make any secret of the fact that I liked him and that I wanted to see him again.

"Without being cold-blooded about it, I could see exactly what my agenda was, if I wanted to have a really satisfying relationship with him. In one sentence, I had to restore his faith in womankind. I had to show him that not all women are vain and selfish, and that we don't always expect men to wait on us hand and foot, sexually speaking.

"Besides, I don't think that a lot of women realize that if they're more active in their love lives, they'll get a whole lot more excitement out of their relationships. I know that during my last affair, the one I had before Michael, I really had a ball. We *both* really had a ball. We only broke up because Van had to go to Europe to work for a German bank. There were tears, and we missed each other like crazy, but apart from my leaving my job and going to Germany with him, what else could we do?

"The following week, Michael took me to a musical, which was lightweight but a whole lot of fun. Then I invited him back to my apartment for a glass of wine and something to eat. I hadn't made a candelit dinner, nothing like that. Only some ciabatta sandwiches with pastrami and cheese and fruit. Informal stuff, the kind you can eat with your fingers. I opened a bottle of Italian red wine and we sat on the floor listening to George Michael and talking.

"Michael kissed me, and paid me the greatest compliment. He said, 'I feel like we've been friends for years.' And do you know why that was? Because I listened to him, because I paid attention to what he said, so that he felt happy about confiding all of his problems to me. It's not a great secret knack, although the way some women behave, you'd think that it was. Every man has something on his mind, something that's bugging him, some resentment. It could be work, it could be romance. It could be anything at all. But if you get him to talk about it, you'll make him warm to you so quickly . . . and you'll get that problem solved, and out of the way, in case you *do* feel like starting a relationship with him. I had to get Michael's feelings about his wife out of the way, so that he could turn all of his attention onto *us*, and our relationship.

"The second great secret in my opinion is to give a man more than he's expecting. I learned that lesson from my first-ever affair. I was very naive, and I thought that having sex with a man was absolutely the best thing that had ever happened to me. I was like a puppy with two tails. What made it even more exciting was that I spent almost every night at this man's apartment, and up until then I'd been living with my mother. So now I had sexual excitement and I had freedom, both, and wanted to enjoy them right to the limit.

"My friends at work were talking about oral sex one day. There was an article in a magazine saying that something like 98 percent of men said it was their favorite sexual treat. One of my friends said that she didn't like doing it very much because her boyfriend always wanted to come in her mouth. Another girl said that her husband was just the same, he expected her to swallow and she wouldn't. But I thought to myself, if these guys like it so much, why don't they? It's only a little bit of squirty stuff, it's not going to harm anybody.

"So the next morning, while this man was still asleep, I drew back the covers and I started to suck his cock. It was soft at first, and I could get all of it inside of my mouth, but gradually I could feel him wake up, and his cock started to grow bigger and bigger, until it almost choked me. He put his hand down and stroked my hair and my shoulders, and I think he wanted to roll me over and make love to me. But I kept on licking him and sucking him and beating his cock up and down, and after a little while he lay back and I could feel him growing more and more tense. His stomach muscle tightened up, and so did his thighs, and he tried to push himself even further into my mouth. He suddenly gripped my hair and said, 'I'm coming.' So at least he was gentleman enough to give me a choice, you know, whether I wanted to swallow or not. In fact I think he expected me to stop sucking him. But instead I closed my lips right around his cock, and licked his hole with the tip of my tongue, and he said something like 'oh, God,' and I could actually feel his come squirting out of his hole and into my mouth. He squirted again, and again, and I swallowed it all. It has this funny dry taste, but I liked it. I was quite disappointed that there wasn't more. I licked his cock completely clean, and then I climbed up the bed and gave him a long, come-tasting kiss. I remember him looking up at me and slowly shaking his head and saying, 'You're something else. You really are.'

"And I got my reward. About a half-hour later his cock came up again, as hard as an iron bar. I guess he was fantasizing about what I'd done for him! He fucked me for over an hour, until we were both late for work, and I went to the office with a very satisfied pussy!

"I kept trying to think of new things that I could do for him. I never had to worry about my own satisfaction because he always responded to everything I did by giving me all the loving that I could handle, and more. And we always talked about what we liked to do. I'd say something like, 'How about I suck your cock and swallow all of your come?' Or 'How about I piss and you watch me?' That's one thing I learned that all men really love, even though you won't often get them to admit it. They all love to watch women piss. The first time I did it, my man was in the bathtub, and I came in naked and sat down on the toilet right opposite. Instead of sitting like I normally did, I sat right back on the toilet seat and spread my pussy with my fingers. Then I pissed, and I watched him watching me, and his cock came right up through the bubble-bath like a big red submarine! When I was finished, I stood up and went over to the bath, and held my pussy open again. I said, 'Can you lick me clean? I don't like paper. I much prefer a nice warm tongue.' I don't think he could believe what he was hearing, but he stuck out his tongue and he licked all the piss off my pussy. He even put his mouth over my pisshole and sucked at it.

"It sounds as if I was so sexually sophisticated, but I was the opposite. I was so innocent that I didn't have any inhibitions about doing anything at all. I didn't realize that some women won't let their partners watch them on the toilet. I felt totally liberated, I could do anything at all, and all I wanted to do was show my man how much he turned me on. I used to walk around his apartment naked, even when he was dressed, and when he was watching television I used to open up his pants and take out his cock and suck it. Every day was loving and fun, because I always tried to give him something extra, some sexy little surprise.

"Anyhow, when Michael kissed me, I kissed him back, and I took his face in both of my hands. I think that's such an intimate thing to do. It's like saying to the other person, 'Look at your beautiful face, I want to frame it, I want to remember it.' The next thing I did was unfasten my skirt, and take it off. Underneath I was wearing a black lace thong and black self-support stockings. I always think it's a very sexy surprise to take your skirt off first, instead of going through the usual routine of sweater and bra. Blouses have to be unbuttoned, sweaters have to be dragged over your head, bras are complicated for most men. But if you take off your skirt, or your pants, you're still not showing him any more than you'd show him on the beach, say, but you look so sexy and available and it's a clear statement that you don't just want petting, you want him to make love to you.

"What's great about stockings and a thong is that your thighs are bare, and your butt is completely bare, too, so that when he puts his hands around you he can't help cupping your cheeks. By now, of course, he'll have a major-league hard-on. And this is another secret of mine. I never try to tear open a man's pants like I'm a dog who's frantically trying to dig up a lost bone. Instead, I gently stroke his hard-on through his pants, using the backs of my fingers, trailing them gently up and down. My second boyfriend showed me how to do that. He says it feels incredibly sexy, especially if you can manage to do it in unusual places, like the elevator at work, or when he's driving you home. He said it was juicy cock time, guaranteed.

"Once I'd stroked Michael's cock for a while, and kissed him, I very slowly pulled down his zipper, until it was halfway down, and the head of his cock was just peeking out through his fly, still covered by his shorts. I gripped the head of his cock with my fingernails and gently dug them in, and rubbed it up and down a little. That was another trick that my second boyfriend taught me, and he only taught me because I actually *asked* him how he liked his cock to be touched.

"Before I levered Michael's cock out of his shorts, I stood up in front of him and took hold of his head in my hands and ruffled his hair. He was still kneeling on the floor, and he kissed my thighs and slowly massaged my butt, which felt gorgeous. Then I said, 'Why don't you take my panties off for me? With your *teeth*.'

"He loved it. He gripped hold of my black elastic between his teeth, and pulled my thong down, first one side, then the other, then the front. It's a terrific way of turning a man on, because his face is only an inch away from your pussy, and if you're warm and juicy he can actually *smell* you. I always trim my pubic hair, but I don't do it completely bare, because I have very dark hair and it grows back stubbly. I do it with scissors so that it's still soft and silky, but my pussy's still exposed.

"Michael dragged my thong halfway down my thighs with his teeth. Then he kissed me, all around my pussy.

"I said, 'Come on, let's go to bed.' I took off my thong, and then I knelt down beside him and took his cock out of his shorts. He stood up, and dropped his pants, and at the same time I took his cock into my mouth and rolled my tongue around it. When it was good and wet, I said, 'Here . . . do you have a condom?' and he handed me one from his shirt pocket. At least he was prepared—although I do have plenty of my own in the bedroom. I opened the foil and then I took the bulb of the condom between my lips. I love doing this . . . Michael had obviously never had it done to him before, and I think it blew his mind. I rolled the condom onto his cock using my mouth, as far down as it would go, right down to his pubic hair, and when his cock was halfway down my throat I made this little choking noise, like his cock's so enormous that I'm suffocating on it. I wasn't really choking, but it's a fantastic way of telling a man that he has a really huge cock without having to say it in so many words.

"We went into the bedroom. I always like two soft lights, one on each side of the bed, and another light at the end of the bed, slightly brighter, so that when a man makes love to me he can see clearly between my legs. There's another thing I've learned about men, they love to look at your pussy. Just stare at it. With my first boyfriend, I used to sit on the couch all afternoon reading a book and I wouldn't be wearing anything except this little pink angora top. I'd have my legs open and he could happily sit there for hours, admiring my pussy. It's no good being embarrassed, you should be flattered that they love to look at you so much. Sometimes he'd gently stroke my pussy, or open up my lips so that he could see right inside, and then he'd just go back to staring at me. A friend of mine asked me about two weeks ago how she could attract her husband's attention and get him to make love to her more often, and that was what I told her to do. Trim your pubic hair, or shave it all off, and simply sit around the house with only a sweater on, displaying what you've got. It works like magic. It's even sexier if you wear high-heeled shoes as well.

"This was the time for Michael to take off my sweater and my bra. We stood by the bed, very close, so that his hard cock was bumping against my stomach. He bared my breasts, and fondled them, and then I lay back on the bed and held my arms out for him to climb on top of me. I tool hold of his cock and pressed it in between my breasts, while he stripped off his shirt and his T-shirt.

"I squeezed his cock in my cleavage, and he loved it, but I knew that he was dying to get down to business and put it into my pussy. The trouble is, even though I get turned on like you wouldn't believe, it always takes me such a long time. I guess that's one of the reasons I started to do things to men instead of always having them do things to me. I get very aroused by playing with men, watching them grow more and more excited, but when I'm kind of taking the initiative I can slow things down if a guy looks like he's building up to a climax too soon, which is going to leave me only half warmed-up.

"One of my favorite ways of slowing things down for *him* and speeding them up for *me* is to take hold of his hand before he starts making love to me, taking it down and holding it between my legs. I say, 'What does that feel like? Does that feel good for you? Do you know how near you are to touching my clitoris? Ohh . . . why don't you stroke me here . . .' "— and here Pauline demonstrated how she would open her legs wide and look down between them—" '. . .that's my clitoris . . . if you touch it with the very tip of your finger . . .' or however you'd like him to touch you. I like having my clitoris touched directly, but I know a lot of women who find it too sensitive and like to have their pussy-lips massaged instead. But whatever you prefer, you can slow everything down by showing your man what you really enjoy, and have him finger your clitoris and your pussy. *He's* always pleased because you've shown him how to turn you on, because a lot of men—in fact, I'd say *most* men—don't know how to masturbate a woman really well. And *you're* pleased because he's giving you all of that sexy warming-up that you don't usually get.

"I did this with Michael, and he was good . . . he touched me just the way I like it, quickly flicking my clitoris from side to side. At the same time I didn't forget about him. I took hold of his cock and massaged it very, very slowly. He wasn't getting too turned on because he was concentrating on playing with my clitoris, and of course he was wearing a condom, too.

"I began to feel that beautiful sexy tingly feeling between my legs, and I said to Michael, 'Come on . . . your finger's working wonders but what I need is your big hard cock.' He kissed me and I could tell by the look on his face that he was really pleased with the way that he'd turned me on. It made him feel like a better lover. And from then on, he *would* be a better lover, because he'd always make sure that he aroused a woman properly before he started fucking her.

"I've found so many different ways of making sure that a man turns me on before we have intercourse. Not that I've had that many men, but you can't expect the same trick to work every single time you make love, can you? It would be too predictable, wouldn't it? And you'd both begin to get kind of bored of it. So you have to keep thinking of new things to try. Michael used to like it when I wrestled him, so that he would have to fight me to have sex with me. I used to wriggle out from under him and twist myself around so that he could catch me around the thighs, with his face only a couple of inches away from my pussy, and of course he wouldn't be able to resist kissing it and licking it. I struggled and screamed at him to stop, which was a guaranteed way of making him carry on. And that was *very* sexy, being held in a wrestler's leg lock while my pussy was being licked, and knowing that I couldn't stop him from licking me even if I'd wanted to, which of course I didn't.

"A married friend of mine told me that she sometimes used a vibrator when she went to bed with her husband. She said that he loved using it on her, and that he often gave her an orgasm before they even had intercourse. They used it *during* intercourse, too. She liked to push the vibrator up her husband's asshole while he was making love to her. She said it always made him much stiffer, and his climaxes were like an explosion! That's another secret I've learned: that men get so much pleasure when you play with their asshole. I like Michael playing with my asshole, so it must feel just as good for him. I mean, why do gays fuck each other in the ass? Michael loves it when we're making love and I put one finger up his asshole; and sometimes I do it when he's just lying in bed next to me reading or watching TV or whatever. I play with his cock and his balls and then I wet one finger between my legs and work it up his asshole as far as I can. I stir it around and if I keep on doing it long enough I can make him come. Sometimes he doesn't even get a proper hard-on: the sperm just comes pouring out of him like I've turned on a faucet.

"I don't think I'd recommend a vibrator on a first date. The guy's going to think that you're kind of kinky; or else he's going to think that you've been single for so long that you have to get off on a plastic cock; or else he's maybe going to think that you don't have confidence in what he can do for you!

"But after Michael and I had been sleeping

together for maybe two months I sent off for this mail-order catalog of sex toys and lingerie and stuff, and I saw this vibrator that looks exactly like a penis except that it lights up. I showed it to Michael and I said, 'We have to have one of these,' and so he laughed and said okay. I don't know whether he thought I was serious or not, but when it arrived in the mail a couple of weeks later he said, 'We have to try this out tonight.'

"I don't think either of us could wait until we came home that evening. I called Michael at work during the day and told him how much he turned me on and how much I was looking forward to making love to him. That's another great secret, don't you think, calling your man during the day and saying really sexy things to him so that he can't wait to get back and make love to you.

"That night Michael brought home a bottle of French wine. I was waiting for him already, sitting on the couch, wearing nothing but a little white T-shirt. The only light came from two red scented candles, so the living room was very dark and romantic. Michael came in and we were as nervous with each other as if we were first-time lovers. He opened the wine and poured us a glass each and then he came and sat down next to me. I stripped off his necktie and unbuttoned his shirt, and kissed him. Then

I reached under the cushions and produced the vibrator. I switched it on and it lit up. We both laughed but it was that real warm, excited laughter. Michael took hold of the vibrator and slipped it underneath my T-shirt. It shone right through and it buzzed against my nipples so that they both stood up stiff. I'd never had a feeling like that in my nipples before . . . they tingled like your fingers do when they're very cold, and then they start to warm up again.

"Michael circled the vibrator around and around my breasts, and the feeling grew and grew. If he'd kept going, I think he could have given me an orgasm just by vibrating my breasts. But then he drew the vibrator slowly down my stomach, and around the insides of my thighs. I was all lit up, between my legs, even though the room was so dark. Michael slid the vibrator slowly up and down between my pussy-lips, and then he touched it very gently against my clitoris. The novelty of it made it even more exciting, and I felt that I was in some kind of sex heaven. While he was using the vibrator on my clitoris, Michael was kissing me passionately, and I mean *passionately*, and running his hands through my hair, like he could hardly control himself.

"He pushed the vibrator into my pussy, and it was unbelievable because all of my pussy-lips lit up from inside. I was so juicy by then that he didn't have any trouble sliding it right up me, right up the end, and then he slowly stirred it around, and with every stir my pussy made a wet sticky sound.

"He kept on stirring while he pulled his pants open with his left hand and struggled his way out of them. When he was naked, he slowly drew the vibrator out of my pussy and massaged his own cock with it, up and down the shaft, and all around his balls. His cock was sticking up so hard, and it was pulsing with the beat of his heart.

"He took the vibrator and lubricated the end of it with the juice from the tip of his cock. Then he parted the cheeks of my ass and slowly forced the vibrator into my asshole. I thought my asshole was going to be too tight at first, because that vibrator was enormous, as big as Michael's cock, maybe a little bigger. But he kept on forcing it into me, and at last my muscles relaxed and he managed to push it halfway into my ass. My asshole was all lit up red, and Michael opened my pussy with his fingers and you could see the light shining red through the thin skin between my pussy and my asshole. I had this feeling in my ass like I desperately needed to push that vibrator out of me, and at the same time I wanted it to go in deeper. It was like straining to go to the toilet but nearly having an orgasm at the same time.

"Michael pushed the vibrator even further up my ass, and then he knelt on the couch between my legs and pushed his cock into me, too. That was too much. I couldn't hold myself from having an orgasm. I clung onto Michael and I kept having one orgasm after another, I lost count how many. Michael kept on thrusting his cock into me and that vibrator kept on buzzing deep inside my ass and I didn't think my pussy and my ass were ever going to stop twitching.

"We've done plenty of other things. You have to, if you're going to keep your sex life alive. I think you always try new techniques, even if you don't think that you're going to like them. Like, I was not an anal person. I didn't like the idea of anal sex at all. But once you break yourself in—once you get used to the feeling of having a great big man's cock up your ass, you can't get enough of it. Well, I can't. I wouldn't like two men at once, and I don't usually enjoy having a vibrator up my ass at the same time that Michael's making love to me. But I don't honestly know which I prefer—front or back. They're both good."

These were only highlights of my talk with Pauline, which lasted for several hours. She was not only generous to her lovers, she was generous with her insights and completely unembarrassed about describing her sexual pleasures. As she said, "Sex is for sharing. If you discover something that's really exciting, why not tell all your friends?"

The contrast between her attitude toward lovemaking and Melissa's attitude couldn't have been more marked. In their way, each of them was exceptional—Melissa in her exhibitionism and Pauline in her enthusiasm. Most of us are a little less gung-ho about sex than Pauline and a lot less willing to indulge our own vanity than Melissa.

But there's no question that if you make a conscious effort to develop your sexual relationships by taking a tireless interest in your lover's pleasure and satisfaction; and do everything you can to introduce novelty and fun and a sense of sharing into your lovemaking, your relationships stand a far greater chance of being close and creative and highly erotic . . . and of lasting much longer, too.

Take Pauline's comment about anal sex. At first she didn't like the idea of it, and a majority of women don't, before they've tried it. But most men derive intense pleasure from it, because of the physical tightness of the anus, and because of the thrill of penetrating their lover in someplace "forbidden." So Pauline tried it, and eventually grew to enjoy it as much as vaginal penetration.

Texas porn star Julie Meadows (star of *Carnal Secrets*, in which she performed an extraordinary anal scene with Chris Cannon) said, "Sexually I think I'm best at anal sex. It's really an erogenous zone, and I don't think a lot of women realize just how erotic it can be once you've learned to relax. It seems so taboo but once you get over the fact that it's going into your butt, it's very sexy."

Up-and-coming porn actress Silvia Saint, 24, agrees that anal sex is one of her favorite variations, although she doesn't particularly care for double penetrations or dildoes.

Like Pauline, she believes that "everything is worth trying . . . if you don't like it, if *you* don't enjoy it, you don't have to do it again."

Most of us have sexual limits—acts that we wouldn't perform or fantasies that we wouldn't feel happy about discussing with our partners. Quite often, though, these limits can restrict development of our sexual relationships, and can eventually cripple them beyond repair. It's so important to be completely open with your new lover right from the very first time you make love. Be open-minded, open to hints and suggestions, and always willing to talk about anything and everything, no matter how perverse you may think it is.

If your new sexual relationship is going to be wilder and much more exciting than any relationship you've ever had before, you're going to have to be prepared to be ten times more adventurous, and forget about any sexual inhibitions you ever had before. Once a man realizes that he can talk about anything with you, and that you'll enjoy listening, he'll think that you're the most amazing thing that ever happened to him, and he won't want to let you go.

7

Sharing the (Erotic) Dream

"All my life I've had an erotic fantasy about covering a naked girl in cream and fruit and cake. I want to pour chocolate sauce all over her breasts and rub butter frosting into her hair. Then I'd empty a can of maple syrup between her legs and make love to her."

This was John speaking—a 34-year-old insurance executive from Long Beach, California. If he sounds like his sexual tastes are rather unusual, they are. But they're by no means unique. So many men get off on women being smothered in various kinds of mess that there are several magazines and videos devoted exclusively to "dirty girls."

A typical video opens with a girl in black bra and stockings plastering herself with cheesecake and masturbating with handfuls of cream. Another shows a naked girl lying back with her legs wide apart, pouring a gallon of vanilla custard all over her vulva and her breasts and smearing it over her face. Some "dirty girl" videos show girls masturbating with bananas and cucumbers, or urinating over each other's faces. Some of the more extreme productions depict girls spitting and drooling in each other's faces, or breaking wind, or excreting and masturbating at the same time.

Everybody has different sexual tastes and different sexual fantasies. That's what makes sex as exciting and varied as it is. But it does create problems when one partner has an overwhelming urge to perform a particular sexual act and finds it impossible to suggest it to the other partner, for fear of causing upset or embarrassment, or provoking sheer disgust.

Yet if you're going to find yourself a wild new lover, and *keep* him, you'll have to realize that most sexually driven men harbor some pretty outrageous desires (just as many sexually driven women do). Don't make him feel that he can't share these fantasies with you. After all, you won't necessarily have to act them out for real. Talking about them could be enough. Most of all, don't make him feel that they disgust you. Take his fantasies for what they are—fantasies—and make your own judgment about how much you want to make them come true.

Discussing your partner's fantasies, giving him the chance to describe them in detail, and *not* being judgmental—that can often give him all the sexual release that he needs. Let him talk filth. Encourage him to talk dirty, and listen. What he says is going to be the key to your future success in a long-term sexual relationship. Suppose it turns him on to see girls emptying jugs of cream between their legs and masturbating with bananas. Think about it, seriously. Where's the harm? And where's the harm in you going home and doing the same? If he finds you lying in bed with a peeled banana peeking out of your vagina, don't you think he's going to get a whole lot of pleasure out of eating it, and then licking all around your vulva for dessert? And what will you get out of it, except for unmitigated pleasure? Marie-Lou, 27, a bank teller from Chicago, Illinois, said, "Rick always liked to watch me going to the bathroom. Whenever I went in there, he used to come in, too, and sit on the side of the tub and talk to me, even if I was having a shit. I could see his eyes, glancing between my legs, and it really embarrassed me, because that's about the most personal thing you can do, and you don't want your boyfriend staring at you while you're doing it, do you?

"I talked to my mom about it, because we've always had a very close relationship. And do you know what she said? 'Your dad used to like to do that, too.' I couldn't believe that. My dad watching my mother going to the bathroom? But she said, 'When somebody really loves another person, they want to possess them, they want to own them, they want to be part of everything they do. Dressing, undressing, brushing their teeth, falling asleep, waking up. Going to the bathroom. It's not perversion, it's love.' "

Marie-Lou took her mother's advice, and two or three days later, when Rick was coming to bed, she threw back the covers and said, "Look . . . how'd you like a bite out of this?

"I'd pushed a Snickers bar three quarters of the way up my asshole, so that it looked like I was shitting. It was melting, and dripping everywhere. Rick was wearing this towel wrapped around his waist. When he saw me, he dropped it, and he stood there right in front of me with his dick so hard that it was almost touching his belly-button. He thought for a second that I'd actually shit myself, and that I was inviting him to eat it, but even when he realized it was chocolate, it still turned him on. He got down between my legs and he wolfed that Snickers bar out of my asshole, all of it, and licked all the way around, and then he got on top of me and fucked me. We were all sticky and sweet but we loved it, and he took out his cock when he was coming and shot it all over my pussy and all over my chocolatey asshole, and then he licked me again. We kissed like we were going to eat each other, and his mouth tasted of chocolate and sperm, and that's the most erotic flavor combination I've ever experienced. We fondled each other and rolled around the bed so that there was chocolate smeared all over the sheets. It was so messy but it was marvelous. One of my close friends was *disgusted* when I told her about it. She said, 'How can you *do* things like that . . . it's not the real thing, but it's just as bad. It's the *idea* of it. And I would never, ever let my husband watch me on the toilet.' I have to admit that *I* was disgusted at first, until I talked to my mom, and she made me realize that it was totally harmless. Your lover sees you naked. He sees you wash you hair and clean your teeth. If it excites him, where's the harm in him watching you relieve yourself? I loved it and he loved it, and it brought us so much closer, because he knew that I understood what his fantasy was, and that I was happy to indulge it. I don't think it's infantile at all. In fact I think if you can do things you like with your partner, it shows how mature you are."

Has she asked him *why* it arouses him so much?

"I don't think it matters why. I'm not a psychiatrist, I'm not trying to analyze him, and I'm not trying to cure him, either. What's to cure? Now that I've come to terms with it, there's absolutely no problem at all. He enjoys it and I enjoy it because he does, that's all. If I had some kind of special fantasy like that, I think I'd be delighted that my partner wanted to share it with me."

A couple of warnings: make sure that your lover doesn't have any nut allergies before inviting him to eat chocolate bars out of your anus. And never invite him to eat real excrement. My colleague Dr. Gloria Brame, who runs an excellent website for those interested in kinky sex, sums it up very succinctly: "From time to time, people criticize me for not being more open-minded about eating poop. After all, I seem perfectly comfortable with many other extreme types of sex, including ones that make some of my poop-eating fans faint with horror. Am I secretly a prude, after all?

"But you can't eat poop without putting yourself at risk of disease. It is true that some people who do this don't get sick. Some people who step in front of speeding cars don't get run over, either. Human feces, unlike urine, is by its very nature infested with bacteria, and a bacterial infection transmitted by ingesting feces can be fatal. There is no way to protect yourself against getting one.

"So to my mind, ingestion, while a perfectly acceptable fantasy, can never be acted out with any guarantee of safety, unlike many seemingly more dangerous types of sexual behavior."

I began this chapter with this particular fantasy because it shocks women more than almost an other. After that, most of the common male fantasies that you're likely to come across will seem comparatively tame. But even the mildest fantasy or fetish shouldn't be dismissed. If you discover that your new lover has a predilection for some minor sexual kink, you should show him that it doesn't put you off. In fact, you should make every effort to involve it in your lovemaking. You'll find that his heightened response will make your consideration more than worth the trouble.

After years of talking to men about their unfulfilled sexual fantasies, I think I can safely say the four most common of them are these:

1: Bondage. This usually involves tying a woman to a bed or a chair, so that she's completely helpless, and having his wicked way with her. Actually, their way is very seldom wicked. It's the woman's helplessness that they find arousing, and the fact that they can look and touch and caress a woman without her being able to resist. One man wanted to do nothing more than tickle a naked woman with a feather boa, trailing it all over her and pulling it backward and forward between her legs. Another wanted to paint erotic pictures all over a woman's body, while another simply wanted to lick her all over, from her toes to her face. Many men are aroused by the idea of making love to a woman who can't resist and bringing her to orgasm while she's unable to move her arms and her legs. Shaving the pubic area of a tied-up woman also comes high on the list. But only a very small minority showed any interest in sado-masochistic behavior, and even those took care to point out that they would only be interested in S&M with a woman who had given her informed consent, and who actually enjoyed sexual pain. Of this minority, several had a fantasy about dripping candlewax onto a woman's nipples, while others were excited by the idea of attaching clips to her nipples or using extra-large dildoes. As I say, though, almost all of the men who admitted to being aroused by bondage wanted their "victim" to be erotically stimulated in the most pleasant way possible.

Take great care about indulging in bondage with a man you've only just met. If he expresses any interest in it, don't immediately submit to being tied up. Make a mental note of his interest and shelve it until you know him well enough to be 100 percent sure that he will do it safely. You can *talk* about it, though. There's no harm in that. And talking about it will give you a clearer idea of how compelling his fantasy is, and whether it has a dark side to it.

2: Lingerie. An overwhelming majority of men have erotic fantasies about their wives or lovers dressing in sexy lingerie. You can tell by the numbers of purple split-crotch panties that are bought on birthdays and Valentine's Day. Men are strongly aroused by the contrast between naked skin and black lace (or white nylon, or leather, or PVC, or whatever.) It's the sexual vulnerability that excites them: the fact that you're ostensibly dressed, but at the same time you're still exposing your nipples and your genitals, and that you're open to being looked at, and intimately touched, and sexually penetrated—all without taking anything off. The most popular items of erotic lingerie are stockings and garter belts, closely followed by peephole bras that leave your nipples exposed, open-crotch panties, G-strings, and crotchless bodysuits. The most popular colors are black, red, white, and purple.

The problem with erotic lingerie is that women don't like it half as much as men. Over 75 percent of the women I asked about erotic lingerie said that if their husbands or lovers gave them any, they would be "annoyed" and take it back for an exchange or a refund. Women prefer pretty and comfortable lingerie, and the only item of erotic underwear that has gained any mainstream popularity amongst women is the thong—not because it makes you look like Gipsy Rose Lee, but because it doesn't give you a visible panty-line.

"I hate that sexy underwear," said Gina, 28, a nurse from Boston, Massachusetts. "My boyfriend is always buying it for me but whenever I wear it I think I look like a whore."

That, of course, is the whole point of it. Your lover *wants* you to look like a whore. He wants you to look sluttish and available and dirty-minded and cheap. It's a fantasy. He doesn't really think of you that way, not normally, but now and again he wants some variation, some excitement. He want you to behave like a woman with no inhibitions.

A woman who refuses to wear erotic lingerie is failing to understand that her lover is paying her a considerable tribute. He's trying to show her that he thinks she's the sexiest woman in the whole world. He doesn't really see her as cheap. He's trying to explain that, underneath that demure exterior, he sees her as a sexual tigress. He's trying to demonstrate that she excites him.

That's why, if your lover gives you sexy underwear, don't do what most women do which is to lift it out of the gift-box as if it's a string of decaying seaweed and say, "I hope you're not seriously expecting me to wear *this!*" It took him enough courage to buy the underwear in the first place. Don't make him feel like some kind of nasty little pervert. He'll probably put a brave face on it, and take it back, but you'll have done the damage. You've embarrassed him sexually, which is never a good thing to do to the man you're supposed to love. Not only that, you've made it impossible for him ever again to show you how sexy he thinks you are, in every way he wants to.

It will cost you nothing to wear the underwear he buys you. It will cost you nothing to act a little whorish for him. It will cost you nothing to give him a sparkle of appreciation. So you don't like it? So what. Accept it for what it is, which is dressing-up clothes. You used to dress up as a fairy or a queen when you were younger, what's wrong with dressing up as a woman with sex on her mind?

Put it on and take him to bed and see if you don't enjoy yourself. You don't have to wear it all the time, after all. And since he obviously finds you so sexy in flimsy lingerie, why don't you very occasionally buy some yourself, and give him a fashion parade in the bedroom?

There's always the problem of size, of course. Men are notoriously bad at judging their lovers' bra measurements. As one woman said, "He gave me a fishnet bra that you could have used as a trawl net for tuna." But again, don't be tempted to mock. Just exchange it, and make sure that you wear the replacement.

Many men are aroused by dirty, vulgar sex. I've personally known several highly respectable professional men who regularly visited prostitutes and who enjoyed having sex in cheap hotels with women they picked up on the streets. Just because you've shown your lover that you're not prepared to indulge his fantasy by wearing erotic lingerie, that doesn't mean that he's not going to think about it anymore. In the long term, the result could be that when he wants a whorish woman, he's going to go looking for a real one.

Women regularly ask me, "If I don't

like his fantasy, why do I have to help him to act it out?"

The answer to that question is that seeking to understand and satisfy each other is what couples do. It's what makes a sexual relationship develop and grow, and endure. Remember that you're equally entitled to expect him to act out *your* fantasies, too.

3: Risky sex. A *soupcon* of danger can greatly intensify a man's sexual excitement, and many men have fantasies about making love in the open air, in the office, in an elevator—anyplace where there's a chance of discovery. Occasionally couples make love in public, without making any pretense at concealment—in the park, on the beach, in automobiles and airplanes. It's often mistakenly thought that they've been so overwhelmed with lust that they've been unable to control themselves. But the reality is that they make love in front of other people quite deliberately, because it hugely increases their sexual arousal. *Here we are, doing the most intimate thing that two people can do together, and we're doing it where everybody can see us.* Other couples play out this fantasy slightly more discreetly by going to group sex parties or partner-swapping evenings, but they're still enjoying the thrill of doing something private in front of other people.

What if your new lover suddenly starts getting extremely fresh in risky surroundings? How you respond depends entirely on you. If you think that the chance of your being discovered is comparatively minimal, or if you don't seriously mind if somebody catches you at it, then you might well be tempted to go ahead. But your lover shouldn't be too upset if you tell him no—especially if you promise him a good time when you get home tonight.

You can play on his fantasy when you're in bed by making up risky or exhibitionistic scenarios, such as making love in front of an audience, or climbing onto your table in a fashionable restaurant and having noisy and unrestrained intercourse amid the knives and forks.

Alison, a 26-year-old hair stylist from Seattle, Washington, said that her new lover, Jim, a 29-year-old aeronautical engineer, exhibited a penchant for taking sexual risks "almost from day one of our relationship.

"In another guy, it might have been irritating, but Jim was always such fun. We were invited to a party three days after we met. I got all dressed up and Jim came around to collect me. He said I looked absolutely irresistible. I was wearing this tight pale-blue sweater and this short navy skirt. I introduced him to my folks and my dad offered him a beer. They sat together talking while I went upstairs to finish my hair. The next thing I know, my bedroom door flew open and it was Jim. He said, 'Quick—I told your old man that I had to go to the john!' He took hold of me and kissed me, and then he pulled up my skirt around my hips and started to pull down my pantyhose. I said, 'Stop it! What are you doing?' He said, 'I can't resist you . . . I can't wait a second longer!' He tugged open his pants and took out his cock . . . and, yes, I could see that he couldn't resist me. It was so big! He took hold of my hand and wrapped my fingers around his cock and said, 'Feel that? It's straining for you . . . it has to have you.' He turned me around and bent me over so that I was holding on to my dressing-table. Then he pushed his cock right up me, from behind. I could see my face in my dressing-table mirror, and I was staring at myself and thinking, 'My God, this is me being fucked . . . I'm actually being fucked.' It was out of this world. His cock was flying in and out of me and I was starting to get real wet. Then suddenly my dad called out from downstairs, like, 'Alison, have you seen my reading glasses anyplace?' and he started to climb up the stairs. Jim gave me two or three quick thrusts with his cock and then he whipped his zipper up and by the time my dad came into the door he was right across the other side of the room looking at my high school pictures. He was still hard, though; his cock made his pants stick up like a tent!

"On the way to the party he kept trying to slide his hand up my skirt. I said, 'No, come on, Jim, you're driving.' He said, 'Let's find someplace to park and we can finish what we were doing.' He took a side-turning and we ended up in this parking lot that overlooks Shilshole Bay. It was dark and there was nobody else there. I said that maybe we should wait till later, but Jim said, 'Look at my cock . . . how can I walk around all evening with my cock poking out like this?' The way he said it, he made me laugh so much. Anyhow, we climbed into the back of the car. Jim took his pants right off and he pulled my pantyhose right down to my ankles. He climbed on top of me and I took hold of his cock and guided it into my pussy. I was so uncomfortable; I had the door handle pressing against the side of my head, but I didn't care. Jim's cock was so big that I felt totally filled up . . . I just wanted him to fuck me and fuck me all night.

"I was panting and screaming and I felt like I was close to having an orgasm when the whole car was filled up with light. All of these cars arrived, seven or eight of them. It was a whole party of fishermen, they were laughing and shouting and slamming their car doors. One of them parked so close that he hit Jim's car when he opened his door. I looked up and I could see his face peering into the window. He shouted out to all of his friends, and they all came running. I was trying to struggle off the seat. I was so embarrassed. But Jim said, 'Stay here. Let's finish it. Let's make them jealous.' And he kissed me, and stroked my hair, and he slowly carried on fucking me while all of these fishermen were standing around the car.

"We didn't hurry. We fucked real slow, and we enjoyed every moment of it, because we knew that all of these guys were watching us, they were watching Jim's cock sliding in and out of my pussy. They started to clap in time to us fucking. It was like a dream. I'd never let anybody see my pussy before, except the guys that I'd slept with, and to think that all these strangers were standing around staring at it with their tongues hanging out, that was so exciting. I started to come. I grabbed hold of Jim's hair and I pulled at his ears and scratched his face. My hips were bouncing up and down, I couldn't help it. And then Jim came too, but his cock slipped out of me, and his sperm was flying all over my sweater, and the fishermen were slapping the roof of the car and shouting, 'Go! Go! Go!'

"We climbed out of the car and those guys stood around and laughed and clapped for us. They were so good-natured about it, I couldn't be angry. Jim gave them high-fives and before I got back into the passenger seat, I lifted up my skirt and I gave them a twirl, so that they could see my pussy and my butt, and I until I sat down I didn't realize that I had sperm running down my thighs.

"Jim never left me alone. He was always wanting to put his hand into my panties or squeeze my breasts, and he always liked to do it when there was a risk of somebody coming into the room. I think he loved the idea of fucking a woman in front of people, so that they could see what a great stud he was.

"I went along with it for a while, and I'm not going to tell you that I didn't enjoy it, because I think that every woman is an exhibitionist. Those girls you see in men's magazines, with their legs wide apart, don't tell me they do it for the money. They love to show themselves off. But in the end I had to tell Jim that I wanted to cool it. I didn't need all of that danger. I didn't want to share him with the rest of the world, I wanted us to make love together, in private.

"He was okay. He didn't get upset. And everything's fine, so long as I let him put his hand up my skirt now and again, when we're at my parents' house; or if he sneaks into the bathroom with me when we're visiting friends, and I suck his cock while I'm sitting on the can. I don't mind risky sex at all. Sometimes it's very exciting. And it shows that Jim wants me just as much as he did when he first met me."

4: Masochism. A lot of men are aroused by the idea of being disciplined by a dominant woman and being made to perform submissive sexual acts. My Dutch friend

Monique von Cleef, who was a notorious S&M madam in her day, told me that a majority of her clients were senior executives, police chiefs, and men with highly responsible jobs. At the end of the day, they wanted to forget all of their stress and be treated like slaves, with no responsibilities whatsoever. They wanted to be punished, too, because they felt guilty about the decisions they had made during the working day—hiring people, firing people, and wrecking people's careers. They wanted to be spanked, and handcuffed, and given enemas. They wanted to have their penises locked up in cages filled with spikes, and sit on stools with enormous dildoes in the middle of them while they were obliged to listen to a children's story.

Not all men have masochistic inclinations as pronounced as these. But whatever they tell you, most men are sexually aroused by being punished or hurt, especially in the throes of making love. Gene, 31, a realtor from North Bergen, New Jersey, admitted that he adored his girlfriend digging her fingernails into his scrotum just before he climaxed, and "pulling my skin so hard that she almost wrenches my balls off." He said that he couldn't decide if it was pain or pleasure. "It's pretty damned sore afterward, that's for sure, but while she's doing it, it's Shangri-La."

Henry, 28, a construction engineer from Westbrook, Maine, told me, "I used to have this fantasy that I was chained in a dungeon. I was lying on a stone floor, naked. Every couple of hours, this fantastically beautiful woman would come down to see me. She had short, slicked-back hair and she was dressed in a black leather outfit that left her breasts bare and exposed her cunt. She would stand there and insult me, call me every filthy name you ever heard of. Cocksucker, mother-fucker, everything. She would spit on me, spit in my face. Then she would lash me with her whip, slashing my cheeks and my chest and making sure that she whipped my dick. She whipped it until I screamed. Then she wrapped that whip around my cock and tugged at it, and she would tell me that I was a pathetic fail-ure, and an ass-licker. And she would keep on tugging my dick until I climaxed, and then she would whip me again, until there was blood and sperm flying everywhere, and she would tell me how useless I was.

"I guess, in the final analysis, I was looking for a woman to dominate me, to

tell me what to do. I spend all day shouting at my staff. I wanted somebody to put
my life into perspective. Power is erotic,
you know, having power over other people. But complete lack of power, complete
humiliation, that's erotic, too. Having to
lick some woman's shoes, I think that's
very sexual. Having to sweep her floors
and polish her furniture while you're totally naked, I think that's very sexual, too.
I think all men have a masochistic streak
in them. They want women to scratch
them and bite them and insult them and
piss in their faces. It's an important part
of evaluating your position in the world.
It's an important part of assessing your
own value."

You can test your new lover's responsiveness to pain by scratching his back
during intercourse, or biting his ear lobe,
or nipping his nipples. A man's nipples
are extremely tender, and if you find that
your lover enjoys you chewing on them
quite hard, then it's quite likely that he's
receptive to more than a little pain and
punishment. Try sinking your teeth into
his buttocks; or biting his neck; or inserting three or more fingers into his anus,
without any lubrication. You'll soon find
out how masochistic he is. Non-

masochists say "Ouch!" while masochists say "Ohhhh . . . ."

Remember, though, that not every man is a masochist all the time. The pain that he was able to enjoy during the delirium of last night's sex may not be tolerable in the cold light of day. So don't expect to be able to carry on where you left off. A bite in the middle of lovemaking can be ecstasy. A bite during your morning coffee break can be an irritating nuisance.

How far you want to act out his pleasure-and-pain theatricals is up to you. If you're a reasonably straight woman, and you don't really want to get involved in any kind of S&M scene, then the best thing you can do is go looking for somebody else. Masochism isn't a disease that you can cure. It's an essential part of somebody's sexual personality. Either decide that you'd like to get involved in his sexual games, and that you'd get pleasure out of them, too, or hit the trail and find somebody else.

Having a masochistic lover can actually be a whole lot of fun. He might want you to tie him up and make love to him while he's helpless (see Bondage); or he might want you to paddle his behind or force him to clean out your bathrooms with his tongue.

Celia, 29, an accountant from Tulsa, Oklahoma, said, "One hot night we were both lying on the bed, side-by-side, naked, reading books. I said to Ken, 'Will you fix me a drink?' and he said, 'No.' So I slapped his ass and said, 'Fix me a drink, you lazy bastard, or I'll give you another one.'

"I slapped him again, and then again, and then again, until the cheeks of ass flushed quite red. I said, 'Fix me a drink, will you?' and I was angry now because he seemed like he was enjoying himself. I lost my temper and I slapped his ass again and again, very hard. He closed his eyes for a while, I'll never forget that, then he said, 'Okay . . . you win . . . I'll fix you a drink.' He climbed up off the bed and his cock was hard and there was semen dripping from the end of it, and semen all over the sheet. I said, 'You've come. I can't believe it.' He shrugged and said, 'What did you expect, spanking me like that?'

"Spanking's part of our sexual repertoire now. I don't do it too often. It's supposed to be a special punishment, for when I'm really angry about something. But it helps to relieve all of our tensions.

It means that I have a way of showing that I disapprove of something he's said, or done, or *not* done. And he gets such a thrill out of it. I can spank him when he's standing up, and it only takes two or three spanks before his cock comes up; and six or seven more before he comes. I don't touch his cock at all, and neither does he. His semen just comes spurting out on its own."

Some women are alarmed when their partner displays masochistic tendencies. *I expected him to behave like a man. I expected him to look after me. But he wants me to whip him on his bare ass when he's done something wrong.*

But if a man derives erotic pleasure from pain or humiliation, that doesn't make him any less of a man. It's the flip side to his personality, and often the strongest and most reliable of men are those who have the most extreme masochistic desires. Enjoying pain and subjugation isn't an illness, unless it's taken to extremes. It's a natural part of human sexuality, and if you introduce it into your love life with care, it can be a source of immense pleasure and emotional relief. I say "with care" because there are sensible limits to every aspect of human sexual behavior. Without being judgmental, some of them are inadvisable for both your physical and emotional health, and some of them (as we have already seen from the eating of feces) are class-A dangerous.

I was approached some time ago by a woman who was extremely worried about her boyfriend's sexual practices. Anesthetized with codeine, he was using a craft knife to reshape the head of his penis, cutting slices from it on either side in order to make it more "rocket-shaped." He said that his penis was extra-sensitive once scar tissue had formed over his wounds, giving him a unique combination of pain and pleasure.

A banker's wife told me that her husband had slit his penis in half, all the way from the head to the root, so that essentially he had two half-penises. Other self-mutilations include piercing the scrotal sac and inflating it with a drinking straw during oral sex (extremely risky, since human breath contains so many bacteria); and in one case, the complete removal of the scrotum, so that the testes were exposed.

I always hesitate to use the word "bizarre," but I believe that any form of serious self-damage shows that somebody has sexual problems that require psychiatric care. There is a self-destructive streak in everybody's sexual personality. Lately, it has been often displayed through body-piercing and tattooing and decorative scars, which have become more popular. To a certain extent, it's exciting and erotic. But if you find that your new lover is interested in more than a little spanking or a pair of sterling-silver nipple rings, you may be wise to cool your relationship and look for somebody whose sexuality is on a slightly more even keel. While I am a devoted believer in creative and varied sex, I am also a believer in taking care of yourself, and protecting yourself from people whose sexual obsessions may be too deep and dangerous for you to cope with.

I know that many women are disconcerted when, quite early in their relationships, their partners suddenly come out and express a sexual preference that they simply weren't expecting. "I thought he was just a normal, straightforward guy," said 27-year-old Sylvia, a travel agent from New York. "He treated me like a lady. We shared a whole lot of interests in common . . . music, good food, laughing. For the first time I believed that I might have found a soul mate. Then, the second time we went to bed together, he asked me to keep my shoes on. I couldn't handle it. Was he making love to me, or my shoes? I had to ask him to leave."

"Why can't he accept me the way I am?" asked a 25-year-old Michigan homemaker whose new husband had suggested that she remove her pubic hair. She said that having no pubic hair made her feel "defenseless," and that her husband's request had made her suspicious that he had an obsession about prepubescent girls.

Several women (including the porno actress Silvia Saint) have said that they don't like the idea of being tied up. "My partner is always dropping heavy hints about how much it would turn him on if he tied me up to the bed," said Jennie, 28, a hairdresser from Alexandria, Louisiana. "But the whole idea of it scares me. If he doesn't feel that he can assert himself sexually without tying me up . . . like, what's going on here? It upsets me."

"I know that my partner wants me to give him oral sex, but I'm not too sure about it," said 19-year-old Susan, a student from Madison, Wisconsin. "He lies next to me in bed, with his penis only a couple of inches away from my face, and once I woke up in the night and found that he was stroking my lips with it. Do you think there's something wrong with me, that I don't want to do it?"

I've heard similar reservations from dozens of women, and all I'll say is this: when you enter into a new sexual relationship, looking for a wild new lover, you're going to have to put some of your inhibitions where they belong, and that's back in the past, with all of those relationships that didn't quite work out. This is the new you, the you who's going to be adventurous and carefree in bed. The you who's going to give your new lover the time of his life, and who is going to have the time of her life in return.

You have certain inalienable sexual rights. You have the right not to be forced or argued with or blackmailed into performing any sexual act that you dislike. You have the right to enjoy yourself in bed. You have the right to find yourself a man who pleases and satisfies you, but along with that right you have the responsibility to please him and satisfy *him*.

Unless a sexual act is obviously painful or dangerous, give it at least one chance. You'll be surprised how variations like oral or anal sex can become acquired tastes, and add a new dimension to your new love life.

Most of all, look at the man you've just found, and ask yourself what he's been looking for. Maybe he's been looking for a wild new lover, too, and you're her.

8

Twenty-five Wild New Things You Can Do Today

1: Decorate your navel and your vulva with felt-tip flowers and hearts and cherubs.
2: Call your lover at work and tell him that you're masturbating with a handful of honey.
3: Draw a picture of yourself sucking your lover's penis (trace a photograph of yourself if you're not very good at drawing . . . try to make it a good likeness). Tuck it into his briefcase when he leaves for work.
4: Record yourself masturbating and slip the cassette into your lover's car. Call him on his mobile phone and tell him to listen to it on his way to work. Use the dirtiest language you know.
5: Go visit him at work wearing nothing but a coat, and open it up when nobody else is looking.
6: Put bright red lipstick on your anus and invite him to kiss it.

7: Take a series of Polaroids of yourself wetting your panties, and put them in an envelope for him to open at work. Be sure to enclose the wet panties, too.

8: When he comes home, greet him completely naked except for high-heeled shoes and a large pink daisy in your vagina.

9: Send off for two matching vibrators, and invite him to use one on you while you use one on him. All's fair in love and war!

10: Have a naked picnic in bed, and use the food to arouse your lover in any way that you can think of. Hot dog, anyone?

11: When he comes out of the bathroom tonight, lie on the bed waiting for him, naked and smothered from head to foot in baby oil.

12: Before he's even awake in the morning, start to massage his penis with scented oil.

13: Make an erotic video of yourself during the day and show it to him when he comes to bed.

14: On his birthday, greet him in the living room, naked with your legs wide apart and a lighted candle in your vagina.

15: Go through a sex-aid catalogue together and choose two items. The catch is, each has to choose one for the other, and promise to use them.

WILD SEX FOR NEW LOVERS

16: Join him in the shower or tub, fully dressed, and give him a sexy soaping.

17: Wake him up in the morning by sitting on his face (not too hard, you don't want to suffocate him!).

18: Write him an "anonymous" letter, filled with all of the filthiest fantasies you can think of. Really let your imagination rip! You'll be surprised by what you're capable of putting into words, and he'll be staggered by how sexy you are!

19: Book a room at a hotel and ask him to meet you there after work. When he arrives, greet him with a bottle of chilled champagne and the most outrageous lingerie you can find.

20: The second he walks in the door, open his pants and take out his penis. Don't even let him put his briefcase down before you push him into the living room and give him enthusiastic oral sex.

21: Come to a deal: each of you writes on a piece of paper a sexual favor that you would like the other to perform. Play a game of Trivial Pursuit for it, or Monopoly, or toss a coin if you're too impatient. The winner gets the favor, no questions asked.

22: Find a place to make love in the open air. A wood, a lake, maybe your balcony, if you live in the city, or a corner of your yard where nobody can see you. Have sex completely naked . . . it adds to the thrill.

23: Ask him to teach you how to masturbate him so that it really feels good and he really comes quickly. Use sexy magazines as an aid, ask him to show you which girls turn him on the most. Don't be jealous . . . they're only pictures!

24: Teach him how to masturbate you the way you really like it.

25: Do one erotic thing tonight that you've never done before, and do another one tomorrow, and every day for a week.

Good luck with your new love life. I hope that whatever pleasure you give, you'll get back a hundred times over.

Structured Analysis
and Design
of Information Systems

A. Ziya Aktas

A RESTON BOOK
PRENTICE-HALL, INC.
Englewood Cliffs, New Jersey 07632

Library of Congress Cataloging-in-Publication Data

AKTAS, A. ZIYA. (date)
  Structured analysis and design of information
systems.

  Includes bibliographies and index.
  1. Electronic data processing—Structured
techniques. 2. System analysis. 3. System design.
I. Title.
QA76.9.S84A37 1987   004.2'1   86-15483
ISBN 0-8359-7117-1

Editorial/production supervision and
  interior design: *Carol L. Atkins*
Cover design: *20/20 Services, Inc.*
Manufacturing buyer: *Ed O'Dougherty*

To Anadolu

Printed in the United States of America

10 9 8 7 6 5 4 3 2 1

ISBN 0-8359-7117-1   025

Prentice-Hall International (UK) Limited, *London*
Prentice-Hall of Australia Pty. Limited, *Sydney*
Prentice-Hall Canada Inc., *Toronto*
Prentice-Hall Hispanoamericana, S.A., *Mexico*
Prentice-Hall of India Private Limited, *New Delhi*
Prentice-Hall of Japan, Inc., *Tokyo*
Prentice-Hall of Southeast Asia Pte. Ltd., *Singapore*
Editora Prentice-Hall do Brasil, Ltda., *Rio de Janeiro*

Contents

PART III   METHODOLOGIES

Foreword

By enabling us to gather a wealth of information on myriad subjects at an ever increasing rate, computers have ushered in an "information explosion." As a result we are gaining a new appreciation of information itself as an organizational resource. Our appreciation calls for even greater reserves of information and, accordingly, more efficient and effective ways to analyze and design successful information systems.

In this highly readable text, Dr. A. Ziya Aktas explains how structured system development methodologies surpass the capabilities of the classical approach in expanding the efficiency of information systems. Structure, he argues, is essential because it imposes order and thus improves the comprehensibility of complex systems. The structured approach presented herein is a combination of common sense and the rigorous application of some very useful tools.

Dr. Aktas writes as an accomplished teacher and researcher. He is currently Chairman of the Department of Computer Engineering at Middle East Technical University (METU) at Ankara, Turkey. During his fifteen years of teaching, Dr. Aktas has published several books and many papers in prestigious international journals. He received his B.S. and M.S. degrees in civil engineering from METU and his Ph.D. in civil engineering from Lehigh University.

While taking a two-year leave from METU, Dr. Aktas served on the faculty of the Computer Technology Department of Purdue University School of Engineering at Indianapolis, part of Indiana University–Purdue University at Indianapolis (IUPUI). During that time our faculty and students were fortunate to be introduced to many of the ideas and techniques presented in this text. We have witnessed their proven effectiveness.

I believe this book reflects Dr. Aktas' dedication to excellence. Both students and practitioners will find the text invites careful reading. Most assuredly the book will provide the reader with an increased awareness of the advantages and the necessity of the structured approach. If offers timely information regarding the tools and methodologies employed in the approach as well. Overall, it is an important contribution to the study of systems analysis and design.

R. Bruce Renda
Dean
Purdue University
School of Engineering and Technology
at Indianapolis

Preface

Both technical and nontechnical media have recently emphasized the growing need for systems analysts in the information systems field. The crucial point stressed repeatedly is that the number of available systems analysts is quite below the number that is demanded. A logical step in solving the problem would be to include some courses in systems analysis and design in the curricula of computer science, computer technology, information systems/science, computer engineering, business, or similar programs. This is in fact what is being done in many schools in the United States and Europe.

It has been observed, however, that teaching a systems analysis and design course is quite difficult. Perhaps the major limitation of conventional systems analysis and design courses is the lack of awareness of how to apply engineering tools and methods. If we begin by defining a structured approach as an engineering approach for information systems development, or as a well-defined and standard set of methods and tools for problem solving, we can then go on to teach how to use the structured tools and methods/methodologies in such courses.

The major objectives of this book are threefold: to present material that will clearly convey what are the available tools and methodologies for structured analysis and design of information systems, to compare these tools and methodologies, and to give examples of their applications. Hence it can be used either as a textbook or as a reference by the practicing systems analyst in a business or nonbusiness organization. A quite thorough review of recent publications in the field and a brief discussion of future research directions in the information systems

development area are other contributions of the book. Some exercises and examples are provided within each chapter to illustrate the material, and a short case
study is provided in the appendix to show the application of some commonly used
methodologies such as SD (Structured Design), W/O (Warnier/Orr), and JSD
(Jackson System Design). Relevant references will be given at the end of each
chapter.

Some of the outstanding features of the book include:

- A discussion of classical approach vs. the structured approach in Part I should
  help clarify some often confusing terms and concepts.
- A practical life cycle for an information system is proposed.
- Objectives of the structured approach are elaborated.
- A thorough discussion of the available tools and methodologies of the structured approach reveals the entire spectrum of possibilities and the differences
  between tools and methodologies.
- The material is up-to-date and contains applications of various methodologies to the same or similar problems to facilitate comparison.
- Measurement of software properties using quantifiable metrics has been a
  relatively recent topic in software engineering area.
- A short chapter of the book is devoted to a relatively important and promising
  research topic now being directed at applying concepts to the measurement
  of properties of information systems.

It would be very appropriate to use this text for a senior or a graduate course
that is taught after a classical systems analysis and design course. The book is
primarily intended to be used as a text book for any course similar to CIS-5 Structured Systems Analysis and Design of the DPMA Curriculum. It can, of course,
also be used by professional systems analysts and programmers as well.

I am indebted to many people who aided in the preparation of the book. It
is now my pleasure to acknowledge some of these very fine people who encouraged, helped, and gave me the strength that I needed to finish the manuscript. First
I would like to acknowledge B. Elderd of Reston/Prentice-Hall, Inc. Her continuous interest and care gave me the courage to start and to pursue my efforts in
manuscript preparation. I would like to thank her, Reston/Prentice-Hall, and the
discipline editors, J. Sulzycki and T. Buchholz, and editorial associate J. Kinzer
for their care, interest, and support in the preparation and review of the manuscript.
Actually, executive editor J. F. Fegen, and production editors C. Atkins and N.
Menges, of Prentice-Hall made editing and publication of this book possible. It is
my real pleasure to express my gratitude and sincere thanks to them and to all other
members of Prentice-Hall who contributed to the editing, production, and manufacturing. Many thanks are due various anonymous reviewers who contributed
greatly by their comments, criticisms, and encouragements. It is another pleasure
to express my thanks to B. Renda and R. Crozier of Purdue University School of

Engineering and Technology at Indianapolis, the dean and the department chairman, respectively, for their support and encouragement during the manuscript preparation. How can I forget the late J. Williams? I owe him and our dear friend E. Solinski many thanks for the very valuable discussions that we held together and also for their encouragement in my work. A few chapters of the book were drafted by J. Keely and the rest were drafted and typed by G. Oskay. It was later retyped a few times by A. Yardim. It is difficult for me to express my gratitude and thanks to her and others. My students in Indianapolis and in Ankara contributed a lot by their care, interest, questions, and comments during and after my lectures on structured approaches. I thank them all. I also thank Z. Aykanat and H. Sarrafzadeh for their assistance in preparing the manuscript. Last but not least, I want to express my sincere thanks to my family: my wife, our boys, and our parents. Without their patience, understanding, and sacrifice I would never have been able to finish this work.

A. Ziya Aktas
METU—Ankara

Chapter 1

Fundamental Concepts

1.1 SYSTEMS CONCEPT AND INFORMATION SYSTEMS

"System" is a term that is commonly used in many disciplines. Its use increased remarkably after the late fifties especially due to the rapid growth of electronic data processing (EDP) activities and to the appearance of some interdisciplinary studies such as cybernetics and biophysics. Social, educational, industrial, business, and engineering systems are only a few examples of systems in today's world. Obviously there exist many definitions of system.

Although the word "system" is used in many seemingly unrelated areas, all systems have some common properties: They have elements, environments, interaction between their elements and with the environment, and most important of all, they have goals to be fulfilled. Hence, one may define a system as an organized collection of people, machines, procedures, documents, data, or any other entities such that they interact with each other as well as with the environment to reach a predefined goal. A "subsystem" is a system which is an element of a larger system. The large system is called a "super system" or "supra system."

Very similar to the word "system," the word "information" is also a very much used and confused word. It is used by EDP people, by communications people, by librarians, and by many others. "Data" is another word that is used with information or even as its synonym. Yet a third word, "knowledge," is closely related to the other two. In fact fifth-generation computer systems are being referred to as knowledge-information processing systems (TL 82). An attempt to

1

clear that confusion around the terms data/information/knowledge needs to refer to another term: message. A message is a group of characters that is stored, processed, and transmitted in the information system of an organization. In other words, information in an organization is stored, processed, and transmitted as messages. The content of messages that flow through the information system of an organization has different levels of meaning depending on whether the messages carry data, information, or knowledge. As pointed out by Taggart (Tag 80), we recognize three levels of meaning for messages included in an information system: data, information, and knowledge (Figure 1.1).

- knowledge
- information
- data   meaning value

Figure 1.1   Meaning levels of messages

Data are groups of characters recognized as having the lowest level meaning. They are raw facts and opinions. *Information* has more meaning than data in that it is useful in a present decision situation. *Knowledge* has the highest level of meaning because it represents information that can be potentially useful in future decision situations.

As a comparison of these three terms, consider the following illustration:

Data: Employees have submitted their vacation requests.
Information: Summer is the vacation season, but we have already received production orders for summer.
Knowledge: Employee vacation dates should be arranged to handle the summer production properly.

There is still difficulty in distinguishing data from information or knowledge, however, because a certain data element may be information to a user at one time and knowledge to the same user at a different time or place. We, therefore, use the term "information" in the text as a general term, without differentiating the meaning level of the messages.

The information system of an organization may be defined as a system that serves to provide information within the organization when and where it is needed at any managerial level. Such a system must take the information received and store, retrieve, transform, process, and communicate it using the computer system or some other means. Bryce (BrM 83) states: "Equating information systems with computer systems is a misconception born of decades of preoccupation with technology." He defines an information system as a logically interrelated set of business processes that accomplish organizational goals.

As noted by Taggart (Tag 80), information in an information system environment has the following common requirements:

- It must be understood by its recipient in the proper frame of reference.
- It must be relevant to a current need in the decision-making process.

- It must have a surprise value, that is, what is already known should not be presented.
- It must lead its users to make a decision. A decision could be to take no action.

Brookes et al. (BGJL 82) stated that for an information system to yield information with the above characteristics, it must have some attributes. We may rearrange them as follows:

- Effective processing of information. This refers to proper editing of input data and efficient utilization of hardware and software.
- Effective management of information. Stressed are care in file management operations and in security and integrity of the existing data.
- Flexibility. The information system should be flexible enough to handle a variety of operations.
- User satisfaction. Of prime importance are user understanding of and satisfaction with the information system.

Any action in an organization depends on the result of a decision-making process at the proper managerial level of that organization. Obviously, then, the right information, available at the right time, is vital for the process of optimal decision making. In some decision-making/action processes the available data can be used directly. In most cases, however, data are grouped and summarized in various forms and finally transformed to become information to be used in decision making. The result of action(s) following a decision-making process can also be used for another decision and action activity (i.e. feedback process in systems terminology). The relationship between data and action is illustrated in Figure 1.2 and draws on that given by Konsynski (Ko 80).

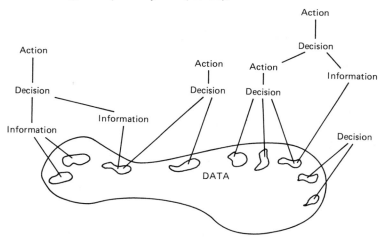

Figure 1.2   Data/action relationship in an organization

1.2 SUBSYSTEMS OF AN INFORMATION SYSTEM

The information system of any organization contains information related to three basic types of operations, namely, transaction processing, control, and strategic planning. Following Davis (DaG 74), one could group them into two as operating level and management level activities as in Figure 1.3.

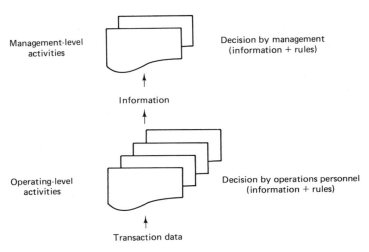

Management-level
activities

Decision by management
(information + rules)

Information

Operating-level
activities

Decision by operations personnel
(information + rules)

Transaction data

Figure 1.3   Operating level and management level activities

It is almost conventional now to represent management level activities as a triangle and to base it on a rectangle as a symbol of operating level activities (Figure 1.4).

Let us first consider the management level activities. In strategic planning, the executive or top management of the organization decides on the objectives of the organization, on the resources to be used to attain these objectives, and on the policies that are to govern the acquisition, use, and disposition of these resources. Activities have a long time range—one to ten or more years. As seen in Figure 1.4, the control function has both management and operational components. In *management control*, middle-level managers assure that resources are obtained and used effectively and efficiently to accomplish the organization's objectives. Activities have year-to-year or monthly time range. In *operational control*, supervisory management assures that specific tasks are carried out effectively and efficiently. Activities have day-to-day or weekly time range (e.g., IBM 78).

The rectangular block under the management triangle in Figure 1.4 is used to represent *transaction processing*, which means the daily routine business operations of the organization.

When we consider the relationship between the information system of an organization and its activities, common practice has been to define two subsystems

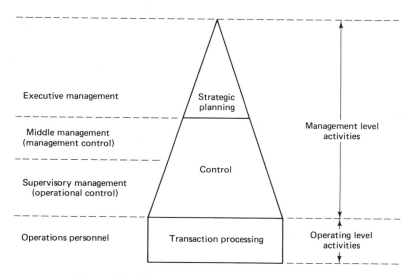

Figure 1.4   Information-related activities of organizations

as MIS (Management Information System) and OIS (Operations Information System) as in Figure 1.5. Comparing Figures 1.4 and 1.5, one concludes that OIS is the information subsystem relevant to transaction processing of the organization, and MIS is the information subsystem relevant to managerial decisions for control and strategic planning purposes.

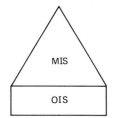

Figure 1.5   Information subsystems of an organization

1.3 AN EXAMPLE

Consider a small manufacturing company, Central Circuits Co., whose primary business objective is to produce custom-engineered printed circuit cards for larger electronic component manufacturers. When we review the types of activities of this company, we can combine Figures 1.2, 1.3, and 1.4 into a schema as shown in Figure 1.6.

In that figure data/information/knowledge (decision) relations are illustrated

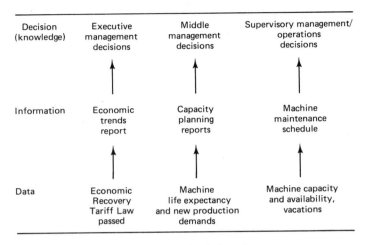

Decision (knowledge)	Executive management decisions	Middle management decisions	Supervisory management/ operations decisions
Information	Economic trends report	Capacity planning reports	Machine maintenance schedule
Data	Economic Recovery Tariff Law passed	Machine life expectancy and new production demands	Machine capacity and availability, vacations

Figure 1.6   Example of an information system

using some examples of decisions that would be made by executive management, middle management, and supervisory management.

1.4 EDP/MIS/DSS

We have conceptualized the information system of an organization as consisting of two subsystems: MIS (Management Information System) and OIS (Operations Information System). Quite often the OIS of an organization is referred to as EDP (electronic data processing) if the information flow is supported by computers. In addition, the tendency now is to break down the MIS subsystem of an information system into MIS and DSS (Decision Support Systems). Various papers and books have appeared to refine the DSS idea (e.g., BHW 81, SC 82, Th 83) and to define the boundaries between EDP, MIS, and DSS (e.g., Di 81, RB 82).

As stated by Raho and Belohlav (RB 82), the flood of information presents both a threat and an opportunity for the manager. The information overload that can inundate a manager at any managerial level of the organization may be a threat. More information, however, is an opportunity for the manager to make better in-formed decisions. The effective collection, storage, transformation, and commu-nication of information in an organization is a function of EDP, MIS, and DSS. Understanding the differences between EDP, MIS, and DSS will, therefore, help managers to cope with the dynamic information systems they are living with.

Referring to Raho and Belohlav (RB 82) again, we may state that data are of primary interest in an EDP system which functions at an operational level within the organization. The internal output of an EDP system consists mainly of factual reports and summary reports.

In an MIS, information is data which has been processed to become meaningful to a variety of potential users, primarily middle and upper management. In contrast to the EDP system, an MIS views not just the transformation of data but how it can be turned into useful organizational information. The major output of an MIS consists of standardized reports and interrogative reporting. An MIS is designed from an organizational perspective rather than from a business transaction perspective.

In DSS, the emphasis is on decision making at all levels of management in the organization. DSS is a tool to help managers in their decision-making activities by providing them with the necessary information. The information produced by a DSS consists of interactive/iterative reports and unstructured reports oriented to the individual manager. An important distinction between DSS on the one hand and EDP and MIS on the other has to do with development of the system structure. In EDP and MIS, the systems designers develop the system structure, whereas in DSS the manager not only provides the input but he/she defines the structure as well. Another definition of DSS is given as: "DSS means marrying analytical tools with computer technology and putting it out in executive users' offices" (Th 83).

1.5 OTHER ASPECTS OF INFORMATION

Information is not only a resource but an asset for an organization, empowering it to produce changes in its environment. "Today, businesses are recognizing data more and more as a resource that is as important as personnel, cash, facilities, or materials. They see the need to consolidate the key data files and make information available not just to individual functions as departments but throughout the business, in order for management to gain an overall view of the business and be able to make multifunctional decisions" (IBM 81). It is also predicted that "the organizations that will excel in the 1980s will be those that manage information as a major resource" (BrM 83). In the proceedings of a conference, Oren (Ore 81) quotes a comment to the effect that "a number of countries in the West are now passing into a post-industrial phase of society where the strategic resource is knowledge as opposed to raw materials or financial capital which were the strategic resources in pre-industrial and industrial societies, repectively." Defining knowledge as high-level information, one sees the significance of information in the technical development of countries.

The data communications system of an organization is another topic that is closely related to the information system of that organization. The transmission of data/information from one point to another in the organization by any means—for example, telephone lines or coaxial cables—is data communications, and it seems that more and more, data communications and information systems of organizations are becoming inseparable. Hampel (Ha 81) noted the convergence of information processing and data communications systems of organization and defined the eighties as a "decade of information" (Figure 1.7). As if to prove the validity of Figure 1.7, in 1982 AT&T restructured itself to enter the computer area. In the same year IBM emerged from an antitrust suit unharmed and announced its deci-

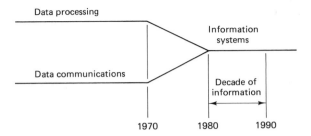

Data processing

Information
systems

Data communications

Decade of
information

1970   1980   1990

Figure 1.7 Information systems in the 1980s

sion to become more deeply involved with data communications. Taggart predicted these developments in AT&T and IBM as early as 1980 and described the situation as a "battle of giants" (Tag 80, p. 28). Clearly every year in this decade is witnessing the fact that information is becoming a key issue. "Information engineering" degree programs in some European countries indicate the significance of recent developments in this area.

The fast growing use of databases (DB) and database management systems (DBMS) is also closely related to data processing/data communications and information systems, and the proper application of these systems definitely improves the value of information in organizations. One of the major advantages of DB applications is data integrity or data correctness. A DB also improves the value of information by minimizing data redundancy. Another major advantage of DB is that the same set of data is available for different applications.

Looking again at our hypothetical small company, Central Circuits Company, we may describe its DB as in Figure 1.8.

As can be seen from the figure, the major groups of data are raw material data, machine capacity data, process data, demand data, product definition data, and personnel resources data. The capacity planning system, work order control system, and economics and market analysis system are the main systems utilizing the DB. In the figure it is intended to describe the data as the content of a single DB. For a large organization, however, each or some combination of these data form an individual DB.

Another important factor related to the success of information systems as they impact on decision-making activities is the reliability of the information in the database system. Zakay (Zak 82) considers the reliability of information as a potential threat to the acceptability of decision support systems. He suggests three main potential sources as the major causes for an unreliable database: (1) information that is held back by users and not entered into the system, (2) biased information entered into the system, and (3) incorrect updating of the database.

The developments in "knowledge-based expert systems," or "knowledge system" for short, are expected to lead over time to the construction of extremely valuable "knowledge bases," a basic unit of the new discipline of "knowledge engineering." It is predicted that knowledge systems will increase individual and

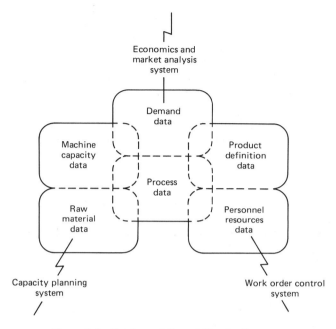

Figure 1.8 Database of Central Circuits Company

social potential by preserving know-how, by distributing knowledge more effectively, and by improving the performance of tasks that require expertise (HR 84). It was argued by Keen (Kee 81) that information systems development is an intensely political as well as a technical process and that organizational mechanisms are needed to provide MIS managers with authority and resources for negotiation. Finally, it was pointed out that MIS can be improved by understanding the behavioral processes by which humans process information and make choices (BT 82).

In a recent survey conducted by Computerworld about the problems of data processing (DP) managers, applications backlog was identified as their biggest headache (Com 83). The next most pressing problems were found to be keeping up with technology and budget cuts. Obviously rapid advances in hardware/software components of computers are rapidly increasing the number of computer-based applications. Thus the demand for information-processing professionals with problem-solving capabilities continues to grow. Trying to meet that demand necessitates revising the curricula of existing academic programs and encourages the proposal of new curricula.

SUMMARY

''System'' is a term that is common to many disciplines. All systems have some common properties: They have elements, environments, interaction between their elements and with the environment, and goals to be fulfilled. A system may be defined as an organized collection of people, machines, procedures, documents, data, or any other entities, such that they interact with each other as well as with environment to reach a predefined goal.

Information, data, and knowledge are closely related terms. They may be defined as the meaning content levels of messages flowing in an information system.

The information system of an organization may be defined as a system that serves to provide information in the organization when and where it is needed at any managerial level. Information in an information system must be understood by its recipient in the proper frame of reference; it must be relevant to a current decision-making process, it must have a surprise value, and it must lead its users into action. Effective processing and management of information, flexibility, and user satisfaction are some of the desirable attributes of an information system.

Any action in an organization depends on the result of a decision-making process at the proper managerial level of that organization. The right information, available at the right time will, therefore, be vital in the decision/action activities of managers.

Transaction processing, control, and strategic planning are those operations of an organization for which information is kept in the information system. Information about these operations may be defined in two subsystems as MIS (Management Information System) and OIS (Operations Information System). Recently computer-based and information-related activities of an organization are grouped under EDP, MIS, and DSS.

The value of information in organizations is a critical issue. It is generally accepted now that information is an asset as well as a resource for an organization.

Data communications is another topic that is highly related to the information system of organizations.

Databases (DB) and database management systems (DBMS) are closely related to data processing/data communications and information systems, and their proper applications improve the value of information in organizations.

Reliability of information in the databases, behavioral aspects of information systems, and problem-solving capability of information systems professionals are some of the recent issues relevant to information and information systems.

EXERCISES

1. Give three examples of systems.
2. What are the common properties of systems?
3. Define a system.
4. What is a message?
5. Define data, information, and knowledge.
6. What is the information system of an organization?

7. What are the common requirements for information in an information system environment?

8. What are some attributes of an information system?

9. What is the significance of information in decision-making/action process?

10. What are the basic types of operations for which information is kept in the information system of an organization?

11. What is strategic planning?

12. What are the control activities of an organization?

13. What is transaction processing in an organization?

14. What are the subsystems of an information system?

15. Comment on the differences between EDP, MIS, and DSS.

16. Discuss the value of information for organizations.

17. What is the relationship between the data communications and information systems of an organization?

18. Why do we call the eighties a "decade of information"?

19. What are the major advantages of DB applications?

20. What is the effect of reliability on information systems?

21. What are the major points in the behavioral aspects of information systems?

SELECTED REFERENCES

(BGJI 82)   Brookes, C. H. P. et al. *Information Systems Design*. Prentice-Hall, 1982.

(BHW 81)   Bonczek, R. H., C. W. Holsapple, and A. B. Whinston. *Foundations of Decision Support Systems*. Academic Press, 1981.

(BT 82)   Benbasat, I., and R. N. Taylor. "Behavioral Aspects of Information Processing for the Design of MIS," *IEEE Transactions on Systems, Man, and Cybernetics*, Vol. SMC-12, No. 4 (July/August 1982), pp. 440–450.

(BrM 83)   Bryce, M. "Information Resource Mismanagement," *Infosystems*, No. 2, February 1983, pp. 89–92.

(CCEH 81)   Cotterman, W. W. et al. *Systems Analysis and Design*, North Holland, 1981.

(COM 83)   *Computerworld*, Weekly Newspaper, CW Communications/Inc., April 11, 1983, p. 1.

(DaG 74)   Davis, G. B. *Management Information Systems: Conceptual Foundations, Structure, and Development*. McGraw Hill, 1974.

(Di 81)   Dickson, G. W., "MIS: Evolution and Status," in *Advances in Computers*, ed. M. C. Yovits. Academic Press, 1981, pp. 1–37.

(Ha 81)   Hampel, W. E., "Fact Retrieval in the 1980's," NATO/AGARD Conference Preprint No. 304, August 1981, pp. 6: 1–36.

(HR 84)   Hayes-Roth, F. "Knowledge Based Expert Systems," *IEEE Computer*, October 1984, pp. 263–273.

(IBM 78)   IBM. *Business Systems Planning*, GE 20-0630-0, November 1978.

(IBM 81)   IBM. *Information Systems Planning Guide*, GE20-0527-3, July 1981.

(Kee 81)   Keen, P. G. W., "Information Systems and Organizational Change," *Comm. ACM*, Vol. 24, No. 1 (January 1981), 24–33.

(Ko 80)   Konsynski, B. "Data Base Driven System Design," in *Systems Analysis and Design*, ed. W. W. Cotterman et al. North Holland, 1981, pp. 251–278.

(Ore 81)   Oren, T. I. "Foundations for an Information Technology," *Proc. of 1981 Winter Simulation Conf.*, ed. T. I. Oren et al., ACM/IEEE, 1981, pp. 201–208.

(RB 82)   Raho, L. E., and J. A. Belohlav, "Discriminating Characteristics of EDP, MIS and DSS Information Interface," *Data Management*, December 1982, pp. 18–20.

(SC 82)   Sprague, R. H., and E. D. Carlson. *Building Effective Decision Support Systems*. Prentice-Hall, 1982.

(Tag 80)   Taggart, W. *Information Systems*. Allyn and Bacon, 1980.

(Th 83)   Thiel, C. T. "DSS Means Computer-Aided Management," *Infosystems*, No. 3, 1983, pp. 38–44.

(TL 82)   Treleaven, P. C., and I. G. Lima, "Japan's Fifth-Generation Computer Systems," *IEEE Computer*, August 1982, pp. 79–88.

(Yov 81)   Yovits, M. C. *Advances in Computers*. Academic Press, 1981.

(Zak 82)   Zakay, D. "Reliability of Information as a Potential Threat to the Acceptability of DSS," in *IEEE Transactions on Systems, Man, and Cybernetics*, Vol. SMC-12, Nol. 4 (July/August 1982), 518–520.

Chapter 2

Information Systems Life Cycles

2.1 INTRODUCTION

In the mid-sixties, there occurred a number of large, costly, and embarrassing failures in EDP applications for large systems, in large part because of poor or nonexistent system development techniques (e.g., Fr 79). Following these failures, an understanding of the significance of information systems development methodologies began to emerge in the late sixties and early seventies. Since then various methodology proposals have been made and their applications reported. Designers of almost all of these information systems development methodologies have had a common point: They have realized that, computer-based or not, any information systems development process is, or rather must be, like an engineering systems development process.

With a view to construction and operation of various types of buildings, power transmission lines, various machines, and chemical plants as examples of engineering system development, we can summarize the major phases in such a development process as

1. Planning
2. Analysis
3. Design
4. Implementation or construction
5. Maintenance

In the planning phase, the engineer gathers information about the problem and the requirements. He/she then sets criteria and constraints for a solution and generates a number of alternative solutions. In the analysis phase, the engineer tests the alternative solutions against the criteria and constraints. The analysis is a pivotal point in the entire development process. As noted by various authors (e.g., EJMN 79, In 78a), a great deal of engineering education deals with teaching engineers how to analyze. The laws of nature, the rules of economics, and common sense (often referred to as engineering judgment) are the main elements of analysis conducted by engineers. The next major phase in the engineering system development, namely design (or synthesis), may be defined as the creation of a new system in accordance with a preconceived plan from the analysis phase. The design or synthesis phase may also be defined as "the optimum solution to the sum of the true needs of a particular set of circumstances" or as "a creativity activity—it involves bringing into being something new and useful that has not existed previously" (In 78a, p. 8). The designed system is constructed and operated. Maintenance is performed on every system which is operational.

The "life cycle" of a system is a term used to describe the major phases and their steps in its development process. Clearly then, life cycles of engineering systems and information systems should be the same or similar and the same general principles should be held valid in information systems development. In the following sections this point will be seen more clearly by comparing the life cycles of information and engineering systems; later a life cycle for information systems will be given.

2.2 INFORMATION SYSTEMS LIFE CYCLE VS. ENGINEERING SYSTEMS LIFE CYCLE

As noted earlier, to be able to see the similarity between development processes of information systems and engineering systems, one should compare their life cycles. In Table 2.1 we tabulate the life cycles for four information systems between 1960 and 1983 (Op 60, Kel 70, BBA 80, and DaW 83). Examining the life cycles for information systems that have been proposed by different authors at various times during the last 20 years, one notes their similarity. But the most crucial point is that information systems life cycles are very close to those followed by engineering systems; that is, planning, analysis, design, implementation, and maintenance are also the major phases for developing information systems. This is not a coincidence; once more it should be stressed that an information system development process is an engineering process and as such has to follow the same steps and obey the same general principles, as we shall elaborate in the next chapters. One should also refer to the term "software engineering" to recall the engineering nature of the software development process, which is a subsystem of an information system.

Another interesting conclusion from the above information systems life cycle

TABLE 2.1 Information Systems Life Cycles for Two Decades

Steps	1960 (Op 60)	1970 (Kel 70)		1980 (BBA 80)		1983 (DaW 83)
1	Analyze the present system	Scope definition	} System Survey	Initial investigation	} Systems Planning	Problem definition
2	Develop a conceptual model	Survey study		Feasibility study		Feasibility study
3	Test the model	Data collection and analysis	} System Analysis and Design	Operations and system analysis	} Systems Requirements	Analysis
4	Pilot installation of the new system	System design		User requirements		System design
5	Full installation of the new system	Implementation planning	} System Development	Technical support approach		Detailed design
6		Development		Conceptual design and package review		Implementation
7		Testing		Alternatives evaluation and planning		Maintenance
8		Cutover		Systems technical specifications	} Systems Development	
9		Maintenance		Technical support development		
10				Applications specifications		
11				Applications programming and testing		
12				User procedures and controls		
13				User training		
14				Implementation planning		
15				Conversion planning		
16				Systems test		
17				Conversion and phased implementation	} Systems Implementation	
18				Refinement and tuning		
19				Post-implementation review		

15

study is the fact that although information systems life cycles have been known to consist of more or less the same steps for almost 20 years, the naming and even the adherence to these steps has not sufficed to develop successful information systems. As we shall discuss further in the next chapter, there has been something missing in information systems development efforts. The missing piece is the fact that in any engineering system development there are some tools and methodologies to be used in parallel with the system life cycle. Failure in determination of user requirements and in user participation for system development has been another critical reason for unsuccessful information systems, in addition to hard sell from computer manufacturers, inadequate staff, unrealistic deadlines, ignorant management, and some other common causes.

2.3 A PROPOSAL FOR AN INFORMATION SYSTEMS LIFE CYCLE

Table 2.2, graphically represented in Figure 2.1, proposes a new life cycle for information systems.[1] A common misinterpretation of tables like Table 2.2 is the impression that the whole process is linear: It looks as if all the phases and steps follow each other in a sequential manner. This is, however, not the reality. All the phases and their steps of the development process have an iterative nature; that is,

[1]Table A.1, given in Appendix A, includes the key considerations and end products of the development steps depicted in Table 2.2.

TABLE 2.2   Information Systems Life Cycle

I. Planning
  1.1. Request for a system study
  1.2. Initial investigation
  1.3. Feasibility study
II. Analysis
  2.1. Redefine the problem
  2.2. Understand the existing system
  2.3. Determine user requirements and constraints on a new system
  2.4. Logical model of the recommended solution (conceptual, logical, or architectural design) or functional specifications
III. Physical Design
  3.1. System design (or general design or system specifications)
  3.2. Detailed design (or specific design)
IV. Implementation or Construction
  4.1. System building
  4.2. Testing
  4.3. Installation/conversion
  4.4. Operations (refinement/tuning)
  4.5. Post-implementation review
V. Maintenance
  5.1. Maintenance and enhancements

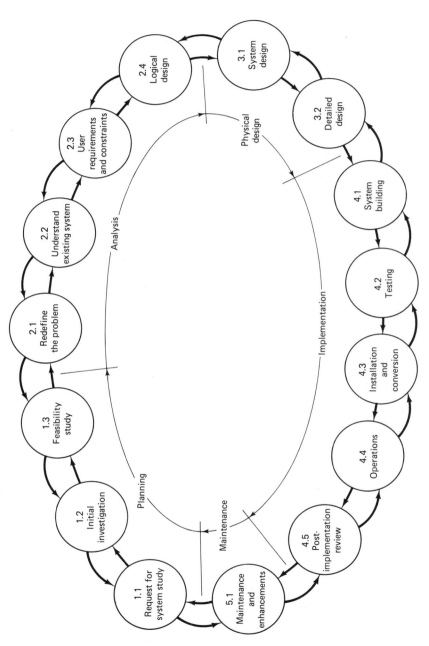

Figure 2.1 Information systems life cycle

work on a step or a phase often requires to go back to the previous step(s) or even phase(s), and whatever has been done up to that point may need to be completely revised. Maintenance of a system usually requires the repetition of the whole development process starting with the planning phase. In order to depict the cyclic nature of the information system development process, we have used an elliptical shape in Figure 2.1. The reverse directed arrows between the steps are used to indicate the iteration of some steps and phases, that is, to imply the nonlinear character of the development process.

A number of methodologies for information systems development consisted simply of following steps similar to those given in Table 2.2 or Figure 2.1. Such a methodology or approach is commonly known as "classical systems approach" or "classical (traditional or conventional) analysis and design of information systems."

Although there may be some variations among individual steps, the "classical systems approach" states that following the steps of an information system life cycle will yield a successful information system. Unfortunately, however, this practice has not been sufficient to yield a successful information system; in addition to naming the stages of a system life cycle, one has to have some standard tools and techniques to develop that system. Beginning in the early seventies, some tools and methodologies were gathered under the name of "structured approach" or "structured systems development methodologies" or "structured analysis and design methodologies." They basically provided the systems analyst with additional tools and techniques, besides the idea of an information system life cycle. The need for such an approach will be discussed further in the next chapter.

We should mention here that although there have been continuous efforts to develop and reevaluate current information systems, the emphasis of the classical approach has been on technical personnel, not on the user. Only recently has it been realized that user understanding and user support for a system being developed is vital for the success of the final system. One of the main contributions of structured methodologies for information systems development is thus user participation and consequently user commitment. Of course, this commitment ideally begins with the executive management of the user organization.

SUMMARY

The major phases and steps of a system development process are commonly known as a "life cycle." Life cycles of engineering systems and information systems are very similar, if not the same. The classical approach to information system development emphasizes the use of a life cycle and documentation for system development. Since the early 1970s, however, there is a new approach called the structured approach, which provides the systems analyst with some tools and methodologies in addition to the life cycle concept to develop a successful information system.

EXERCISES

1. What are the major phases of an engineering system development process?

2. Compare the information systems life cycles for the period 1960 to 1983. What are the similarities and differences?

3. Is information system development an engineering process? Why?

4. What do we mean by a cycle and by the iterative nature of an information system life cycle?

5. What is the basic idea behind the classical approach to information systems development?

6. What is the basic difference between the "classical approach" and the "structured approach" to information systems development?

SELECTED REFERENCES

(BBA 80)   Biggs, C. L., E. G. Birks, and W. Atkins. *Managing the Systems Development*. Prentice-Hall, 1980.

(BGJL 82)   Brookes, C. H. P., P. J. Grouse, D. R. Jeffery, and M. J. Lawrence. *Information Systems Design*. Prentice-Hall, 1982.

(DaW 83)   Davis, W. S. *Systems Analysis and Design*. Addison-Wesley, 1983.

(EJMN 79)   Eide, A. R., R. D. Jension, L. D. Mashaw, and L. L. Northrup. *Engineering Fundamentals and Problem Solving*. McGraw Hill, 1979.

(Fr 79)   Freeman, P. "A Perspective on Requirements Analysis and Specification," Auerbach Publishers Inc., Portfolio No.: 32-04-01, 1979.

(In 78a)   Infotech State of the Art Report: Structured Analysis and Design, Vol. 1: Analysis and Bibliography, Infotech International Ltd., Maidenhead Berkshire, UK, 1978.

(Kel 70)   Kelly, J. F. *Computerized Management Information Systems*. MacMillan, 1970.

(Op 60)   Optner, S. L. *Systems Analysis for Business and Industrial Problem Solving*. Prentice-Hall, 1960.

Chapter 3

Classical Approach

3.1 INTRODUCTION

As noted earlier, the ''classical approach'' to information systems development consists of following steps similar to those given in Table 2.2. Because of the complicated nature of information systems, however, accepting and following the steps of the life cycle has not been enough to develop a successful information system. Remember, every engineering discipline—electrical, mechanical, structural, and so on—has its own methodology that has helped concretize system life cycle definitions. Unfortunately, until recently no one realized that following the life cycle alone would not yield successful information systems. Now, however, it is understood that the systems development approach requires some tools and techniques to make it successful. Such an approach is what we commonly call a ''structured approach'' or ''structured analysis and design of information systems.''

In the following sections, the classical approach and its problems will be reviewed first. Recent trends in information systems life cycles will be discussed later.

3.2 PROBLEMS OF THE CLASSICAL APPROACH

In order to understand the need for a structured approach in information systems development, let's consider briefly the problems we have had using classical approach for information systems development:

3.2.1 Character of Classical Approach

As noted by McGowen and McHenry (McGMcH 80) the classical approach appeals to many because it is a contractual model. It is a familiar model embodied explicitly in contracts and institutionalized as the development and documentation standards in many organizations, more a managerial than a technical tool. Indeed the classical approach emphasizes documentation almost to the exclusion of development. Although documentation is a must in information systems development, the number of critical problems and failures in information systems has already shown that documentation alone is not enough for successful information system development. The development process itself must receive more emphasis than documentation, and documentation should be viewed simply as a by-product of a development process.

3.2.2 Hardware/Software Cost

Another reason for using a structured approach is the trend of software/hardware cost. Ramamoorthy et al. (RPTU 84) stated the following:

> Computer users first became aware of a software crisis 15 years ago. Software projects were being delivered far behind schedule, quality was poor, and maintenance was expensive. And as more complex software applications were found, programmers fell further behind the demand and their results were of poorer quality. The high demand and comparatively low productivity drove software costs up. In the US in 1980, software cost approximately $40 billion, or two percent of the gross national product. Dolotta estimates that by the year 1985 the cost of software will be approximately 8.5 percent of the GNP, while Steel points to 13 percent by 1990.

A relatively old prediction made by Boehm (Bo 76) is given as Figure 3.1. There are some arguments in the literature about the validity of Boehm's prediction; for

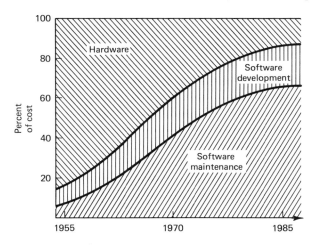

Figure 3.1   Computer-based information systems cost trends

example, an article by Cragon provided some numerical data to lower the ratio of software to hardware (Cr 82). It is clear, however, that the cost of software is continuously increasing while that per unit hardware is decreasing. Yet the demand for software is also increasing at an even faster rate. A few years ago Myers (MyW 78) pointed out that the need for software was increasing because access to inexpensive hardware brought with it many new applications requiring innovative software. The need is even greater now because of the microcomputer explosion that we are all witnessing. If we consider software to be an information subsystem, clearly the classical approach has failed to decrease these costs.

3.2.3 Maintenance Cost of Existing Information Systems

Another important reason for using the structured approach in information system development has to do with the maintenance cost of existing software and the information system as a whole (e.g., Ak 82, MyW 78, Ca 81). Normally corrective and/or enhancement maintenance of software accounts for about 70 percent of the total software cost. (Actually, two recent articles use the figure of 67 percent [CW 82, RPTU 84].) The overall cost of software and maintenance in the United States is estimated to be roughly 15 to 25 billion dollars per year. Although structured programming techniques have increased programmer productivity, that increase, which is estimated to be roughly 5 percent (MyW 78), lags far behind the rate of increase of total software cost. There is obviously a need to decrease the cost of software development, to increase reliability of the product and maintainability of the system, and to increase the productivity of the technical personnel involved in system development. Boehm (Bo 77) indicated that from two to four times the cost of development can be spent on system maintenance. Connor (Co 80) likened maintenance to the body of the cost iceberg (Figure 3.2).

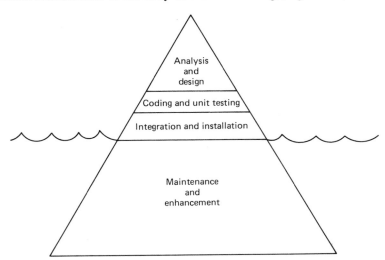

Figure 3.2   Computer-based information systems development and maintenance cost

3.2.4 User Requirements, Responsibility, and Involvement

The most critical shortcoming of the classical approach has been very limited reflection on user requirements in the completed information system. Ongoing communication with the user during development of the information system and after implementation is vital for the success of the project. The classical approach assumed that users know and state their requirements very clearly and correctly by the end of analysis phase—that is, before the physical design of the system. Experience has shown that in most cases users' requirements are not very clear and/or correct throughout almost the entire system development phase. As a result, system designers are now trying to involve users during the entire system development process and to have a development process that is flexible and allows changes in user requirements during the development of the system and even after the implementation. Structured system development approaches that emphasize user participation and communication begin with a request for system study—as reflected in Table 2.2—that includes a statement of the problem as well as its requirements. During the determination of user requirements in the analysis phase, the systems analyst tries to understand the requirements and defines specifications to meet requirements. Any errors made in specifying requirements have an enormous impact on the system being developed. They inevitably lead to user dissatisfaction with the application systems and eventually the larger information system failures (e.g., In 78a).

Another key to the success of an information system that is responsive to the user is the commitment of the executive management of the user organization. It is an essential ingredient to the success of both the classical and the structured methodologies. However, the structured approach makes it easy to define the system and thus makes it easily understandable by the user management.

3.2.5 Testability of the Developed System

The purpose of testing a system is to find and correct any errors before implementation and operation. In a modular system each module is tested separately after which the integrated system is checked to ensure the proper interaction of all modules. Testing an information system before its implementation is critical because correction of any system error will be much more costly after the system is implemented and made operational. Some research results indicate that the untestability of systems requirements during the system development phase has been a major source of system errors. This is reflected in Table 3.1, which categorizes requirements and shows their relative frequency (In 78a, p. 107).

As can be seen from Table 3.1, errors due to "incorrect, untestable, or overrestrictive" requirements exceed all other errors. The point at which errors are introduced and the point at which they are discovered are especially critical in the development of computer-based information systems. This is represented in Figure 3.3 (Co 80).

TABLE 3.1   Requirements Errors in Systems Development

Type	Percentage
• Incorrect/untestable/overrestrictive	35
• Missing/incomplete	20
• Untraceable or out of scope	15
• Unclear/ambiguous	10
• Inconsistent/incompatible	10
• Typographical errors	10

The classical approach, however, does not provide the systems analyst with a means for systems testing, and it does not even consider testing as a part of system development process.

3.2.6 Other Problems

A monolithic view of the system and the "big-bang" implementation have been indicated as some of the other problems in the classical system development process (To). Because the classical systems approach takes a linear view of the application, it has a hard time dealing with large and complex systems. The big-bang occurs when an existing system is replaced by a newly developed system with no transitional period; most often the user organization will have great difficulty coping with such an event. Because of the lack of user input during the classical system development process, the user is actually introduced to the system only after the implementation so that change requests are likely to build up from that point. Thus, there is a significant gap between user expectations and system capabilities—again a main reason of user frustrations and system failures.

Another problem with the classical approach is its unsuitability to project management techniques. Poor estimations of manpower requirements may be a major reason of system problems in many applications. The estimates may be in

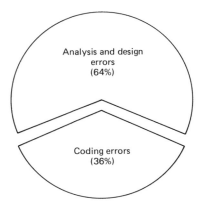

Figure 3.3   Computer-based information system errors

the form of missed deadlines, cost and resource overrun, and unsatisfactory quality of delivered systems in terms of poor maintainability, poor extensibility, poor performance in relation to cost, and low user satisfaction, for example.

Finally, inability to integrate applications into a system is another problem of classical approach. Traditionally, many applications such as payroll, accounting, and stock control, which are often tied to the existing organizations, are developed separately. Quite often serious problems of integration and dependence occur when we try to integrate such individual applications into a large, single system.

3.3 RECENT TRENDS IN INFORMATION SYSTEMS LIFE CYCLES

There have been various estimates about the cost distribution of individual steps in the classical approach to information systems development. In terms of computer-based information systems, Orr (Orr 81a) estimated that when the systems were developed using the classical approach, the planning, analysis, and design steps of the information systems life cycle took only 20 percent of the total development cost, while implementation step took almost 80 percent. Referring to other estimates given by Ramamoorthy and So (RS 78), Richardson and his colleagues (RBT 80), and Taggart (Tag 80), one can portray the hypothetical cost distribution for the classical approach as shown by the broken lines in Figure 3.4. The results obtained using classical approach have not been satisfactory, as noted before. It is indicated that "many of the problems of the software production process have arisen from a failure of those involved with software production to understand the role and nature of the design process" (In 78a, p. 8). Also "generally

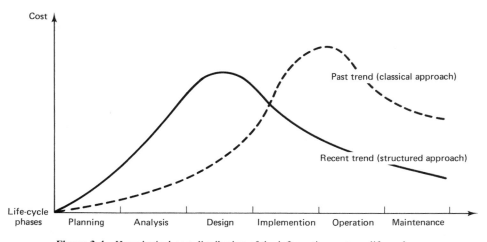

Figure 3.4   Hypothetical cost distribution of the information systems life cycle

speaking, previous experience with large scale software development has been depressing. The symptoms of the inadequacy of our software design and development methodology are high costs, inexpensive products, slippage of production schedules, and difficulties in system operation and maintenance'' (RS 78). Ramamoorthy and So (RS 78) further state that design errors account for a high percentage of the total, in fact from 36 to 74 percent. They conclude that there is a need for methods to reduce design errors. Recall that before the design phase, Table 2.2 and Figure 2.1 both descibed planning and analysis phases in the information systems life cycle. These two initial phases of systems development are sometimes termed ''requirements engineering'' (RS 78). In other research results, Ramamoorthy and So (RS 78) state that requirements problems are indeed serious and that classical means of analyzing and stating requirements are not satisfactory. The classical approach generally results in incorrect, inconsistent, and unclear requirements, causing 85 percent of the total requirements problems. Their conclusion is that a successful analysis methodology coupled with an advanced design and implementation (coding) methodology should reduce the cost elements of total development, operations, and maintenance. Taggart (Tag 80) and Orr (Orr 81a) indicate that the cost distribution pattern of the information systems life cycle has been changing. Compared to the classical approach, the earlier steps of the information system life cycle are now being allocated a higher percentage of the total development cost. This recent trend appears as the solid line in Figure 3.4.

In summary, the following tendencies can be noted:

- The analysis and design phases of information systems development processes now constitute between 70 and 80 percent of the total development cost.
- Maintenance of the existing information system claims more than half the time and effort of the technical staff of an information systems department.
- The value (in money and its effects on the total organization) of information systems has made it imperative that there must be some approaches to develop successful information systems.
- Information system development process is an engineering process, therefore similar approaches should be used.

''Structured approach'' is the name of the recent approach for information systems development. It is also called ''structured systems development methodologies'' or ''structured analysis and design methodologies'' in the literature (e.g., Ak 82).

SUMMARY

The classical systems approach is based on following the systems life cycle steps for a system development process. This has proven insufficient for developing a successful information system, which, similar to any engineering discipline, requires the proper methodologies. Such a methodology is commonly known as a "structured approach" or "a structured system development methodology."

The main problems with the classical approach for information systems development are the contractual character of the classical approach, hardware/software cost trends, high maintenance costs of existing information systems, and very limited participation of the user during development and implementation. A monolithic view of the system, "big-bang" implementation, and lack of project management capabilities have been indicated as some of the other problems in using a classical approach to information systems development.

A recent trend in information systems life cycles is that the analysis and design phases are getting more than half of the total development effort. In the past this had been just the opposite, and implementation and testing had been the major cost elements. The new trend lays special emphasis on the determination and specification of systems requirements.

EXERCISES

1. Why do we need a structured methodology of information systems development?
2. What are the major problems in using a classical systems approach for information systems development?
3. Try to obtain estimates of hardware/software cost ratios in 1960, 1970, and 1980 and indicate any trend you observe.
4. What is system maintenance? Why is it important for information systems?
5. Discuss the significance of testing in systems development.
6. Compare the recent trend in systems development to the past trend for information systems development.
7. What is the "structured approach"?

SELECTED REFERENCES

(Ak 82)   Aktas, Z. "Discussion of Structured System Analysis and Design Strategies for Information Systems." ACM Annual CS Conference, February 9–11, 1982, Indianapolis, IN.

(Bo 76)   Boehm, B. W. "Software Engineering," *IEEE Transactions on Computers*, Vol. C-25, No. 12 (December 1976), 35–50

(Bo 77)   Boehm, B. W. "Software Reliability: Measurement and Management." International Software Management Conference, London, Spring 1977.

(Ca 81)   Canning, R. G. "Easing the Software Maintenance Burden," *EDP Analyzer*, Vol. 19, No. 8 (August 1981).

(Co 80)   Connor, M. F. "Structured Analysis and Design Technique," *SoftTech, Inc.*, May 1980.

(Cr 82)   Cragon, H. G. "The Myth of the Hardware/Software Cost Ratio," *Computer*, Vol. 15, No. 12 (December 1982) 100–101.

(CW 82)   Collofell, J. S., and S. N. Woodfield. "A Project-Unified Software En-
               gineering Course Sequence," *ACM-SIGCSE Bulletin*, Vol. 14, No. 1
               (February 1982) 13–19.

(In 78a)   "Infotech State of the Art Report: Structured Analysis and Design," Vol.
               1: Analysis and Bibliography, Infotech International Ltd. Maidenhead,
               Berkshire UK, 1978.

(McGMcH 80)   McGowan, C., and R. C. Mc Henry. "Software Management," in *Re-
               search Directions in Software Technology*, ed. P. Wegner, MIT Press,
               1980, pp. 207–253.

(MyW 78)   Myers, W. "The Need for Software Engineering," *Computers*, Vol. 11
               (February 1978), 12–26.

(Orr 81a)   Orr, K. "System Methodologies for the 80's," *Infosystems*, June 1981,
               pp. 78–80.

(RBT 80)   Richardson, G. L., C. W. Butler, and J. D. Tomlinson. *A Primer on
               Structured Program Design*, Petrocelli, 1980.

(RPTU 84)   Ramamoorthy, C. V., A. Prakash, W. Tsai, and Y. Usuda. "Software
               Engineering: Problems and Perspectives," *IEEE Computer*, October 1984,
               pp. 191–209.

(RS 78)   Ramamoorthy, C. V., and H. G. So. "Software Requirements and Spec-
               ifications: Status and Perspectives," in *Tutorial: Software Methodology*,
               ed. Ramamoorthy and Yeh, IEEE, 1978, pp. 43–164.

(Tag 80)   Taggart, W. *Information Systems*. Allyn and Bacon, 1980.

(To)   Tommela, D. R. *A Strategy for Systems Implementation*, Auerbach Pub-
               lishers Inc., Portfolio No: 3-10-24.

Chapter 4

Structured Approach

4.1. OBJECTIVES AND MODELLING IN THE STRUCTURED APPROACH

Both problems with the classical approach and recent trends of the information systems life cycle have signalled the need for a different approach. This approach, which started to appear in early 1970s is called the "structured approach," or—more recently—the "operational approach" (Zav 84). Like the engineering approach to problem solving, the structured approach adopts some well-defined, standardized procedures and documentation, or at the least a methodology to be followed in developing a well-defined and standardized information system as the product. The resulting system will have a well-defined structure. Structure imposes order and improves comprehensibility of complex systems. It should, therefore, be an essential feature of information systems design. Structure "may pertain to the manner or form in which something is constructed or may refer to the actual system as constructed. Descriptions of structure focus on interrelation of the various parts as dominated by the general character or function of the whole. Designing structure is a process of identifying, analyzing, and selecting among alternatives with design categories" (Tau 79, p. 233).

The need for a methodology in information systems development is also expressed by Brookes et al. (BGJL 82, p. 16) as follows: "Although the systems life cycle is a useful framework within which to consider the whole systems analysis-design process, those persons responsible for carrying out the tasks need a more detailed representation or methodology to follow. Without an adequate methodology, less experienced analysts/designers may have difficulty knowing what aspect of the project should be worked on at any given time. In addition, it is usually important for all the individuals working on systems development within the one organization to follow the same procedures in terms of the sequence of steps and the means for documenting the results of their analysis and design work to assist in both project control and the interchangeability of staff.'' Structure and structured systems analysis and design concepts are not new. Assembly line techniques in factories and circuit design for electronic devices are just two examples of that idea that have been used for some time in industry. It is, however, relatively new to use these concepts in methodologies to develop information systems such that the product satisfies user needs. Through a structured approach, more complex problems of business and other organizations are solved, and the resulting system is easy to maintain, flexible, more satisfactory to users, better documented, on time, and within budget. Duran and McCready stated the major benefits of structured approaches as increased productivity, a higher quality (error-free) system, easier maintenance of the resulting systems, and greater capability of attracting and retaining quality people (DMcC 81).

Referring to Nauman et al. (NDMcK 80), one may state that to determine, define, and meet the information requirements of an organization accurately and completely is the task of the organization's information system. The most important ingredient of that system is people: managers, users, systems development personnel, and operations personnel. It is, however, difficult to obtain a correct and complete set of information requirements from an organization. Davis (DaG 82) gives three reasons for such a difficulty:

1. The limitations of human beings as information processors and problem solvers
2. The variety and complexity of information requirements
3. The complex patterns of interaction among users and analysts in defining requirements.

During system development, the information requirements of the organization are usually documented in the form of a ''functional specification'' or ''logical design'' and represent an agreement between the users and the developers of the system (NDMcK 80). This process has recently been referred to as ''requirements engineering'' in various sources and been recognized as the most important and critical part of the information systems development process.

As we shall see in the later chapters, there are various structured system development methodologies, but any of these should specify the following:

- How to recognize a good design
- How to create a good design
- How to communicate a good design

In addition, an effective methodology will incorporate purposeful structuring and modularity of the system under consideration. The resultant information system will then have most, if not all, of the following properties (e.g., DMcC 81, RDMcG 77, Sch82, TPW 81):

- Acceptability—users find the quality and efficiency satisfactory
- documentation—clarity of goals and methods documented during development results in better communications among users, developers, and managers
- testability—chances of future failures and/or user dissatisfaction are minimized
- cohesiveness—maximum interaction within each component (module)
- compatibility—the system "fits" the total, integrated system
- economy—the system should be cost effective within the given resources
- efficiency—resource utilization is optimal
- fast development rate—relatively less time is needed for development
- feasibility—resultant system should satisfy all feasibility criteria
- flexibility—it is easy to modify, add, or delete components
- logic/hierarchy—components of the system are logically/hierarchically related to each other
- low degree of coupling—there is minimum interaction between components (modules)
- maintainability—future maintenance and enhancement times and efforts are reduced
- modularity—the system has relatively independent and single-function parts that can be put together to make a complete system; modularization, decomposition, parsing are the terms that are used interchangeably
- reliability—error rate is minimized; outputs are consistent and correct;
- visibility—it is easy to perceive how and why actions occur (they are traceable)
- simplicity—complexity and ambiguity are minimized
- timeliness—the system should operate well under normal, peak, and recovery conditions
- uniformity—the structure of the components (modules) should be uniform
- user friendliness—the system meets user needs and acts as a catalyst in achieving objectives.

The above properties may be stated as the objectives of a structured systems development methodology for an information system; they are summarized as Table 4.1.

Structuring the information system during development—that is, during the analysis and design phases, as well as during implementation, operation, and

TABLE 4.1 Some Properties of a Structured
Information System

• acceptable	• Logical/hierarchical
• better documented	• low coupling
• better tested	• maintainable
• cohesive	• modular
• compatible	• more reliable
• economical	• observable/visible
• efficient	• simple
• fast development rate	• timely
• feasible	• uniform
• flexible	• user friendly

maintenance—has been the common property of a group of methodologies known as ''structured methodologies.''

Although it is now common to use structured documentation, structured testing, structured walk throughs, structured validation and verification, and structured project management during an information system development process, the crucial phases are structured analysis (or requirements specification) and structured design.

As stated by Duran and McCready (DMcC 81), structured analysis is used to define and describe the system that best satisfies user requirements, given certain time and budget constraints. The objective of structured design is to minimize the lifetime cost of an information system by emphasizing maintainability, because maintenance is the most costly component in a system's life cycle. The critical point in design is to match the solution to the problem.

Although there are a variety of ways to implement structured analysis and structured design, some of the features all methodologies share are the use of graphical models, emphasis on user communication (and hence user involvement), repetition of the previous phase(s) and step(s), and reviews. In the structured analysis process, the models should represent the functions of the system rather than the means to accomplish them; in other words, emphasis is on the logical components of the system rather than its physical components. Consideration of design and implementation issues is postponed until agreement has been reached between designers and users on the function, or objectives, of the system. In some structured design methodologies, a set of evaluative criteria is also provided as part of the methodology as a kind of checklist for the systems analyst.

The models that are used in structured analysis and design and their interrelation are depicted in Figure 4.1. The first model describes how the current system operates by depicting its physical components. The second model is a logical abstraction of the current system, prepared to show what the existing system does. The third model represents the planned operation of the new system. By adding general physical components to the logical model of the new system we then arrive at a physical model of the new system—number 4 in Figure 4.1—that details the actual implementation.

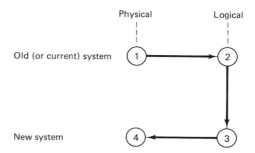

Figure 4.1 Models in structured analysis and design

4.2 SOME TERMINOLOGY

A number of terms are commonly used in the structured approach and need to be clarified at this point. The dictionary (Web 75) defines these terms as

algorithm	A step-by-step procedure for solving a problem
method	A systematic way, technique, or process of or for doing something; a body of skills and techniques
methodology	A body of methods, rules, and postulates employed by a discipline
strategy	The art of devising or employing plans toward a goal
technique	The manner in which technical details are treated
tool	Something (as an instrument or apparatus) used in performing an operation or necessary in the practice of a vocation and profession.

Freeman (Fr 79) defined a method as a way of doing something; by extension, methodologies are collections of methods and tools chosen to complement one another, along with the management and human factor procedures necessary for their application. Techniques are defined as informal methods and tools as objects such as programs, languages, or documentation forms that help us use a method. Davis (DaG 82) defined a method as an orderly or systematic procedure and a methodology as a set of methods and techniques. He also stated that strategies are general approaches for achieving objectives and that methods and methodologies are the detailed means for doing it. Comparing the terms ''method'' and ''methodology,'' Infotech Report (In 78a) notes that a method is a procedure for carrying out a particular task and that a methodology consists of an integrated set of methods, based on a reasoned set of basic principles, along with rules for applying them. Griffiths (Gr 78) observes that the distinction between method and methodology has never been made explicit and indicates that a design methodology provides, in some measure, reasons for all the steps in the design process; furthermore, these reasons may be understood completely without reference to a particular application.

As is clear from the definitions on p. 33, the terms "method," "methodology," and "strategy" have very close meanings. For our purposes in this text, we shall use the term "method" to signify a way to solve a problem; strategy and methodology will be taken as synonyms to mean a group of methods and tools along with certain rules for the development and operations of an information system. Also, the phrase "structured system development methodology" will be used to mean "structured approach" and vice versa.

4.3 STRUCTURED TOOLS

The tools that are used in the structured approach are sometimes grouped as analysis and design tools. Howden (How 82) also mentions some verification tools—such as file comparator, test harness, and performance monitor–and management tools and techniques such as automated project control system, project control system, and project status report generators.

A shared property of the tools that are used in the structured approach is that they are graphical. There are also some nongraphical tools. In fact, the phrase "a picture is worth a thousand words" is the basic idea behind most of the tools and methodologies that are employed in the structured approach.

Another common characteristic of most of the structured tools is that they are based on the "tree concept." One may recall the applications of trees for data and expression representation or as decision and game trees. If one examines the structured tools of such methodologies as the hierarchy diagram, structure chart, Jackson diagram, or Warnier/Orr diagram, it will become evident that they are just an application of the tree concept.

Many of the tools that will be discussed in the following chapters are components of their respective systems development methodologies. SADT, HIPO, the Jackson diagram, Warnier/Orr diagram, data flow diagram (DFD), and the structure chart are some of the examples of that category.

The literature reveals several attempts to classify the tools of the structured approach. For example, Peters (Pes 81) classifies them as architectural, structural, behavioral, and database techniques. The difficulty with such a classification is that often a particular tool will easily fit several categories. We, therefore, prefer to classify them broadly as graphical and nongraphical tools and to treat HIPO, data flow diagrams, structure charts, SADT, Jackson Diagrams, the entity-relationship model, and Warnier/Orr Diagrams as the typical graphical tools. Data Dictionary, Structured English, and pseudocode will be treated as typical nongraphical tools that are used in structured approach.

Almost all of the tools that are used in the structured approach are identical to those that are proposed and used for software development. A thorough survey and classification of such tools is given in a U.S. Department of Commerce publication (Hou 82).

Another tool that is often used together with structured tools is the classical flowchart. Flowcharts are used to describe the programming logic of a problem but also to describe the physical components of an information system. Such a flowchart is called a "system flowchart," and some of the symbols that are used in it are tabulated in Figure 4.2.

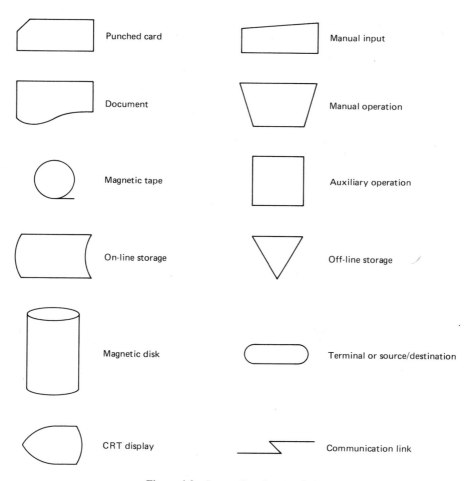

Figure 4.2   System flowchart symbols

4.4 STRUCTURED METHODOLOGIES

There are numerous methodologies available for the development of information systems. A partial listing of available packaged information systems development methodologies is given by Benenati (Be 82). Atena, Auto Flow, Cara Systems

Development Standards, Dauphin, Domonic, Glossary, HIPO, Jackson Design, Prosim (Long Range Planning Models), Mentor Systems Project Methodology Plus, Nichols Project Management Control System, Odyssey, PACII, PRIDE, Program Design Management (PDM), Project Control/70, (System Development Methodology) SDM/70, PROVOC, PSL/PSA, PSDM, SADT, Software Life Cycle Management (SLCM), Spectrum-1, SREM, Structured Design, and War-nier/Orr Diagrams are some of these packages.

Unfortunately, the industry has not yet established clear standards. However, some methodologies are being successfully used in a number of organizations, among them Structured Design, Warnier/Orr, Jackson System Development, and SADT. In the third part of the book, the most commonly used methodologies will be grouped together and the typical ones of each group will be discussed. Applications of some of these methodologies will further be demonstrated on a case study presented in the Appendix.

4.5 OTHER ISSUES PERTAINING TO THE STRUCTURED APPROACH

Another point for discussion has to do with the type of user, or the potential application, of the structured approach. From time to time certain methodologies are proposed exclusively either for business systems or for nonbusiness areas such as engineering. It is our belief that a good system development methodology should be applicable to any system, business or nonbusiness.

A few words are now in order about the psychological dimension of the information system development process. Remember, it has already been stated that people are the most important ingredient of an information system. It is, therefore, no surprise to witness a resurgence of interest in the psychological dimension of information systems development (e.g., Mor 81). Another human factor is Miller's magical number seven (Mil 56). In that paper, he was referring to the seven wonders of the world, the seven primary colors, the seven basic notes of the musical scale, seven days of the week, the seven categories for absolute judgment, the seven objects in the span of attention, and the seven digits in the span of immediate memory. The number seven has a special meaning in some religions too. For example, seven is a ''perfect number'' in Islam and in the Judaeo-Christian tradition links the threefold nature of the cosmos with the four earthly elements; water, air, fire, and earth. In structured systems design methodologies 7 ± 2 has been the number that is used for limiting the number of modules and/or the number of hierarchical levels of the system being developed in order to deal with the issue of complexity and improve the clarity of the resulting information system. The subject of system complexity and its relation to human capacity is another recent important issue relevant to structured systems development methodologies for information systems (Ze 82).

Next we would like to address a criticism about the structured system development methodologies for information systems. Recently Kimmerly (Ki 82) claims that ''our inability to match hardware advances lies, at least partially, in the failure of both practicing systems analysts and computer science academicians to stress adequately the importance of aesthetics, imagery, and other precursors of creativity in the methodology of the discipline, particularly with respect to definition of problems and the conceptualization of solutions. As a result, a significant imbalance now exists between the emphasis being placed on high levels of structure on the one hand and creativity on the other.'' He later concludes that ''due in part to the legacy of the various 'structured revolutions' creativity has not only been comprehensively de-emphasized, but has come to be regarded as something to be avoided altogether.''

It is appropriate at this point to recall the ''art vs. science'' debate in the area of programming languages in the late sixties and early seventies. As we all know the answer to that debate has been structured programming, a methodology that is both teachable and learnable. Such a program is much more efficient and valuable to an organization than ''clever or tricky or artistic'' programs. Similarly, structured systems development methodologies for information systems are proving that the information systems development process can be teachable and learnable, just the same as any engineering system development process. Of course, however, there is always a need for human judgment at critical decision points. Just as ''engineering judgment'' is an integral part of developing an engineering system, so there is always a need for systems analysts to interject their opinions and judgments during the information systems development process. This is where a certain degree of creativity is essential in structured information systems development.

SUMMARY

Sometimes an approach for information system development is labelled ''structured'' if the classical information system life cycle-steps are followed closely and some relevant tools (known as structured tools) are used during these steps. Mostly, however, a structured methodology refers to a strategy that will yield a successful information system. Such a stragety applies to the analysis and/or design phase of systems development and employs structured tools and a life cycle concept as in the classical approach.

The major objective of a structured systems development methodology for an information system is to produce a well-defined and standardized information system using well-defined and standardized procedures and documentation. The resulting information system has most of the following properties: It is acceptable, better documented, better tested, cohesive, compatible, economical, efficient, feasible, flexible, hierarchical, maintainable, modular, more reliable, observable, simple, timely, uniform, user friendly, and has a fast development rate and low coupling. System modelling is very important in the structured approach, which employs both logical and physical models.

Algorithm, method, methodology, strategy, technique, and tool are some terms that are used relevant to the structured development processes.

Structure is an essential feature of a development process, since structure imposes order and hence improves the comprehensibility of complex systems. Structuring of the information systems during development, that is, during the analysis and design phases, as well as during implementation, operation, and maintenance, has been the common property of a group of methodologies commonly known as "structured methodologies." There are numerous structured analysis and design methodologies. Use of graphical models, emphasis on user communication and hence user involvement, nonlinearity or iteration, and repeated reviews are some of their common features.

Almost all of the tools that are used in the structured approach are those that are proposed and used for software development. In addition, system flowcharts may be used together with structured tools.

There are a number of structured methodologies for information systems developments. Some of them are manual and some are computerized.

The psychological dimension of the information systems development process is getting more attention lately. Some of the criticism levelled at the structured approach reminds us of the "art vs. science" debate in the area of programming languages in the late sixties. The most important feature of any structured systems development methodology is that it is teachable and learnable.

EXERCISES

1. What is meant by the "structured approach"?
2. What is the main objective of a structured system development methodology?
3. What are the properties of a structured system? Explain them.
4. What is the significance of structure to a development process?
5. What are the common features of structured analysis?
6. What are the common features of structured design?
7. What is the relationship between physical and logical models in structured analysis and design?
8. Define the terms *algorithm*, *method*, *methodology*, *strategy*, *technique*, and *tool*.
9. What is the difference between a method and a methodology?
10. What is the difference between a methodology and a strategy?
11. What are some properties of structured tools?
12. Give any two examples of graphical and nongraphical tools.
13. What is the main reason for using a system flowchart?
14. Give any two examples of structured methodologies.

15. Is there a need for different methodologies for business versus nonbusiness applications? Discuss.

16. What is the idea behind the magical number 7?

17. What is the significance of the human factor in information systems development?

18. What is "requirements engineering"?

SELECTED REFERENCES

(BGJL 82)   Brookes, C. H. P., P. J. Grouse, D. R. Jeffery, and M. J. Lawrence. *Information Systems Design*, Prentice-Hall, 1982.

(DaG 82)   Davis, G. B. "Strategies for Information Requirements Determination," *IBM Systems Journal*, Vol. 21, No. 1 (1982), 4–30.

(DMcC 81)   Duran, P., and A. McCready. *Structured Techniques*. Auerbach Publishers, Inc., Portfolio No: 3-10-20, 1981.

(Fr 79)   Freeman, P. *A Perspective on Requirements Analysis and Specification.* Auerbach Publishers, Inc., Portfolio No: 32-04-01, 1979.

(Gr 78)   Griffiths, S. N. "Design Methodologies," in *Info Tech State of the Art Report: Structured Analysis and Design*, Vol. 2, p. 139, Infotech International Ltd., Maidenhead, Berkshire, UK 1978.

(Hou 82)   Houghton, R. C. *Software Development Tools*, NBS Special Publication, No: 500-88. U.S. Dept. of Commerce, March 1982.

(How 82)   Howden, W. E. "Contemporary Software Development Environments," *Comm. ACM*, Vol. 25, No. 5 (May 1982), 318–29.

(In 78a)   *Info Tech State of the Art Report: Structured Analysis and Design*, Vol. 1: Analysis and Bibliography, Infotech International Ltd., Maidenhead, Berkshire, UK 1978.

(Ki 82)   Kimmerly, W. C. "Restricted Vision," *Datamation*, November 1982, 152–60.

(Mil 56)   Miller, G. A. "The Magical Number Seven, Plus or Minus Two: Some Limits on Our Capacity for Processing Information," *Psychological Review*, Vol. 63, No. 2 (March 1956), 81–97.

(Mor 81)   Moran, T. P. "An Applied Psychology of the User," *Computing Surveys*, Vol. 13, No. 1 (March 1981), 1–11.

(NDMcK 80)   Naumann, J. D., G. B. Davis, and J. D. McKeen. "Determining Information Requirements," *The Journal of Systems and Software*, No. 1 (1980), 273–81.

(Pes 81)   Peters, L. J. *Software Design.* Yourdon Press, 1981.

(RDMcG 77)   Ross, D. T., M. E. Dickover, and C. McGowan. *Software Design Using SADT*, Auerbach Publishers, Inc., Portfolio No: 35-05-03, 1977.

(RPTU 84)   Ramamoorthy, C. V., A. Prakash, W. Tsai, and Y. Usuda. "Software Engineering: Problems and Perspectives," *IEEE Computer*, October 1984, 191–209.

(Sch 82)   Schach, S. R. "A Unified Theory for Software Production," *Software Practice and Experience*, Vol. 12 (1982), 683–89.

(Tau 79)   Tausworthe, R. C. *Standardized Development of Computer Software*, Part II, *Standards*. Prentice-Hall, 1979.

(TPW 81)   Thayer, R. H., A. B. Pyster, and R. C. Wood. "Major Issues in Software Engineering Project Management," *IEEE Transactions on Software Engineering*, Vol. SE-7, No. 4 (July 1981), 333–42.

(Web 75)   Webster's New Collegiate Dictionary, G. & C. Merriam, 1975.

(Zav 84)   Zave, P. "The Operational Versus the Conventional Approach to Software Development," *Comm. ACM*, Vol. 27, No. 2 (February 1984), 104–18.

(Ze 82)   Zeigler, B. P. "Systems Complexity, System Methodology and the Human Capacity to Manage Them," Wayne State University, Department of Computer Science, 1982.

Chapter 5

Hierarchy Charts and HIPO

5.1 INTRODUCTION

A hierarchy chart is also called a function chart. As its name implies, a hierarchy chart shows the hierarchical relations of the modules (i.e., components) of a system under consideration. In such a diagram, each individual module of the system is described by its main function in terms of a verb and an object. As an example, consider the basic modules of a program that updates an inventory master file in Figure 5.1. As seen in Figure 5.1, a hierarchy chart is quite similar to an organization chart where each diagram at any level is a subset of the level above it. A hierarchy chart shows the modular hierarchy of a system as well as its modular partitioning and functions. For example, data retrieval, process, and write functions and their subfunctions are shown in Figure 5.1. However, major loops and decisions involved in a system and communication within the modular hierarchy of the system are not shown.

Well-structured programs or systems are most commonly characterized as "hierarchical" or "tree-structured." As noted by Turner (Tu 80), the distinction between hierarchy and tree is rarely made. He defines a hierarchy as any program (or system) structured in levels, where the modules on a given lower level may or may not be shared by the modules on the higher levels. Tree is then defined as a specific type of hierarchy where sharing is not allowed.

41

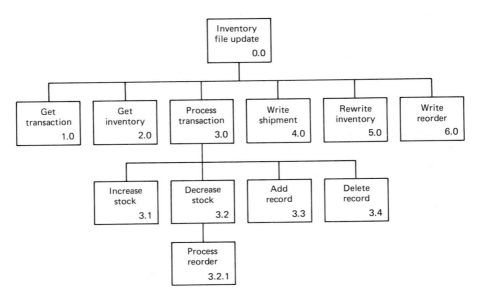

Figure 5.1   Basic functions to update an inventory file

5.2 HIPO

HIPO is an acronym for Hierarchy plus Input-Process-Output. It is a package that consists of a set of diagrams that graphically describe the functions of a system from the general level to the detail level. Initially each major function is identified and then subdivided into lower-level functions. HIPO is developed and supported by IBM (Au, IBM 75, Ka 76).

5.2.1 Uses and Objectives of HIPO

HIPO, similar to many other structured tools of information systems development, is originally a program documentation tool. Flowcharts used in programming describe the program logic. The functions of the program modules, that is, what they do, is not depicted in a flowchart. As noted in an IBM publication (IBM 75), some IBM personnel believe that programming systems documentation based on function can contribute to the efficiency of a program maintenance effort by speeding the location in the code of a function to be modified. HIPO is thus developed as a technique to document functions of programs. HIPO is now also used as a design aid and documentation technique throughout the information system life cycle.

The major objectives of HIPO as a system development and documentation technique may be summarized as (IBM 75):

1. to provide a structure by which the function(s) of a system can be understood
2. to state the functions to be accomplished by a program rather than specify the program statements to be used to perform the functions
3. to provide a visual description of input to be used and output produced by each function for each level of diagrams

The most important objective of a system is to produce output that is correct and meets users' requirements. A HIPO diagram allows one to see how input to a system is transferred into output. Automated programs such as HIPODRAW are available to provide computer-generated and computer-maintained HIPO documentation. Such a program accepts user-written statements describing the desired HIPO documents and produces on a standard line printer all components of a HIPO package.

5.2.2 Kinds of Diagrams in a HIPO package

A typical HIPO package contains three kinds of diagrams:

1. Visual Table of Contents (VTOC): One or more hierarchy diagrams.
2. Overview diagrams: A series of functional diagrams, each of which is related to one function of the system.
3. Detail diagrams: A series of functional diagrams each of which is related to one subfunction of the system.

These diagrams may further be summarized as follows (IBM 75):

1. Visual Table of Contents (VTOC) or hierarchy diagrams:
   Such a diagram contains the names and identification numbers of all the overview and detail HIPO diagrams in the package and shows the structure of the diagram package and relationship of the functions in an hierarchical fashion. A description section is also included to describe each function. (See Figure 5.2 as an example.)
2. Overview Diagrams
   These are high-level HIPO diagrams that describe the major functions and reference the detail diagrams needed to expand the functions to sufficient detail. Overview diagrams provide, in general terms, the inputs, processes, and outputs of a particular function. The input section contains those data items that are used in the process section. The process section contains a series of numbered steps that describe the function being performed. Arrows connect the input data items to the process steps. The output section contains those data items that are created or modified by the process steps. Arrows

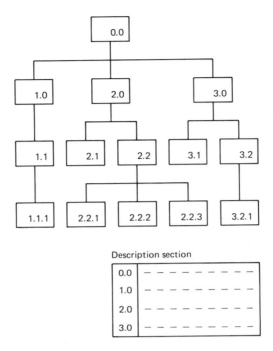

Figure 5.2   Visual table of contents (or hierarchy diagram)

connect the process steps to the output data items (see Figure 5.3a). An extended description area is included in an overview diagram and can amplify the process steps and input and output data items. The extended description also refers to lower level HIPO diagrams, non-HIPO documentation, and code. As is stated in an Auerbach Portfolio (Au), extended description is a table containing prose explanations of a process depicted in the diagram. The extended description can be on the same page as its associated diagram or on an adjacent sheet, depending on the available space. Entries in the extended description are keyed to the detail diagrams by a numbering scheme. Entries also contain cross-references to other documentation (flowcharts, program specs, and so on) or to the implementation itself (module names, subroutines, or labels). The extended description feature of the HIPO package thus serves to tie together the diverse elements of system documentation that may be produced in addition to the diagrams.

3. Detail Diagrams

These are lower level HIPO diagrams that contain the fundamental elements of the package. They describe the specific functions, show specific input and output items, and refer to other detail diagrams. Similar to overview diagrams, detail diagrams may also have an extended description (see Figure 5.3b).

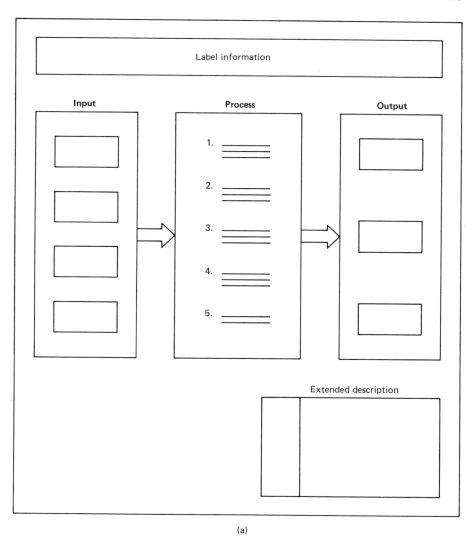

(a)

Figure 5.3   (a) Overview diagram, (b) Detail diagram

No hard-and-fast rule exists to determine the maximum number of levels permitted in the hierarchy diagram (i.e., VTOC); however, the 7 ± 2 rule appears to set a practical limit beyond which the package becomes cumbersome. The number of levels is generally a function of the complexity of the system being documented.

Two available aids for preparing HIPO diagrams are the HIPO Worksheet (Figure 5.4) and the HIPO Template (Figure 5.5), both provided by IBM.

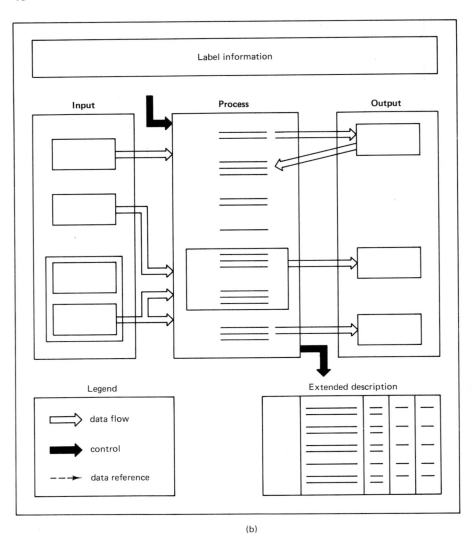

Label information

Input   Process   Output

Legend

data flow

control

data reference

Extended description

(b)

Figure 5.3 *(cont.)*

The strongest features of HIPO are

- its simplicity
- the ease with which users can learn it
- the efficiency of analyst-user communication

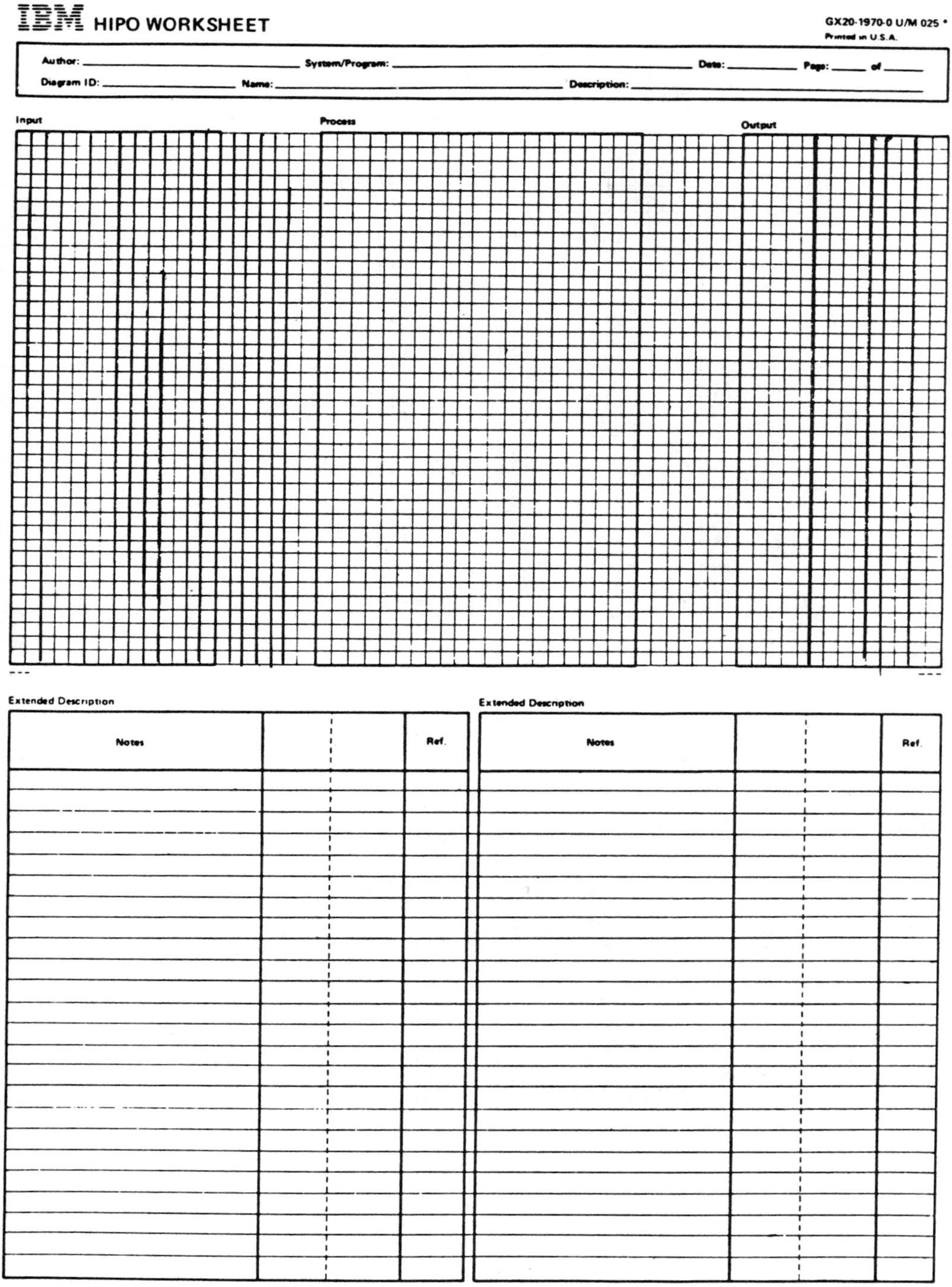
IBM HIPO WORKSHEET

GX20-1970-0 U/M 025 *
Printed in U.S.A.

Author: ______ System/Program: ______ Date: ______ Page: ______ of ______
Diagram ID: ______ Name: ______ Description: ______

Input | Process | Output

Extended Description

Notes		Ref.

Extended Description

Notes		Ref.

Figure 5.4 HIPO worksheet

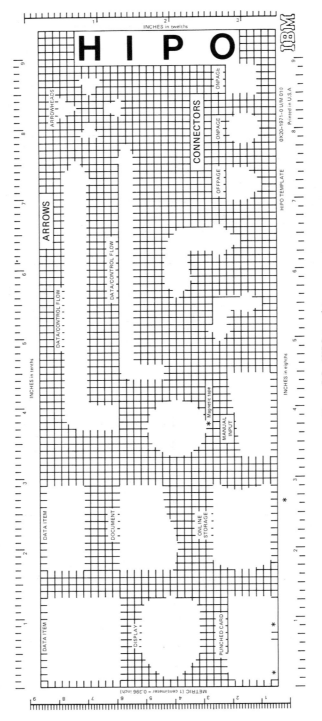

Figure 5.5 HIPO template

48

There are also some challenges in using HIPO. Although users can comprehend the terms used in the notation, large systems of HIPO diagrams are very difficult to change manually and to verify for consistency. Also, data feedback is difficult to describe.

HIPO has been used as a program documentation tool in a variety of business applications. However, the rippling effect (changes in related diagrams associated with changes to systems) can make HIPO impractical for very large system applications. This becomes particularly true when HIPO is used as a system architecture documentation tool.

5.2.3 An Example

The following example illustrates the three different kinds of diagrams in a HIPO package: the hierarchy diagram, overview diagram, and a detail diagram (see Figures 5.6–5.8). The problem relates to a traffic control system.

5.2.4 Steps in Creating HIPO Diagrams

The following steps may be suggested as a guide in drawing both overview and detail diagrams:

1. Prepare empty input, process, and output boxes of HIPO sheets.
2. List any known output in the output box.
3. Develop the contents of the input and process boxes next and fill in any intermediate output not previously specified.
4. Using as few words as possible, state each function in the process box.
5. Connect the corresponding input items and process steps with arrows; connect the corresponding process steps and output items with arrows.
6. Try to combine related data items into logical groupings using boxes.

Some visually important points in developing HIPO diagrams are (IBM 75):

- Arrows generally go from left to right adjacent to the referenced or connected items, and from items higher on the page to those lower on the page.
- Where the tail of the arrow starts and where the tip of the arrow ends must be clear.
- Arrow types must be consistent with the legend.
- Boxes should contain only functionally related items.
- Abbreviations should be avoided in overview diagrams.

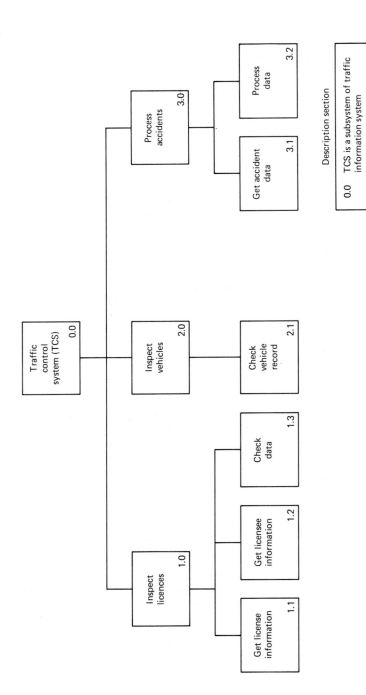

Figure 5.6 Hierarchy diagram example

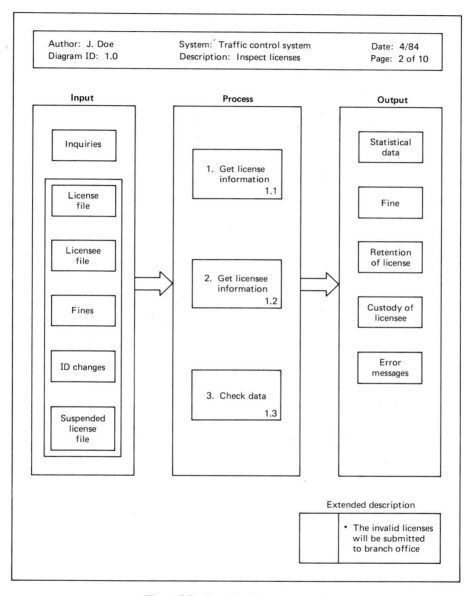

| Author: J. Doe | System: Traffic control system | Date: 4/84 |
| Diagram ID: 1.0 | Description: Inspect licenses | Page: 2 of 10 |

Figure 5.7 Overview diagram example

- All terms and labels should be defined in the extended description when first used.
- Data in overview diagrams should be generally described to minimize arrows.

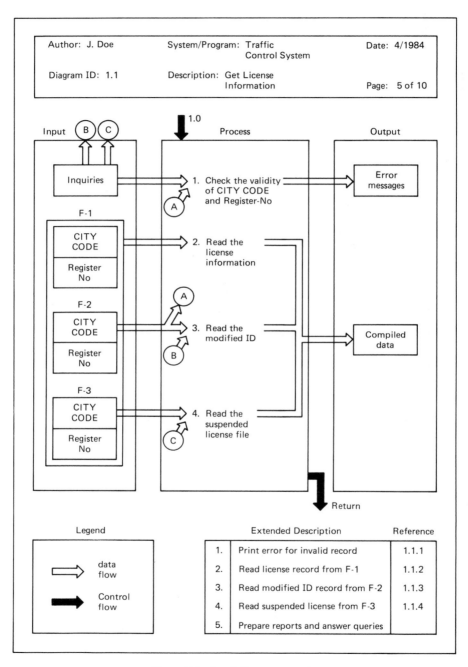

Figure 5.8 Detail diagram example

5.2.5 Types of HIPO Packages

HIPO diagrams are a means for system documentation. During systems development the output from one phase is input to the next phase of the systems life cycle.

Basically, there are two kinds of HIPO packages: the initial design and the detail design. An optional third kind, the maintenance package, is sometimes used. See Figure 5.9.

Initial design package: The designers communicate and validate their ideas by using HIPO diagrams. This package is then used for design reviews by management and other groups, including users.

A review of the initial design package should look for content, consistency, and both technical and functional accuracy.

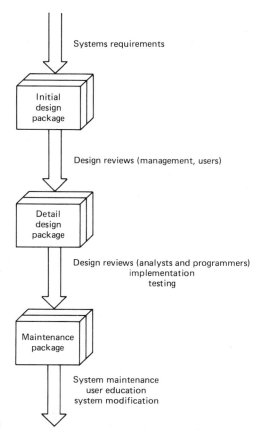

Figure 5.9   Three kinds of HIPO packages

Detail design package.   Using the initial design package as a base, analysts and programmers now add the details, including more levels to the HIPO diagrams, and use the resultant package for implementation and comparison with the initial design package to ensure that all requirements have been met. Frequently this package is the final HIPO documentation and is used as the maintenance package.

In addition to the points that are looked for in the review of the initial design package, appropriate names should be given to such items as programs, files, and tables that are used consistently in the package. Detail design package diagrams should be compared to initial design diagrams to avoid any error.

Maintenance package.   This package is used for corrections, changes, or additions to the system.

As is shown in Figure 5.9, the detail design package is input to the maintenance phase of system development. Reviews of the maintenance phase HIPO package may be conducted for the following purposes:

1. To educate user personnel
2. To check the HIPO package for clarity, legibility, and completeness
3. To optionally delete or add some low-level diagrams or to make some modifications

5.2.6 HIPO and Its Relations to Some Other Tools

Some structured tools such as top-down development, structured programming, chief programmer team, and structured walk-throughs are usually referred to as IPT (Improved Programming Technologies) of IBM.

Combining top-down development with structured programming results in a software of extreme modularity, and HIPO diagrams are valuable and practical tools for such a development effort. Again, the use of HIPO diagrams is reported to be beneficial for structured walk-throughs and for chief programmer team organizations, both of which are used with top-down development and structured programming. Combining top-down development and structured programming results in a program of extreme modularity both in function and logical structure. HIPO diagrams are a logical extension of the functions identified in top-down development and provide the necessary documentation from the start of a project through implementation. Another concept that is being used with top-down development and structured programming is the chief programmer team organization. Structured walk-throughs have been implemented within programming groups that rely on top-down development, structured programming, and chief programmer teams.

5.3 A VARIATION OF HIPO DIAGRAMS

Overview diagrams and detail diagrams of a HIPO package are usually referred to as IPO Diagrams. Instead of using a different format for these diagrams from those shown in Figure 5.3, some authors have reported using the same format for both. Figure 5.10 represents such an alternative format (DaW 83).

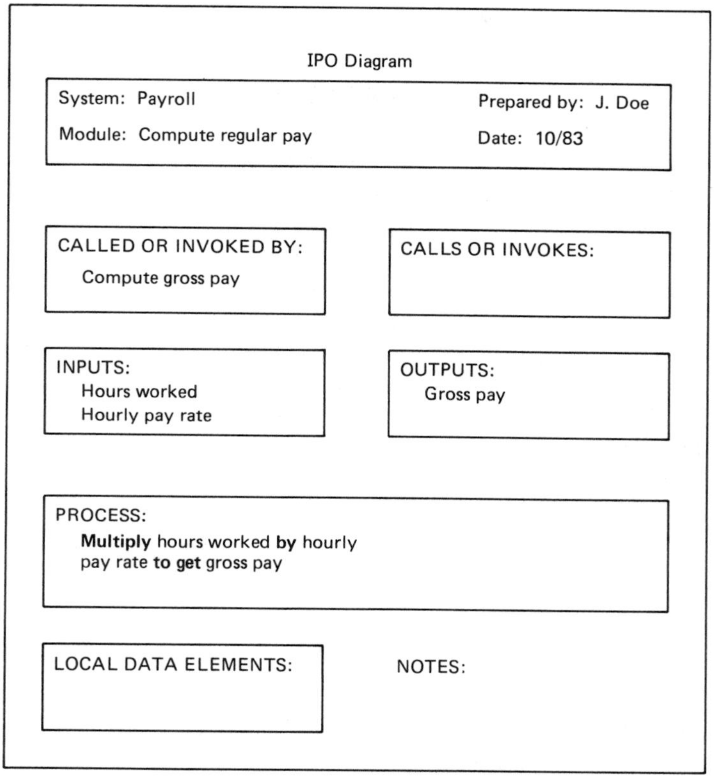

Figure 5.10   A different format for HIPO diagrams

SUMMARY

A hierarchy chart, or function chart, shows the hierarchical relations of the modules of a system under consideration.

HIPO is an acronym for Hierarchy plus Input-Process-Output. It is a package that consists of a set of diagrams that graphically describe functions of a system. A tool developed for programming, it is now used for system development and documentation. A typical HIPO package contains three kinds of diagrams: a visual table of contents (or hierarchy diagram), overview diagrams, and detail diagrams. The available aids for preparing HIPO diagrams are the HIPO worksheet and the HIPO template.

Although it is a practical tool for relatively small systems, HIPO becomes impractical for very large systems.

The initial design package, a detail design package, and a maintenance package are three kinds of HIPO packages. The use of HIPO has been reported with some other structured tools such as top-down development, structured programming, chief programmer team, and structured walk-through.

EXERCISES

1. What is the difference between a hierarchy chart and a function chart?
2. For what do the letters "HIPO" stand?
3. What are the major objectives of HIPO?
4. What type of diagrams are contained in a HIPO package?
5. What is the rippling effect? How good is HIPO against the rippling effect?
6. Give the names of HIPO documentation packages.
7. What is the relationship of HIPO to some other tools such as top-down development, structured programming, chief programmer team, and structured walk-through?
8. Considering a company that you are familiar with, prepare HIPO packages for
   a. Daily sales
   b. Daily accounts payable
   c. Daily cash receipts procedure
   d. Daily inventory procedure
9. Consider the daily sales of a small trading company. A sales operation for a customer consists of the following major functions:
   a. check customer credit
   b. check goods inventory
   c. process order
   d. print shipping order
   Prepare a HIPO package to represent the daily sales of the company.
10. ABC is a regional airline company. Daily operations of ABC are summarized as ticket sales, plane movements, and personnel operations. Ticket sales consist of local flights and international flights. Plane movements include daily plane landings and plane take-offs. Personnel operations mainly consist of checking the attendance of the personnel. Prepare a HIPO package to represent the daily operations of ABC airlines.

SELECTED REFERENCES

(Au)   Auerbach Publishers Inc. *HIPO*, Portfolio No.: 32-04-06.

(DaW 83)   Davis, W. S. *Systems Analysis and Design*, Addison Wesley, 1983.

(IBM 75)   IBM. "HIPO—A Design Aid and Documentation Technique," Publication No. GC20-1851-1, May 1975.

(Ka 76)   Katzan, H. *Systems Design and Documentation*. Van Nostrand Reinhold, 1976.

(Tu 80)   Turner, J. "The Structure of Modular Programs," *Comm. ACM*, Vol. 23, No. 5 (May 1980), 272–77.

Chapter 6

Data Flow Diagrams

6.1 GENERAL

The idea of representing the flow of data in a system by a chart is not new. As reported by Peterson (Pen 77), in 1962 Petri used circles (called places) and bars (called transitions) to represent the static properties of a system. The nodes, or circles, and bars are connected to each other by directed arcs. In 1967, Martin and Estrin (ME 67) represented computational algorithms by directed graph which had circles and arrows as well as some Boolean operator symbols.

As noted by Gane and Sarson (GS 79, p. 25), it is a relatively new insight to use data flow diagrams at the logical level as a key tool for understanding and working with a system of any complexity, as well as to refine the model for use in analysis. The use of such a tool was first reported by Stevens and his colleagues (SMC 74), although many others later used it under the same name, under the acronym DFD, or as a bubble chart. It has also been used in conjunction with the composite design/structured design methodology of the structured approach that will be discussed in Chapter 15. As we shall see later, the data flow diagram concept has also been used in another methodology, namely in SADT (e.g., RB 76), although the circles are replaced by rectangles.

Data flow diagrams enable us to describe an existing system or a proposed new system at a logical level without considering the physical environment in which data flows (e.g., telephone calls, mail, and so on) or the physical environment in which data is stored (e.g., card file, microfiche, disk, floppy disk, or tape).

6.2 A SIMPLE EXAMPLE

To demonstrate DFD and its various symbols, let us consider the daily operations of a local flower shop, Angora Florists, Inc. It is known that almost three quarters of Angora's business is transacted over the phone, mainly for home and/or work delivery. Customer accounts are maintained in the shop.

Since the customer both delivers the order and receives the flowers plus invoices, the customer is both the source in DFD terminology and the destination or sink. As shown in Figure 6.1, a source or sink is represented by a square in a DFD. The circle at the middle of the figure is the process bubble, the hub of the system, so to say. The open-ended rectangles of Figure 6.1 indicate the storage of goods or data. Thus during the processing of an order, some of the flowers are retrieved from the store. Customer information is also stored in the shop, and it passes back and forth between the file and the processing station in order to access customer address and credit status.

As can be seen in Figure 6.1, there are circle(s), square(s), open-ended rectangle(s) and directed arrows in a DFD. In the following section these symbols are formally defined.

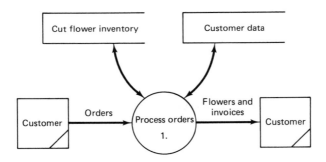

Figure 6.1   Operations of Angora Florists, Inc.

6.3 DFD SYMBOLS

One may define a DFD as a logical model that describes a system as a network of processes (subsystems) connected to each other and/or to data stores and also to source(s) and sink(s) (or destinations). It is now proper to define the basic symbols that are used in a DFD to signify various entities and functions.

1. Data Flow
   An arrow is used to represent a flow of data (information or objects). The name of the data flow is written through or next to the line.

2. Process

   A circle (or bubble) represents an automated or manual task or process. It represents not only the input data that flows into the bubble, but also the transformation of that input data into output, which then flows out of the bubble. A brief descriptive statement and a reference number for the process is written inside the bubble. The descriptive statement should be an imperative sentence that consists of an active verb (e.g., verify, compute) followed by an object clause to describe the process explicitly.

3. Edge of the Model or Source/Sink

   A square is used as an external entity symbol to represent an area in which data originates (i.e., source) or terminates (i.e., sink or destination). In modelling a system by DFD, the data flows that enter and leave the system define the boundary of the system. The name of the originator/terminator entity is written inside the square box, in singular. A more general definition of source and sink may be as follows: A source is an independent system that produces data flows which our system then processes. Similarly, then, sink is another independent system which receives the data flows that our system produces. Thus, a system can be both a source and a sink, and we are allowed to duplicate the symbol if the same outside system appears as both source and sink on a data flow diagram.

4. Storage

   An open-ended rectangle represents a store of information or objects, irrespective of the physical storage medium. The name of the store is written inside the symbol and it should be chosen to be most descriptive to the user. The store symbol identifies a time delay for its content. Quite often data elements do not flow from one process to the next directly but are delayed—that is, stored—while other operations or reordering of data elements occurs. The open-ended rectangle enables us to show such delays in DFD.

   If a data store is only updated during or after a certain process, then an arrow from that process leading to that store is used to indicate the data flow into the store. If, however, the data from the store is used in the process, then one should use a bidirectional arrow. If the name of data store defines clearly the incoming and/or outgoing data, it is not necessary to name the data flows. If, however, the incoming and/or outgoing data are only a portion of the data elements of the stored data, one then should name the data flow(s) properly.

5. Naming

   The names that are used for data flows, description of processes, source/sink, and storage must be defined in the Data Dictionary (DD) of the system development work. DD will be discussed in Chapter 11.

6. Additional Conventions

The crossing of data flow lines should be minimized. In doing this, the same external entity and/or data store can be drawn more than once on the same DFD. The duplicate external entities (source/sink) are identified by an inclined line (/) or by an asterisk (*). The duplicate data stores are identified by a vertical line (|) or by an astrisk (*). If we have more than one type of duplicated entities, one then uses two or more duplication symbols to indicate that. Figures 6.2 and 6.3 show the symbol duplications.

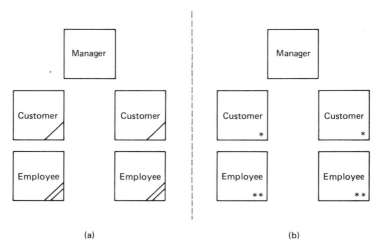

(a)   (b)

Figure 6.2   Example of external entity symbol duplications

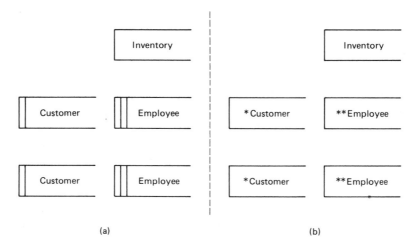

(a)   (b)

Figure 6.3   Example of data store symbol duplications

Customer and employee are the duplicated external entities in Fig. 6.2. Considering customer and employee as data stores, they are shown as duplicated data stores in Figure 6.3.

As shown in Figure 6.4, a little loop is used when it is inevitable that one data flow has to cross another.

Figure 6.4 Data flow line crossings

7. Summary of DFD Symbols
The basic DFD symbols that we have discussed may be summarized for a hypothetical system and presented as Figure 6.5.

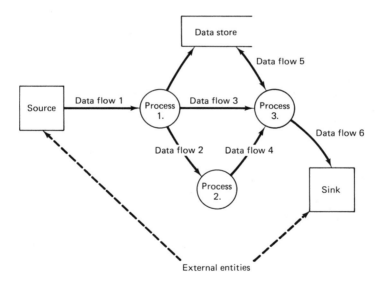

Figure 6.5 Summary of DFD symbols

6.4 OTHER SYMBOLS

Although the symbols defined earlier in this chapter are the most commonly used ones, there are some other symbols in the literature. Several of these are summarized in Figure 6.6. These symbols are given here only for general reference and will not be used in the text.

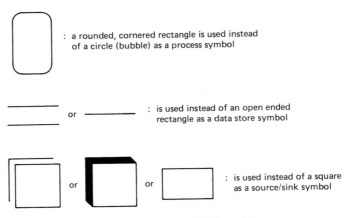

Figure 6.6 Additional DFD symbols

6.5 LEVELS OF DATA FLOW DIAGRAMS

In preparing a DFD the systems analyst tries to identify the typical flows of data and the proper processes that transform them. They are then summarized as a pack of Data Flow Diagrams. In preparing a DFD, the systems analyst uses a top-down approach so that the top page or the first page of the diagram pack shows the boundaries of the system under consideration. This top page is called a context diagram. The major processes of the system and the relevant data flows are described on the next lower level diagram, which is known as an overview diagram or zero-level diagram. On any one page, the 7 ± 2 rule is applied to the number of processes described. Any process on a higher level DFD is further decomposed into an entire new page of DFD on lower level pages, such that incoming and outgoing data flows to the process are also shown on the diagram. Just as processes are decomposed, data flows on DFDs may also be decomposed into their elements on lower level diagrams. Going upward in DFD levels, one then ensures that detailed processes and/or data flows are summed up in the higher level diagrams. The decomposition or explosion process of data flow diagrams is described in Figure 6.7. For example, an explosion of bubble 3 is shown in the level-1 diagram, and an explosion of bubble 3.1 is shown in the level-2 diagram.

6.6 GUIDELINES FOR DRAWING DATA FLOW DIAGRAMS

The basic steps of preparing data flow diagrams are given by various authors (e.g., DeM 78, GS 79, Jo 80, Wei 80, and YC 79). A guideline for drawing data flow diagrams is summarized below:

Step 1:   Identify all the sources and destinations of the system.
Step 2:   Identify all outputs and inputs of the system and draw the context diagram.

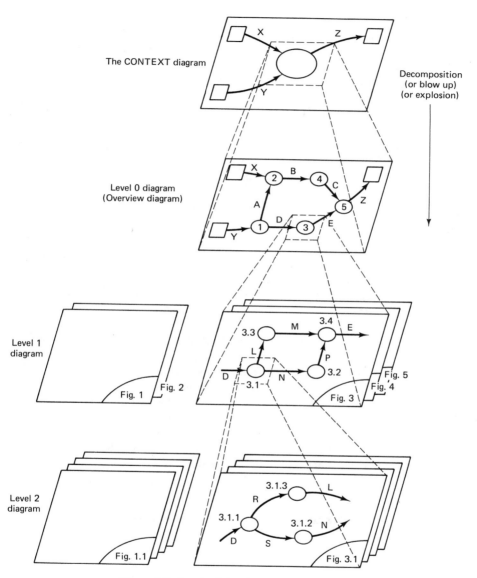

Figure 6.7 Levels of data flow diagrams (DFD)

Step 3:   Taking each source on the left-hand side of the paper, draw the
           data flows, processes, and data stores that will be needed to arrive
           at the proper destination(s) on the right-hand side of the paper.
           When you reach a standstill, you may then take the destinations
           first and come to the middle of the diagram; in some cases, you

may even work your way from the middle—that is, the processes of the diagram—towards the sources and/or destinations.

Step 4:   Label all data flows and data stores to indicate their composition and include them in the Data Dictionary (DD).

Step 5:   Label all processes or transformations (i.e., bubbles), if possible, by means of a transitive verb and an object which is also included in the DD. In labelling processes, consider their inputs and outputs.

Step 6:   Draw the first draft of the diagram free hand, including everything needed except error checking, exception analysis, decision making, initialization (e.g., OPEN FILE), and termination (e.g., CLOSE FILE).

Step 7:   When you are finished with the first draft, check over your list of inputs and outputs that were developed in Step 2. If it is necessary, go over the diagram again. Remember, one may need several drafts.

Step 8:   Next prepare a neater draft using a template and/or other tools. You may use duplicates of data stores and external entities if it helps you to minimize crossing of the data flows on the diagram.

Step 9:   If possible, conduct a review on the revised draft with a user and/or colleague to determine whether the diagram truly represents the system under consideration. If needed, make the necessary modifications.

Step 10:   For each process defined in the final revision of the DFD, work out a lower level decomposition or explosion. Use the proper numbering for parent and children diagrams. If necessary, go back and make additional changes and corrections in the parent DFD.

Step 11:   Repeat the previous step for each process in the DFD until each process has been defined in sufficient detail or in terms of its most elementary inputs and outputs.

6.7 LIMITATIONS AND ADDITIONAL CAPABILITIES OF DFD

As stated earlier, a DFD shows

- partitioning of the systems into subsystems
- data flows in the system
- data stores and in-flowing and out-flowing data
- external entities, that is, sources and sinks of the system

On the other hand, a DFD normally does not show

- composition of data flowing in the system
- data access requirements of data stores
- decisions in the system
- loops in the system
- calculations
- quantities for data and/or processes

It is, however, possible that by defining some relational operators, the capabilities of a DFD can be improved (e.g., Wei 80, YC 79). These operators are:

* denotes a logical AND connection (both a and b);
⊕ denotes an exclusive OR (or XOR) connection (only a or b)
○ denotes an inclusive OR connection (a or b or both).

If both AND and OR operators appear together, the AND operator (i.e.,*) will be performed first and then the OR operator (i.e., ⊕ or ○). An example of how these symbols operate is shown in Figure 6.8. The inclusive OR connection is used for transactions 1 through 4. After editing, a transaction is either valid or rejected. Hence an exclusive OR is used. After an update operation, both a new master file and a list of updates are obtained; hence the AND operator is used.

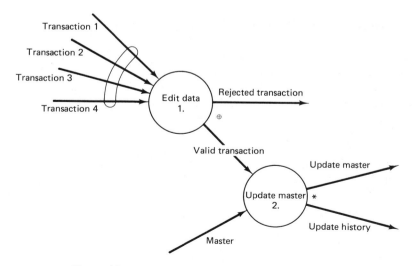

Figure 6.8   Example of logical operator symbols on a DFD

6.8 AN EXAMPLE OF DFD

As an example of drawing a DFD, consider the activities of Hoosier Feed, Inc. Hoosier Feed receives orders from local farmers for cattle and hog feed. It orders bulk feed from Happy Mill and breaks the bulk shipment down for individual farmers. A context diagram and an overview diagram of the activities of this company are given in Figures 6.9 and 6.10, respectively.

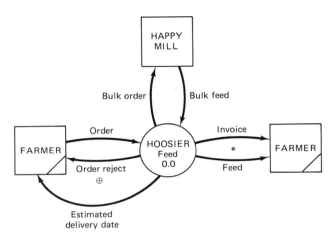

Figure 6.9   Context diagram for the activities of Hoosier Feed, Inc.

6.9 COMMON ERRORS IN DATA FLOW DIAGRAMS

The most common errors in using DFDs may arise from the misuse of several symbols that have been defined earlier for external entities, stores, and so on, or they may result from missing and/or extra data flowing into or out of a process bubble. Obviously, data needed to produce a certain data outflowing from a bubble must be inflowing to the bubble for processing.

6.10 MAJOR REASONS FOR USING DATA FLOW DIAGRAMS

The major reasons for using DFDs may be summarized as follows (StW 82):

1. They help systems analysts
   - to summarize information about the system
   - to understand the key components of the system and to define reusable functions

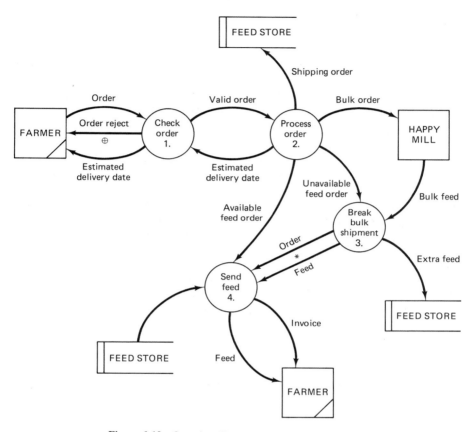

Figure 6.10   Overview diagram for Hoosier Feed, Inc.

- to understand the relationship between subsystems and subassemblies
- to effectively carry through development of the application

Each data flows and the contents of every store in the DFD should be defined in a Data Dictionary (DD), which serves as a first step in developing a database of the system.

2. Recall the fact that communication between user(s) and system analyst(s) is vital in the development of an information system. A DFD serves as an excellent communication tool between these two groups by reducing complexity and by providing a kind of ongoing review of the application.

3. Examining the timing requirements of the various processes in the DFD as a guide, the system analyst is able to draw a number of automation boundaries to develop physical system alternatives. Opposite to decomposition, an automation boundary shows the integration of a group of DFD bubbles into a single process.

SUMMARY

A data flow diagram, DFD, or bubble chart is a logical model to describe an existing system or a proposed new system. A circle is used for process, an arrow for data flow, a square for source/sink, and an open-ended rectangle for data storage. The data names used in a DFD should be defined and their compositions should be described in an accompanying Data Dictionary (DD).

To achieve greater clarity, DFDs are prepared at several levels. The highest level is the "context diagram," which merely shows the boundaries of the system under study. The processes are further decomposed in the lower level diagrams.

A DFD may show the subsystems, data flows, data stores, and external entities of a system. However, it does not show data composition, data access requirements of data stores, decisions and loops of the system processes, calculations, or quantities. Sometimes logical operators such as AND and OR are also used to increase the descriptive capabilities of DFDs.

Common errors in DFDs include misuse of symbols and missing inflowing and/or outflowing data.

Basically DFDs are practical tools to help systems analysts during the analysis and design phase of systems development. One of its major benefits is, however, the fact that it facilitates communication between users and systems analysts.

EXERCISES

1. What is wrong with the following DFDs? Correct them where possible.

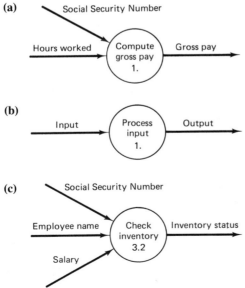

(d)

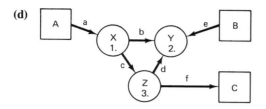

(e)

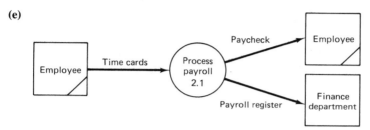

(f)

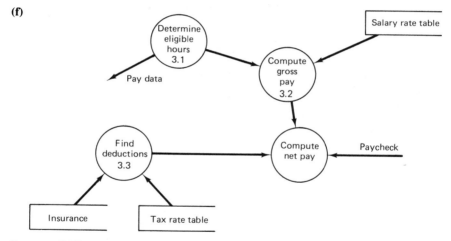

2. Prepare a DFD to describe the activities for
   (a) getting a plane ticket through a travel agent
   (b) eating a doughnut
   (c) pumping fuel into your car
   (d) APM (Auto Parts by Mail) Corporation that stocks auto parts and supplies them by phone and/or mail order
   (e) any other activity of your choice
3. BMB is an international trade corporation. Customer orders are received via phone and telex. Customer order processing, correspondence, and accounting are some of the major processes. Customer file, vendor file, and materials and equipment specifications are some of the data stores in the company. Using DFD, represent the activities of this company.
4. Represent activities of the reserved books section of a university library using DFD.

5. Using DFD, represent the activities for getting a student transcript in a university registration office.

6. Using DFD, represent the various stages of a linear programming (LP) application for a business problem.

SELECTED REFERENCES

(DeM 78)   De Marco, T. *Structured Analysis and System Specification*. Yourdon Press, 1978.

(GS 79)   Gane, C., and T. Sarson. *Structure Systems Analysis: Tools and Techniques*. Prentice-Hall, 1979.

(Jo 80)   Jones, M. P. *The Practical Guide to Structured Systems Design*. Yourdon Press, 1980.

(ME 67)   Martin, D., and G. Estrin. "Models of Computations and Systems," *Journal of the ACM*, Vol. 14, No. 2 (April 1967).

(Pen 77)   Peterson, J. L. "Petri Nets," *ACM Computing Surveys*, Vol. 9, No. 3 (September 1977) 223–52.

(RB 76)   Ross, D. T., and J. W. Brackett. "An Approach to Structured Analysis," *Computer Decisions*, Vol. 8, No. 9 (September 1976), 40–44.

(SMC 74)   Stevens, W. P., G. J. Myers, and L. L. Constantine, "Structured Design," *IBM Systems Journal*, Vol. 13, No. 2 (1974), 115–39.

(StW 82)   Stevens, W. P. "How Data Flow Can Improve Application Development Productivity," *IBM Systems Journal*, Vol. 21, No. 2 (1982), 162–78.

(Wei 80)   Weinberg, V. *Structured Analysis*. Prentice-Hall, 1980.

(YC 79)   Yourdon, E., and L. L. Constantine. *Structured Design*. Prentice-Hall, 1979.

Chapter 7

SADT

7.1 GENERAL

SADT is an acronym for *S*tructured *A*nalysis and *D*esign *T*echnique, a tool that was developed by D. T. Ross during the period from 1969 to 1973. It is now supported and marketed by SofTech, Inc. as a tool that can be used in all phases of systems development. Ross and his colleagues described SADT as both a graphic language for describing systems and a methodology for producing such descriptions (RDMcG). A system is viewed as consisting of things (objects, documents, or data), happenings (activities performed by people, machines, or software), and their interrelationships in SADT applications.

There are two types of diagrams that are used in a SADT package:

1. Activity diagrams (called actigrams)
2. Data diagrams (called datagrams)

Actigrams and datagrams are organized separately in a top-down manner; each diagram is either a summary (i.e., parent) diagram or a detail (i.e., child) diagram of the parent.

The activity kit of SADT consists of activity diagrams that are oriented toward exploding the activities of the system. The data kit, on the other hand, consists of data diagrams oriented toward the depiction of data decomposition in the system. The activity and data kits of SADT are also termed models in the literature. Each type of model includes both data and activities; the main difference is on the subject of decomposition. Any SADT diagram is made up of 7 ± 2 boxes and the arrows connecting these boxes.

A special case of SADT is reported by Peters (Pes 81) as SAMM (Systematic Activity Modelling Method) in which only the activity diagrams are utilized.

7.2 SADT ACTIVITY BOX

On an activity diagram of an activity kit (or activity model) of SADT, the boxes correspond to activities and the arrows correspond to data as can be seen in Figure 7.1.

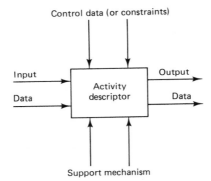

Control data (or constraints)

Input

Activity descriptor

Output

Data

Data

Support mechanism

Figure 7.1   SADT activity box

Each activity represented by a box is named with a verb or verb phrase and an object; an example would be ''sort employee data.'' The phrase ''control data'' as applied to such a box expresses the constraints on that activity. The supporting mechanism of the activity by contrast identifies the department or individual related to and/or responsible for the activity. The support mechanism is also used for cross-referencing models. An example of an SADT activity diagram is given in Figure 7.2. In that figure there are three activities: compute gross pay, compute net pay, and print paycheck. On the figure the data and constraints of the activity boxes are also given.

7.3 SADT DATA BOX

The rectangular boxes in data diagrams of a data kit (or data model) of SADT correspond to data, and the arrows on the diagram indicate the activities related to

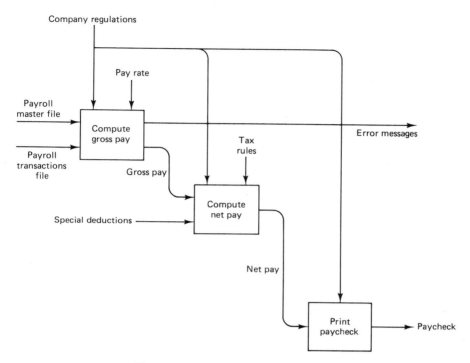

Figure 7.2   Example of an activity diagram

that data, as shown in Figure 7.3. A box on a data diagram is named with a noun or a noun phrase. The control activity at the top of the box is the activity that limits the generation and use of the data. In this case, the box is supported by the storage mechanism (e.g., file), which also serves as a way to cross-reference models, just

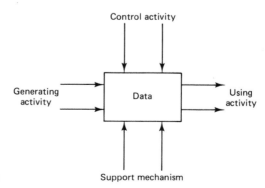

Figure 7.3   SADT data box

as in an activity model. The "generating activity" refers to the activity that generates data, and the "using activity" to the activity that uses data.

7.4 AN EXAMPLE

The sales commission of a salesperson in ABC Co. is computed using the person's rank and monthly total sales. In computing the commission, company policy and company profit for the last six months should be used as control data. The accounting department is responsible for commission computation. Using this information, one can prepare an activity box and a data box of SADT as shown in Figure 7.4a and b, respectively.

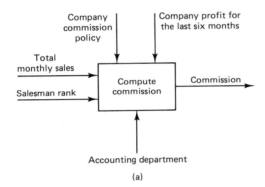

(a)

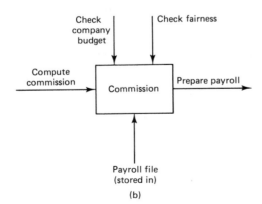

(b)

Figure 7.4 (a) Example activity box, (b) Example data box

7.5 DECOMPOSITION IN SADT

Activity diagrams and data diagrams of SADT are decomposed in the same way that data flow diagrams were exploded in Chapter 6. Figure 7.5 reflects the de-

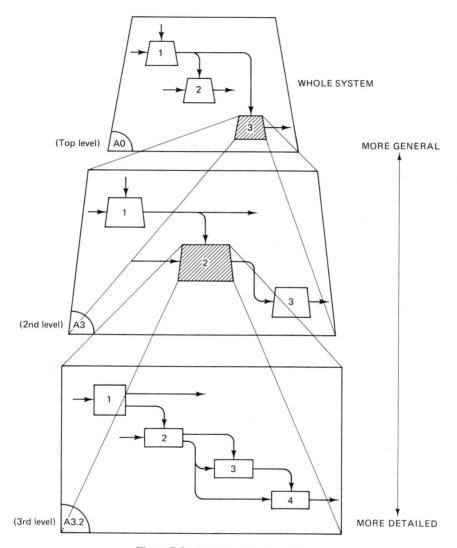

Figure 7.5   Decomposition in SADT

composition of an activity diagram of SADT. An example of SADT in action will be given in Chapter 15.

7.6 GENERAL REMARKS ABOUT SADT

The separate representation of data and activities within the information system, indicating at the same time, however, their links, is the strength of SADT. The major disadvantage of SADT is stated by Peters (Pes 81) as its richness: An SADT diagram contains so much information, it may be hard for users to appreciate it as a proper and correct model for their systems. Further material about SADT may be found in Connor (Co 80).

SUMMARY

As its name implies, SADT (Structured Analysis and Design Technique) is a tool that can be used for both the analysis and the design phases of information systems development. An SADT package consists of two types of diagrams—activity diagrams and data diagrams. Both types of diagrams are organized separately in a top-down manner that recalls the decomposition of data flow diagrams.

An activity diagram of SADT shows the activities, their relations, and their decompositions. A data diagram, on the other hand, is oriented toward the depiction of the decomposition of the data in the system.

EXERCISES

1. What does SADT stand for?
2. What types of diagrams are there in an SADT package?
3. What is the difference between an actigram and a datagram?
4. What is the difference between SAMM and SADT?
5. Prepare an activity diagram and a data diagram of a small information system that you are familiar with.
6. The following DFD is given:

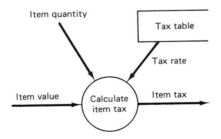

Convert it into a proper SADT diagram.

7. Prepare an activity diagram for a telephone billing project.
8. Prepare the activity diagram and data diagram of the customer billing system of a company.
9. Prepare the activity diagram and data diagram of a student registration system.

10. Prepare the activity diagram and data diagram for the forecasting activities in a production system.

11. Represent an information retrieval system using SADT diagrams.

SELECTED REFERENCES

(Co 80)   Connor, M. F. *Structured Analysis and Design Technique.* SofTech, Inc., May 1980.

(FW 80)   Freeman, P., and A. I. Wasserman, *Tutorial on Software Design Techniques,* 3rd ed. IEEE Computer Society, 1980.

(Pes 81)   Peters, L. J. *Software Design.* Yourdon Press, 1981.

(RDMcG)   Ross, D. T., M. E. Dickover, and C. McGowan. *Software Design Using SADT.* Auerbach, Inc., Portfolio No: 35-05-03.

(RS 80)   Ross, D. T., and K. E. Schoman. "Structured Analysis for Requirements Definition," in *Tutorial on Software Design Techniques,* ed. P. Freeman and A. I. Wasserman. IEEE Computer Society, 1980, 97–106.

(Ro 80)   Ross, D. T. "Structured Analysis (SA): A Language for Communicating Ideas," in *Tutorial on Software Design Techniques,* ed. P. Freeman and A. I. Wasserman. IEEE Computer Society, 1980, 107–125.

Chapter 8

Structure Charts

8.1 GENERAL

Like a hierarchy chart, a structure chart reveals both the modular structure of a system (i.e., it partitions into modules) and the hierarchy into which the modules are arranged. In addition, a structure chart also shows the data and control interfaces among modules. It does not, however, show the decision structure of a system except the major decision(s). Each module in a structure chart is represented by a rectangle identified by a functional module name. The module name consists of a descriptive verb and a single, nonplural object (Figure 8.1a).

Connections and couples are the other two basic elements of structure charts. A connection is represented by a vector joining two modules, and it indicates any reference from one module to something defined in another module. Usually it is used to call other module(s) from a module. A couple is represented by a short arrow with a circular tail. A couple is used to indicate a data item or a control element that moves from one module to another. Data communication is shown by an arrow with an open circle, and control communication by an arrow with a solid circle (Figure 8.1b and c).

In addition to the above elements, a semicircle and a diamond shape are used to represent a major loop and a major decision in a module, respectively. These symbols should be used to represent only the most critical loop(s) and decision(s) in the system to minimize the crowding of the structure chart (Figure 8.1d and e).

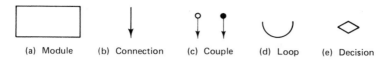

Figure 8.1   Structure chart symbols

8.2 STRUCTURE CHART SYMBOLS AND AN EXAMPLE

The elements of a structure chart—namely, modules, connections, and couples—and their respective symbols are summarized as Figure 8.2.

Figure 8.3 shows an example of a payroll preparation function where em-

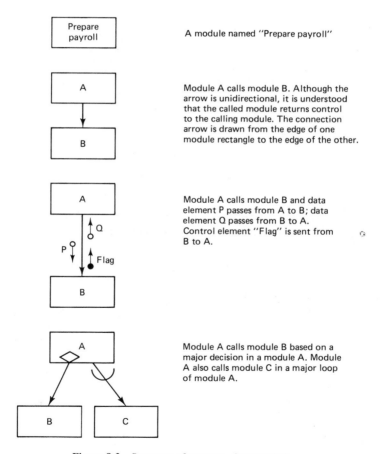

Figure 8.2   Summary of structure chart symbols

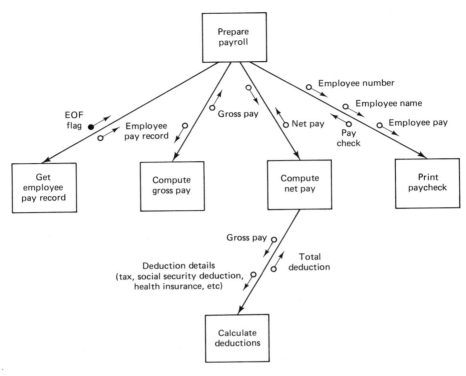

Figure 8.3   Structure chart example

ployee pay record retrieval, gross pay computation, net pay computation, and pay-check printing are considered to be the main modules.

8.3 FINAL REMARKS ABOUT STRUCTURE CHARTS

Structure charts not only illustrate hierarchical modular structures but also indicate the module functions and the data and control communications between modules. They also indicate the fact that higher level modules will be called before lower level ones. As noted by Peters (Pes 80), although structure charts do not permit the documentation of detailed decision information, the sequence of execution is implied in reading from left to right. De Marco (DeM 78), Hassel and Law (HL 82), M. P. Jones (Jo 80), Weinberg (Wei 80) and Yourdon and Constantine (YC 79) are additional references.

SUMMARY

A structure chart shows the modular structure of a system. Inherent in the concept of modular structure is the partitioning of a system into modules or components, the hierarchy into which the modules are arranged, and the interfaces among them. The basic symbols of a structure chart are rectangles to name modules; arrows to represent connections between modules, and couples as a short arrow with a circular tail to show data and control elements communicated between modules. Rarely some additional symbols, such as a semicircle or diamond shape, are also used to show major loop(s) and major decision(s), respectively.

EXERCISES

1. What is the major reason for using structure charts?
2. What is the difference, if any, between the following modular structures?

(a)

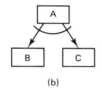
(b)

3. You are given the following figure:

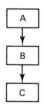

   Is there any difference if you assume this figure is a flowchart over against structure chart?
4. How is a diamond shape used in a structure chart?
5. What is the basic difference between a structure chart and a hierarchy chart?
6. Consider a small farm that produces barley and corn as two major crops. Each year after the harvest, the barley area and corn areas are determined for the following year to optimize the profit of the farm in terms of bushels of yield and selling price of each of the crops.
   Prepare a structure chart for crop planning for this farm by getting the crop record, computing the barley and corn areas, and printing the result.
7. Consider the credit purchase system of a company, and on a structure chart show how to compute and print the monthly schedule of payments resulting from a credit purchase, given the amount of credit purchase and the number of monthly payments planned.
8. Prepare a structure chart for an inventory update operation of a company in terms of the following processes: get transaction, get inventory, process transaction, rewrite inventory, and write reorder.

9. In a government office, birth data is processed to update the birth statistics file. The three major operations during the process are getting the birth record, checking the birth type, and updating a statistics file. The birth type can be normal, or the child is registered to mother only or to father only, or as an orphan child.
Prepare a structure chart to describe the major operations of such an office.

10. One of the current projects of a common carrier company is the editing of the tickets of a telex communication system. The major processes of the tickets editing operation are printing page headings; getting the ticket record; checking the required fields such as call number, country number, sequence number, date and time; storing verified ticket records; and printing an error report.
Prepare a structure chart for such an editing system.

SELECTED REFERENCES

(DeM 78)   DeMarco, T. *Structured Analysis and System Specification*. Yourdon Press, 1978.

(HL 82)   Hassell, J., and V. J. Law. "Tutorial on Structure Charts as an Algorithm Design Tool," *ACM/SIGCSE Bulletin*, Vol. 14, No. 1 (February 1982), 211–23.

(Jo 80)   Jones, M. P. *The Practical Guide to Structured Systems Design*. Yourdon Press, 1980.

(Pes 81)   Peters, L. J. *Software Design*. Yourdon Press, 1981.

(Wei 80)   Weinberg, V. *Structured Analysis*. Prentice-Hall, 1980.

(YC 79)   Yourdon, E., and L. L. Constantine. *Structured Design*. Prentice-Hall, 1979.

Chapter 9

Warnier/Orr Diagrams

9.1 INTRODUCTION

The basic format of the Warnier/Orr Diagrams was developed in the late sixties and early seventies by J. D. Warnier in Paris. It was proposed as a diagram to represent the hierarchical structure of output and input data sets of programs. K. Orr of Topeka, Kansas, later extended some of Warnier's original concepts to information systems analysis and design as well as to database design. The diagrams are, therefore, referred to as Warnier/Orr Diagrams (W/O Diagrams) in the text. They are used to represent data structures as well as processes.

The main tool in a W/O Diagram is the brace "{," also called a universal, which shows decomposition of the system that it depicts. Items that do not decompose further are called elements. If a data structure is represented by a W/O Diagram, the elements are data elements; and if a process of a system is expressed, then its elements are elementary operations.

Other than hierarchy, which is shown in decomposition, the following three simple constructs, representing various data and process structures, can be expressed by W/O Diagrams:

1. sequence
2. repetition (or iteration)
3. selection (or alternation)

In addition, two additional constructs are used as complex constructs:

1. concurrency
2. recursion

The following relational operators are also used in W/O Diagrams:

Symbol	Meaning
$\oplus$	exclusive OR (*a* or *b* but not both)
$+$	inclusive OR (*a* or *b* or both)
$\boxed{/}\ \boxed{*}\ \boxminus\ \boxplus$	arithmetic operator
$\overline{\text{process}}$	negation

Concatenation in data structures and in processes is expressed using a dot:

set name { . attribute = set name . attribute

For example, *employee* { . *name* implies *employee name*.

9.2 GENERAL FORM OF SIMPLE STRUCTURES USING W/O DIAGRAMS

Hierarchy.   The general form of hierarchy in a W/O Diagram is

$$aaa \ \{ \ bb \ \{ \ c$$

which means *aaa* consists of *bb* and *bb* consists of *c*.

Sequence.   The general form of sequence in a W/O Diagram is

$$aaa \left\{ \begin{array}{l} aa \\ bb \\ cc \end{array} \right.$$

which means *aaa* consists of *aa* followed by *bb* and followed by *cc*. Thus, sequence is represented by listing elements serially within a level of hierarchy.

Repetition.   The general form of repetition or iteration in W/O Diagrams is

$$
\begin{array}{ccc}
aaa\ \{ & \text{or} \quad aaa\ \{ & \text{or} \quad aaa\ \{ \\
(1,N) & (N) & (10) \\
& \text{or} & \\
& (0,N) & \\
\\
\text{(i)} & \text{(ii)} & \text{(iii)}
\end{array}
$$

i. (1,N) indicates that *aaa* occurs one to N times
   DO UNTIL (at least once)
ii. (N) or (0,N) indicates that *aaa* occurs zero to N times
   DO WHILE (zero time is possible);
iii. (10) indicates that *aaa* occurs just ten times

In the above forms of (i) and (ii), the value of N is unknown; one time or (1) is also expressed by writing nothing below *aaa*.

Selection (or alternation).   A selection structure is represented by using (0,1) (read as zero or one time) and exclusive OR symbol $\oplus$. The general form is:

$$aaa \begin{cases} bb & \{ \\ (0,1) \\ \oplus \\ cc & \{ \\ (0,1) \end{cases} \quad \text{or} \quad aaa \begin{cases} bb & \{ \\ (0,1) \\ \oplus \\ \overline{bb} & \{ \\ (0,1) \end{cases}$$

9.3 COMPLEX STRUCTURES WITH W/O DIAGRAMS

As noted earlier, concurrency, that is, simultaneous operation, and recursion are also expressed using W/O Diagrams.

Concurrency.   The general form of concurrency is

$$aaa \begin{cases} bb \\ + \\ cc \end{cases}$$

aaa consists of both *bb* and *cc* and their order is not important. Clearly then + serves as a concurrency operator.

Recursion.   A recursive function is a function that calls itself. In systems descriptions sometimes the concept of recursion is used. Recursion on a W/O Diagram is shown by a broken brace:

The general form of recursion in W/O Diagrams is:

$$aaa \begin{cases} bb \\ \\ aaa \begin{cases} \\ \\ \end{cases} \end{cases}$$

and it means that *aaa* consists of *bb* and itself. A simple example is

$$system \begin{cases} system \begin{cases} \\ \\ \end{cases} \end{cases}$$

which means a system has subsystems.

9.4 EXAMPLES OF DATA STRUCTURES USING W/O DIAGRAMS

In the following examples, a hierarchy structure is expressed by using more than one brace to show the decomposition. In addition to hierarchy, other structures are also demonstrated.

Sequence.   The following diagram depicts an employee record:

Number		Name	Date of Birth		
Div.	Ser. No.		Day	Month	Year

Such a record is represented by a W/O Diagram as:

$$Employee\ Record \begin{cases} Number \begin{cases} Div. \\ Ser.\ No. \end{cases} \\ \\ Name \\ \\ Date\ of\ Birth \begin{cases} Day \\ Month \\ Year \end{cases} \end{cases}$$

Repetition.   The repetition structure may be shown by considering an employee file consisting of employee records:

$$\text{Employee File} \left\{ \underset{(1,N)}{\text{Employee Record}} \left\{ \begin{array}{l} \text{Number} \left\{ \begin{array}{l} \text{Div.} \\ \text{Ser. No.} \end{array} \right. \\ \text{Name} \\ \text{Date of Birth} \left\{ \begin{array}{l} \text{Day} \\ \text{Month} \\ \text{Year} \end{array} \right. \end{array} \right. \right.$$

Selection (or alternation).   Consider an account balance check in bank operations to illustrate selection:

$$\text{Balance-check} \left\{ \begin{array}{l} \text{Balance} > 0 \; \{ \text{ payment} \\ \quad (0,1) \\ \\ \oplus \\ \\ \overline{\text{Balance} > 0} \; \{ \text{ print ``overdrafting'' message} \\ \quad (0,1) \end{array} \right.$$

Concurrency.   Now consider the daily operations of a computer system as an example of concurrency:

$$\underset{(D)}{\text{Daily Operation}} \left\{ \begin{array}{l} \text{Batch} \left\{ \begin{array}{l} \text{Editing} \\ \text{Priority} \\ \text{Job Accounting Report} \end{array} \right. \\ + \\ \text{On-line} \end{array} \right.$$

This means batch and on-line operations may occur concurrently.

Recursion.   An assembly problem may be represented using recursion:

$$\text{Assembly} \left\{ \begin{array}{l} \underset{(1,P)}{\text{Pieces}} \\ + \\ \underset{(A)}{\text{Assembly}} \left\{ \right. \end{array} \right.$$

It means that an assembly is defined in terms of another assembly or assemblies. Similarly a part may be defined in terms of other part(s).

9.5 PROCESS REPRESENTATION BY W/O DIAGRAMS

As noted earlier, W/O Diagrams are used to represent processes as well as data structures. For a representation of a process the following general form is used:

$$
\text{Process}
\begin{cases}
\text{Beginning of the Process} & \text{or} & \text{. Begin} \\
\text{Middle of the Process} & \\
\text{End of the Process} & \text{or} & \text{. End}
\end{cases}
$$

As an example of a W/O Diagram to represent a process, consider an operation that updates a customer master file with sales transactions:

$$
\text{Update Master File}
\begin{cases}
\text{. Begin} \\
\text{Customer} \\
\quad \text{(C)} \\
\text{. End}
\end{cases}
\begin{cases}
\text{. Begin} \\
\text{Get transaction} \\
\text{Get master record} \\
\text{Process transaction} \\
\text{Write new master} \\
\text{Store new master} \\
\text{. End}
\end{cases}
\begin{cases}
\text{. Begin} \\
\text{Read transaction} \\
\text{Edit transaction} \\
\text{.End}
\end{cases}
$$

This diagram also shows the hierarchy of operations.

9.6 EXAMPLES OF PROCESS REPRESENTATION USING W/O DIAGRAMS

A common carrier company provides telex communication service. One of the current projects of the company is the computerization of the billing operation of telex communications services. The major steps of the billing operation are creating and updating the master file, and preparing reports. Using W/O Diagrams, these steps of the billing project may be summarized as follows:

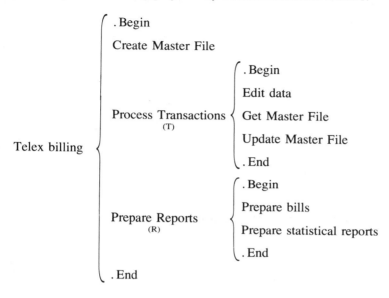

Another example of process representation using W/O Diagrams is the system development life cycle that was discussed in Chapter 2 and presented as Figure 2.1 or as Table 2.2.

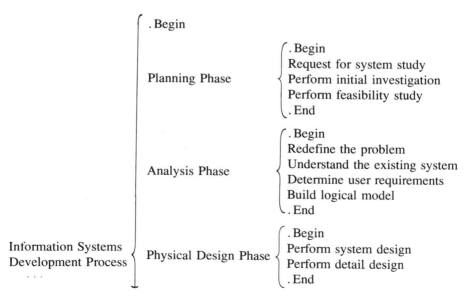

(*cont.*)

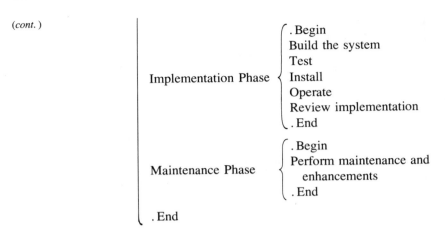

Implementation Phase
- . Begin
- Build the system
- Test
- Install
- Operate
- Review implementation
- . End

Maintenance Phase
- . Begin
- Perform maintenance and enhancements
- . End

. End

9.7 AN EXTENSION OF W/O DIAGRAMS

A combination of systems flow diagram symbols together with W/O Diagram symbols may be used to describe the flow of data in an information system, in particular a database application, where the system consists of three phases: edit, process, and report.

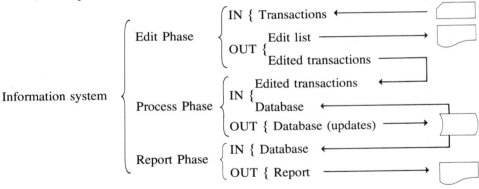

Information system
- Edit Phase
  - IN { Transactions
  - OUT { Edit list / Edited transactions
- Process Phase
  - IN { Edited transactions / Database
  - OUT { Database (updates)
- Report Phase
  - IN { Database
  - OUT { Report

9.8 FINAL REMARKS ABOUT W/O DIAGRAMS

In addition to the publications of J. D. Warnier (Wa 74 and Wa 81) and K. Orr (Orr 77 and Orr 81b), the major references for Warnier/Orr Diagrams are the publications of Higgins (Hi 79 and Hi 83) and the Auerbach Portfolios, particularly No. 12-03-06. The books published by Higgins emphasize design and construction of programs using W/O Diagrams and W/O methodology that will be included in Chapter 15.

SUMMARY

The main element of a Warnier/Orr (W/O) Diagram is the brace {, which indicates decomposition or hierarchy within the system it describes. In addition to decomposition, W/O Diagrams portray the simple structures of sequence, repetition, and selection (or alternation). Concurrency and recursion are two additional structures that may be represented. Exclusive OR and inclusive OR operators are used as logical operators on a W/O Diagram and an arithmetic operator is set inside a box. Negation is expressed in a W/O Diagram by an overbar.

W/O Diagrams are used to describe data structures, processes, and data flows in an information system. In representing data flows, system flow diagram symbols are also used together with braces.

EXERCISES

1. What is the basic element of a W/O Diagram?
2. Can processes also be represented by means of W/O Diagrams? If so, explain how.
3. What are the basic structures represented by W/O Diagrams?
4. What additional structures are also represented by W/O Diagrams?
5. What type of operations are used in W/O Diagrams?
6. Represent your daily activities by using W/O Diagram(s).
7. Take a hypothetical inventory update process and represent it using W/O Diagrams.
8. Describe the situation using W/O Diagrams if you submit your homework or not.
9. Describe your near future after graduation using W/O Diagrams for the description.
10. Represent a customer record of a local bank using W/O Diagrams.
11. Represent the data structure of the available books in a local public library using W/O diagrams. Using W/O Diagrams, represent a search process on the master file of the library.
12. The personnel record of an organization contains the fields of ID, rank and position, personal data, job history, and salary. The ID field consists of number, name, and address; personal data consists of birth date, marital status, sex, and number of dependents; and job history contains date hired and expected retirement date.
    Represent the structure of such a record using W/O Diagrams.
13. The vehicle file is one of the available files of a Traffic Information System of a town. Such a file contains technical and registration data of the recorded vechicles. A vehicle record has ID data, technical specifications, registration data, and vehicle history.
    Represent such a record using W/O Diagrams.
14. Represent a telephone subscription record using W/O Diagrams.
15. Represent the quality control system of an industrial organization using W/O Diagrams.
16. Solve problems 8 through 10 of Chapter 5 using W/O Diagrams.
17. Solve problems 3 through 6 of Chapter 6 using W/O Diagrams.
18. Solve problems 6 through 9 of Chapter 8 using W/O Diagrams.

SELECTED REFERENCES

(Au)   Auerbach, Inc. *Warnier-Orr Diagrams*, Portfolio No: 12-03-06.

(Hi 79)   Higgins, D. *Program Design and Construction.* Prentice-Hall, 1979.

(Hi 83)   Higgins, D. *Designing Structured Programs.* Prentice-Hall, 1983.

(Orr 77)   Orr, K. *Structured Systems Development.* Yourdon Press, 1977.

(Orr 81b)   Orr, K. *Structured Requirements Definition.* K. Orr & Associates, 1981.

(Wa 74)   Warnier, J. D. *Logical Construction of Programs.* Van Nostrand/Reinhold, 1974.

(Wa 81)   Warnier, J. D. *Logical Construction of Systems.* Van Nostrand/Reinhold, 1981.

Chapter 10

Other Diagrams

10.1 INTRODUCTION

In addition to the diagrams discussed in the previous chapters, other diagrams used in structured systems analysis and design include Jackson's Diagrams, Chen's E-R representation, and Leighton diagrams. These tools are defined and discussed in the following sections.

10.2 JACKSON'S NOTATION

Using Jackson's notation, we can represent any program, data structure, or information system in terms of system hierarchy and its elementary and composite components. Elementary components are those that are not further decomposed and have no parts. Composite components are of three types—sequence, selection, or alternation.

There are two types of notations to represent the composite components: a graphical notation which is called a Jackson's Diagram, or Structure Diagram; and a nongraphical notation which is called Structure Text or Schematic Logic (Hic 85, Ja 75, and Ja 83). Jackson's Diagram and structure text notations for sequence, iteration, and selection are given as Figures 10.1 through 10.3.

A sequence has two or more parts which occur once in order. For example, Figure 10.1 shows a Jackson's Diagram and structure text notation for a sequence

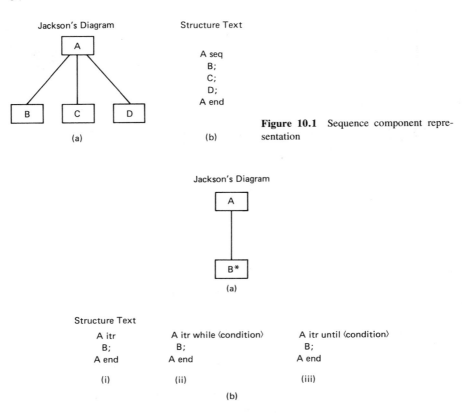

Figure 10.1 Sequence component representation

Figure 10.2 Iteration component representation

component A which consists of one B, followed by one C, followed by one D. In other words, B, C, and D are components of A.

An iteration component has a part which occurs zero or more times for each occurrence of the component itself. In Figure 10.2 the asterisk above B inside the box indicates that component A has an iterated part B; that is, B is repeatedly executed zero or more times for each occurrence of A. Structure text notation of component A is given in three different forms as (i)–(iii) in Figure 10.2b.

A selection component has two or more parts, of which one, and only one, occurs once for each occurrence of the selection component. In Figure 10.3, a diagrammatic representation and structure text notation of a selection component A is given. A has parts such as B, C, and D. The small circles in the boxes for B, C, and D indicate that A is a selection and B, C, and D are its components. It is also possible to show conditions of selection in the structure text similar to a case statement as in (ii) and (iii) of Figure 10.3b. A special case of selection is "null

Jackson's Diagram

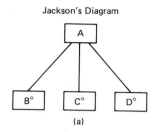

(a)

Structure Text

A sel	A sel ⟨cond-1⟩	A sel ⟨cond-1⟩
B;	B;	B;
A alt	A alt ⟨cond-2⟩	A alt ⟨cond-2⟩
C;	C;	C;
A alt	A alt ⟨cond-3⟩	A alt ⟨else⟩
D;	D;	D;
A end	A end	A end
(i)	(ii)	(iii)

Figure 10.3 Selection component representation

(b)

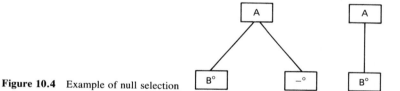

Figure 10.4 Example of null selection

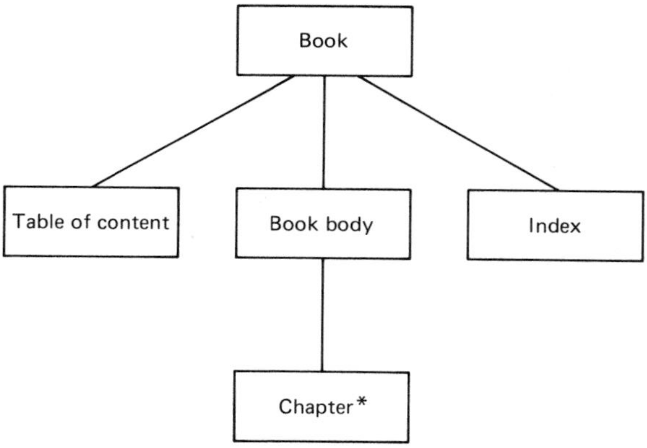

Figure 10.5 Example of iteration in a Jackson's diagram

selection.'' It means ''do nothing'' and is represented by $-^0$. Consider the example given in Figure 10.4 in which A has only one selection component, B.

An example of iteration in a Jackson's Diagram is the structure of a textbook in which the table of contents, body of the book, and the index are sequence components and chapter is the iterated part of the body of the book (Figure 10.5).

The composite components and hierarchy are represented in Figure 10.6. In that figure, A is a sequence component, and B, C, and D are its components. C is a selection component; E and F are its components. E and F are iteration components. F is also a sequence component since H and K are its components.

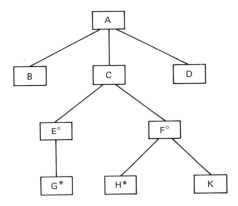

Figure 10.6   Basic structures in Jackson's diagram

A real-life example with Jackson's notation is given in Figure 10.7. In that figure a sales information system is depicted in which a sales clerk is to process sales orders. *Get order record* is an iteration component and it has the following sequence components: *edit customer information, get ordered product information, check ordered quantity*, and *process shippable order. Valid order* and *special order request* are the selection components of *get ordered product information*. Similarly, *process fulfilled order, process partly fulfilled order*, and *process unfulfilled order* are the selection components of *check ordered quantity*. Finally, *process shippable order* is a selection component which has *prepaid order* and *unpaid order* as its elements.

10.3 ENTITY-RELATIONSHIP MODEL (OR CHEN'S E-R MODEL)

E-R Model or Chen's entity-relationship model is a logical model that is used in database analysis and design as well as in the depiction of information systems (e.g., Ch 76, Ch 78, Pan 82). The model has three elements:

- entities
- relationships
- descriptions of entities and relationships or their attributes and values

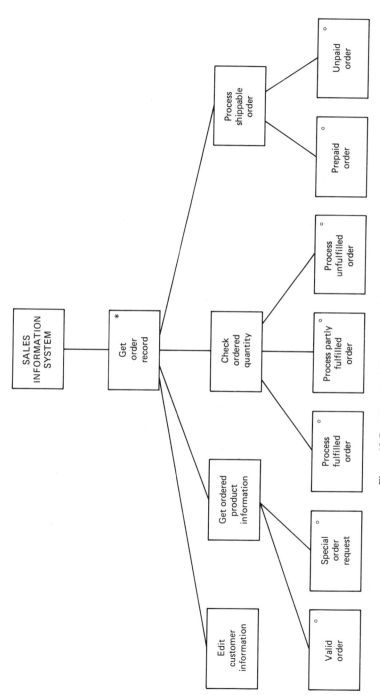

Figure 10.7 A hypothetical system using Jackson's notation

10.3.1 Entities

An entity is a person, place, thing, event, or concept about which information is recorded. For example, in a warehouse the entities are suppliers, parts, shipments, and the like; in a bank, the entities are customers, employees, bank accounts, mortgage loans, and so on. Groups of entities may constitute an entity type, although an entity need not belong to just one type. In an E-R diagram, an entity type is represented by a rectangular-shaped box (some authors prefer an elliptical shape).

10.3.2 Relationships

Relationships—that is, conceptual links—may exist between entities. Relationships are also classified into different types and these relationship types are represented by a diamond-shaped box in an E-R diagram with lines connected to related entity types.

A simple example showing entity and relationship symbols is given in Figure 10.8. In that figure, two rectangles, namely MAN and WOMAN represent entities, and a diamond shape is the relationship, LOVE.

Figure 10.8 Entity and relationship symbols

Relationships in an E-R diagram can be one to one, one to many, and many to many. For example, Figure 10.9 diagrams WORK and PROJ-MANAGER as two different relationship types between two entity types, EMPLOYEE and PROJECT. M, N, and 1 in that figure indicate that there are N projects; M employees

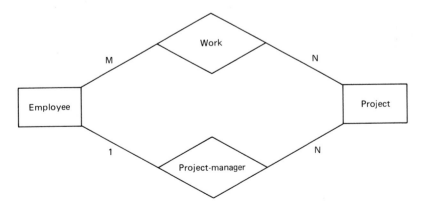

Figure 10.9 Example of entity-relationship (E-R) model

work for these projects, and each project has only one manager. Also an employee can be the manager of many projects. Thus, the PROJ-MANAGER relationship between EMPLOYEE and PROJECT entities is one to many. On the other hand, the WORK relationship between the entities EMPLOYEE and PROJECT is many to many, meaning that each project may consist of several employees and each employee may be associated with more than one project. In the example given in Figure 10.10, the relationship type is MARRIAGE, and it is one-to-one mapping between WOMAN and MAN or among the entity type PERSON.

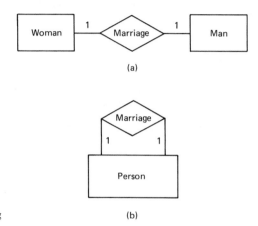

(a)

(b)

Figure 10.10   One-to-one mapping

It is also possible to define a relationship type among more than two entity types. In Figure 10.11, the entities PART, PROJECT, and SUPPLIER are related in a many-to-many relationship: PART-SUPP-PROJ.

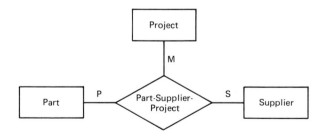

Figure 10.11   Another example of entity-relationship (E-R) model

10.3.3 Descriptions of Entities and Relationships

Every entity has some basic attributes that characterize it. A customer in a bank may be described by such attributes as customer number, name, address, date, and so on. Similarly a house can be described by its size, color, age, and address.

Entities have properties which can be expressed in terms of attribute-value pairs. For example, "SOC-SEC-NO of EMPLOYEE R is 316-88-6972" has SOC-SEC-NO as attribute and 316-88-6972 as the value for the entity EMPLOYEE. Values can be classified into different value types such as SOC-SEC-NO, AGE, COLOR, and QUANTITY. In the E-R notation, a value type is represented by a circle, and an attribute is represented by an arrow directed from the entity type to the desired value type (Figure 10.12). Similar to entities, relationships may have attributes and value types as shown in Figure 10.13.

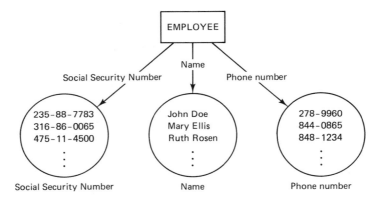

Figure 10.12   Example of entity attributes and value types

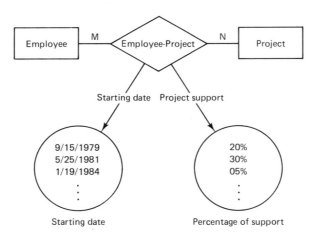

Figure 10.13   Example of relationship attributes and value types

In the example given in Figure 10.13, the STARTING-DATE of an employee in a project depends on both the EMPLOYEE and PROJECT but neither of them alone. Hence STARTING-DATE is an attribute of the relationship EMP-PROJ. Similarly PROJECT-SUPPORT is also an attribute of the EMP-PROJ relationship.

Attribute-value pairs are commonly used to identify entities uniquely. Such attributes of entities are called "entity identifiers" and function the same as primary keys of records in conventional data processing. Relationships are identified by utilizing the identifiers of the entities involved in the relationship.

10.3.4 Special Entity and Relationship Types

Sometimes the existence of an entity may depend on the existence of another entity or entities. Such an entity is called a "weak entity" and it is represented by a double rectangular-shaped box. The relationship box between such entities has "E" to indicate existence-dependent relationship, and an arrow is used to show the direction of dependency. An example is given in Figure 10.14. Figure 10.14 indicates that SPOUSE depends on WORKER. For example, if a worker leaves the company the related spouse data is no longer kept.

Figure 10.14 Existence dependence example

Another special case occurs if an entity cannot be uniquely identified by its own attribute(s). Its relationships with other entities must then be used for identification. If an entity has such a property, it is then said that it has "ID dependency" on other entities. Such a dependency is indicated by "ID" in a double diamond-shaped box, and the direction of relationship is indicated by an arrow. Entity box is also a double rectangle. An example is given in Figure 10.15.

A town is not uniquely identified unless its state is also defined. As indicated by Chen (Ch 78), most ID dependencies are associated with existence dependencies. However, existence dependency does not imply ID dependency.

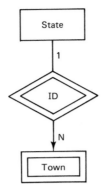

Figure 10.15 ID dependence example

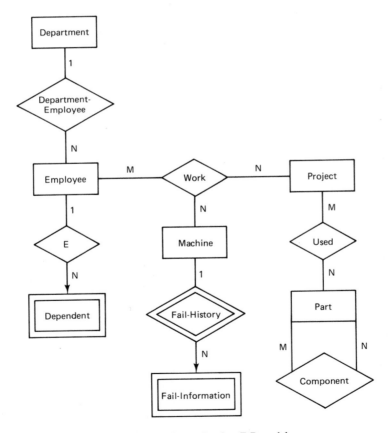

Figure 10.16 Example of an E-R model

Further treatment of special cases in E-R diagrams is presented by Doğaç and Chen (DC 83).

10.3.5 Another Example of the E-R Model

For a further demonstration of the E-R model notation, consider the example given in Figure 10.16 where the entities DEPT, EMP, MACHINE, PROJ, and PART are related through DEPT-EMP, WORK, USED, and COMPONENT relations. DEPENDENT is an existence dependent entity and FAIL-INFO is an ID dependent entity in that example.

10.4 LEIGHTON DIAGRAM

The Leighton diagram is another graphical tool that is available (Pes 80 and Sct 78). Not a very common tool, the Leighton diagram mainly describes the scope

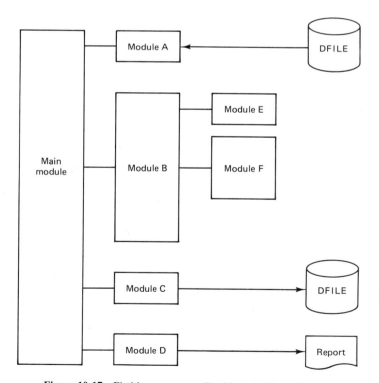

Figure 10.17 Fictitious system outlined by a Leighton diagram

of control, hierarchy, and external interfaces of an information system. Leighton diagrams utilize combinations of

- rectangles
- directed line segment (vectors)
- system flowchart symbols
- connecting lines

A rectangle depicts a module of a system; scope (or span) of control is indicated by the height (i.e., vertical dimension) of the rectangle. Hierarchy is shown by the horizontal dimension of a Leighton diagram, and execution sequence proceeds from top to bottom. A simple example appears in Figure 10.17, which depicts a fictitious system consisting of a main module with four submodules, A, B, C, and D. One may consider Module A as an input module for a disk file. Module B has two process modules, E and F. Module C is an output module for a disk file, and Module D is a reporting module.

SUMMARY

Jackson's notation, Chen's E-R (entity-relationship) model, and the Leighton diagram are other graphical tools that are used in the structured approach in addition to HIPO, DFD, Structured Charts, SADT, and W/O diagrams that were discussed earlier.

Jackson's notation allows us to represent the hierarchy of a system as well as its elementary and composite components. Elementary components are those that are not further decomposed and have no parts. Composite components are of three types—sequence, iteration, and selection. There are two types of notations to represent composite components: a graphical notation, which is called a Jackson Diagram or Structure Diagram, and a nongraphical notation, which is called Structure Text or Schematic Logic.

Chen's E-R model is based on entities, relationships, and their descriptions according to their attributes and values. An entity is a person, place, thing, event, or concept about which information is recorded. A rectangle is used to depict an entity type, which is a group of entities. Relationships—that is, conceptual links—may exist between two or more entities. Relationship types are represented by a diamond-shaped box in an E-R model. Entities and relationships of an E-R model have properties which can be expressed in terms of attribute-value pairs. Existence dependence and ID dependence are special entity types.

The Leighton diagram is another graphical tool that is available. Vertical rectangles, vectors, system flowcharts symbols, and connecting lines are major components of that tool.

EXERCISES

1. What are the basic components of a Jackson Diagram?
2. What are the symbols that are used to represent the basic structures in a Jackson Diagram?
3. What are the basic elements of Chen's E-R model?
4. Define the terms *entity*, *relationship*, *attribute*, and *value*.
5. Investigate the existing student registration system of a college that you are familiar with and represent that system using
    a. a Jackson Diagram
    b. an E-R model
6. Visit a travel agency and examine how the system works. Based on your understanding, represent its major activities using a Jackson Diagram.
7. Give an example for a weak entity and ID dependence.
8. What are the basic components of Leighton Diagrams?

SELECTED REFERENCES

(Ch 76)   Chen, P. P. "The Entity-Relationship Model—Toward a United View of Data," *AMC Transactions on Database Systems*, Vol. 1, No. 1 (March 1976), 9–36.

(Ch 78)   Chen, P. P. *The Entity-Relationship Approach to Logical Data Base Design.* The Q.E.D. Monograph Series, No. 6. Q.E.D. Information Sciences, Inc., Massachusetts, 1978.

(DC 83)   Doğaç, A., and P. P. Chen. "Entity-Relationship Model in the ANSI/SPARC Framework," in *E-R Approach to Information Modeling and Analysis*, ed. P. P. Chen. Elsevier, 1983, 357–74.

(Hic 85)   Hiçyilmaz, C. *Jackson System Development Methodology and an Application.* M.S. Thesis, METU-Dept. of Computer Engineering, March 1985.

(Ja 75)   Jackson, M. *Principles of Program Design.* Academic Press, 1975.

(Pan 82)   Parkin, A. "Data Analysis and System Design by Entity-Relationship Modelling," *The Computer Journal*, Vol. 25, No. 4 (1982), 401–409.

(Pes 80)   Peters, L. J. *Software Design.* Yourdon Press, 1980.

(Sct 78)   Scott, L. R. "An Engineering Methodology for Presenting Software Functional Architecture," in *Proc. 3rd. Int. Conf. on Software Engineering.* IEEE Computer Society, 1978, 222–29.

Chapter 11

Nongraphical Tools

So far we have looked at graphical tools that are used for information systems development. Now we will examine some of the nongraphical tools, including the Data Dictionary/Directory (DD/D), Structured English (SE), and pseudocode. As will become clear later, DD is concerned only with *defining* data, whereas SE and pseudocode are concerned with *processing* data.

11.1 DATA DICTIONARY/DIRECTORY (DD/D)

A Data Dictionary essentially specifies the data admissible to a system through naming, classification, representation or structure, usage, and administration of data; it is also referred to as "data about data" or metadata. The range of information which can be held in a Data Dictionary system may be very large. Although the system may be manual, it is usually computerized.

A Data Directory is generally used to specify the location of data within a database and possibly the most appropriate or efficient database path to be followed during access or retrieval. It may also contain descriptions of report formats, screen displays, translation tables, record, file, or schema definitions, and transaction descriptions. In both logic and development, Data Dictionaries precede Data Directories.

Various Data Dictionary/Directory (DD/D) packages are commercially available. Some of these packages are associated with a specific DBMS while others are more general. Some firms develop DD/D software for their own internal use.

11.1.1 Objectives of DD/D

Although a DD/D is a valuable first step in developing a database (DB) and many DBMS (Database Management Systems) include it, it is fast becoming an indispensable tool in information systems analysis and design. In any organization, a given element of data may be defined differently by different users and/or systems analysts. Use of a DD/D system in such an organization improves communication among systems analysts, users, and management in the analysis phase of systems development. The DD/D system clarifies the flow and content of data items through the information system during the design phase and also supports maintenance efforts. Thus a DD/D system is a useful tool throughout information systems development life cycle, as well as being invaluable in documenting the information system.

Kreitzer (Kr 81) introduces a new term, *Information Resource Management* (IRM), which explicitly recognizes information as the lifeblood of today's organization, a resource that should be managed just as any other critical resource. He also states that the Data Dictionary is a central concept of IRM, in effect, the "hub of the wheel" around which revolve the "spokes" of the information resource.

The basic requirements of a DD system are stated as (KL 83):

- Ease in maintenance
- Ease in reporting
- Comprehensive definition and naming conventions
- Adequacy in documentation

Advantages of Data Dictionaries are summarized as control of data, improved system development and control, and automatic generation capability (Ca 78).

Canning (Ca 78) summarized some of the problems with DD systems as follows:

- Perhaps the first problem that confronts the potential user of a DD system might be termed the what-where-when problem. What will it be used for? Where will it be obtained? When will it be installed in the organization?
- In order to fully appreciate the benefits of a DD system, the user organization must have
  a. a high degree of commitment by management, users, and data processing personnel
  b. an effective data administration function
  c. an effective method for planning the introduction of change into information systems

A data management system (DMS) and its relationship with a DD system is elaborated by Canning (Ca 81). A DMS is defined as a system that includes (1) a DD for defining new files, records, and fields, plus indexes for accessing the records, plus a means for allocating disk space for the files; (2) a means for creating screen formats for inputting and validating data; (3) a means for entering data and updating the database; (4) a record selection and sorting capability; (5) a query capability; (6) a report formatting and column totalling capability; and (7) a means where by specific application logic can be expressed. Thus a DMS can perform most of the routine aspects of a data processing application and in so doing relies heavily on its data dictionary facility.

11.1.2 Content of DD

A data item in a DD may be an element or a group. An element is the lowest level data such that it cannot be decomposed into smaller pieces. Elements may sometimes be components of a group. A group definition shows the component data elements that make up the group and the relationships among them. A set of relational operators are used to define the composition of a group data element, as will be discussed in the next subsection.

The information that is kept in a DD for each data element may include the following identifiers: naming, classification, representation, usage, and administration (e.g., BCS 77).

Naming the information of an element is basically listing its aliases, that is, the variety of names that may be used at different times and in different places to identify the element.

Classification information includes the description of the item in natural language, its ownership, item type (if it is a group[1] or elementary item), privacy and security considerations, and authorization definitions.

Representation information or format may include item length, picture,[2] its composition if it is a group item, and processing units.

Usage information describes the use of the element quantitatively, giving its range of values, frequency of use, conditional values, if any, and so on.

Finally, administration information includes the resources used or required by the element and the processing mode, that is, batch, time sharing, and transaction processing.

11.1.3 Composition Definition of Group Data Items in DD

As noted previously, elements of group data items of DD and their interrelations are defined by means of some formulas using relational operators. The commonly used operators are summarized in Table 11.1 (see DeM 78 and Pes 80).

---

[1]A data item is called a group item if it consists of more than one elementary item.

[2]In COBOL, an elementary item is described by a picture clause, which is a description of the number and type of characters that make up the item.

**TABLE 11.1   Relational Operators for Composition
Definitions**

Symbol	Operation
=	IS COMPOSED OF (or IS EQUIVALENT TO)
+	AND
[ ]	EITHER-OR (i.e., selection)
{ }	ITERATIONS OF
( )	OPTIONAL

In addition to these symbols, a pair of asterisks (*) is used for comments and a pair of quotes for nonnumeric literals which are constants not being used for arithmetic operations. A vertical bar (|) is used for separating options. The upper and lower limits of iterations are also shown outside the iteration braces. For example, iterations from 1 to 10 may be shown by

$$\substack{10 \\ {} \\ 1} \{\text{DATA ELEMENT}\} \qquad \text{or} \qquad 1\{\text{DATA ELEMENT}\}10$$

Default limits are 0 and ∞, meaning that it will be repeated zero or an undefined number of times.

Examples of composition definition using relational operators are as follows for the data items CLASS LIST and PAYMENT:

CLASS LIST = {NAME}

NAME = (INITIAL) + FIRST NAME + LAST NAME

FIRST NAME = 1{ALPHABETIC CHARACTER}10

LAST NAME = 1{ALPHABETIC CHARACTER}30

$$\text{PAYMENT} = \left[\begin{array}{l} \text{``CASH''} \\ \text{``PERSONAL CHECK'' *WITH APPROVAL*} \\ \text{``CREDIT CARD''} \end{array} \right]$$

or

PAYMENT = [``CASH''|``PERSONAL CHECK''|``CREDIT CARD'']

As shown above CLASS LIST consists of NAME. Each NAME has an optional INITIAL, a FIRST NAME and a LAST NAME. FIRST NAME has one to ten letters, and LAST NAME has one to 30 letters. PAYMENT can be in terms of

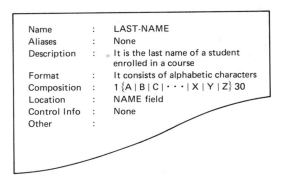

Figure 11.1   DD example

CASH or PERSONAL CHECK or CREDIT CARD. An example of DD is given
in Figure 11.1.

11.1.4 Commercially Available Data Dictionary/Directories

DD/Ds are frequently used in combination with DBMSs. As stated earlier,
this is not necessary and there are numerous DD/D users who still have no DBMS.
Also there are a number of independent DD/D systems developed by specialized
software houses. Some of the commercially available DD/D systems include Control 2000 of MRI Systems, Data Catalogue of Synergetics, Data Dictionary of
Cincom, Datamanager of MSP Inc., DB/DC Dictionary of IBM, Dictionary 204
of Computer Corporation of America, IDMS Dictionary of Cullinane, Lexicon of
Arthur Anderson, and UCC TEN of University Computing Co. (Scl 77, Se 80).

11.2 STRUCTURED ENGLISH

Structured English (SE) is a very limited, highly restricted subset of the natural
language English. In a way SE resembles a programming language and it is an
efficient tool to describe an algorithm. It is quite similar to pseudocode that will
be discussed next. Because of this similarity SE and pseudocode are often mixed.
SE is a better tool to express an algorithm if the main concern is *user* communication. Pseudocode, however, is a better tool if the concern is *programmer* communication. Neither tool is efficient, however, if the algorithm to be expressed has
many decisions. A flow chart, decision table, or decision tree may be a better tool
in such a case. SE's intermediary position is shown illustratively in Figure 11.2
(Yo 81).

Although variations abound and there is not yet a standard SE, the major
characteristics of this tool may be summarized as:

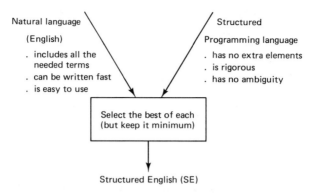

Figure 11.2   A definition of structured English

Limited format for expression.   Simple imperative sentences and/or algebraic expressions are used. Examples of simple imperative sentences are:

Read Master-File.

Multiply Hrs by Wage to get Gross-Pay.

Limited volume of vocabulary.   Sentence objects must be defined in the DD (Data Dictionary), and certain reserved words should be used for logic formulation. For naming the sentence object, a COBOL-like notation may be used.

Limited number of building blocks.   Sequence, selection, and iteration are the basic structures used to put sentences into blocks.

Sequence.   Sequence structure is a sequential collection of imperative sentences, as the following series indicates:

Read First-Record.

Initialize District-Fields.

Add 1 to Counter.

For long algorithms, grouping of some statements into a named block and treatment of such a block as a single statement may be practical. For example, define all individual statements needed to prepare total sales as a block named Total-Sales and reference this block by a single statement:

Perform Total-Sales.

Selection.   For selection (or decision) logic, an if-then-else structure is used, and indentation makes its logic clearer. An example of logic that updates a master file may be expressed as:

```
if Trans-Type = "CHANGE"

    then modify New-Record
    get  Next-Transaction
    else if Trans-Type = "DELETE"

            then delete New-Record

            get Next-Transaction

            else print Error-Msg

            get Next-Transaction.
```

The general form of this structure may be expressed as

```
if <condition>
    then block-1
    else block-2.
```

Iteration.   Iteration (or repetition) logic defines a block (or group of SE statements) that is executed repeatedly until a termination condition is satisfied.

There are two general forms for expressing iteration logic:

```
1. For each <item>
       block-1.


2. Perform until <condition>
       block-2.
```

The following examples demonstrate these forms:

```
1. For each Record
       Process-Record


2. Perform until End-of-File
       Process-Record
       get Next-Record
```

Process-Record in these examples is a block consisting of operations defined elsewhere in the SE statements.

SE is flexible in notation and may consist of various styles. Some of these styles, in addition to the "common style" given above are summarized as follows. The process is group totals of branch office sales for a company.

Common style

```
Print Corporate-Heading
Initialize Corporate-Total
For each Branch
        Print Branch-Heading
        Calculate Yearly-Sales
        Find Max-Sale
            Max-Sale-Val = Sales-Val (1)
            For each Month
                if Sales-Val(Month-No) > Max-Sale-Val
                    then Max-Sale-Val = Sales-Val(Month-No)
        Print Branch-Results
        Add Yearly-Sales to Corporate-Total
Print Corporate-Total
```

Here it is assumed that monthly sales values for branch offices are available. Maximum monthly sales value is computed in a loop checking the monthly sales. The yearly sales total and the maximum monthly sales value for each branch office are computed and printed in an outer loop.

Code style (capitalized common style)

```
        PRINT CORPORATE-HEADING
        INITIALIZE CORPORATE-TOTAL
        FOR EACH BRANCH
            PRINT BRANCH-HEADING
            CALCULATE YEARLY-SALES
                .
                .
                .
```

Outline style (numbered common style)

```
1. Print Corporate-Heading

2. Initialize Corporate-Total

3. For each Branch
   3.1 Print Branch-Heading
   3.2 Calculate Yearly-Sales

   3.3 Find Max-Sale

       3.3.1 Max-Sale-Val = Sales-Val (1)

       3.3.2 For each Month

               if Sales-Val (Month-No) > Max-Sale-Val

                   then Max-Sale-Val = Sales-Val (Month-No)

   3.4 Print Branch-Results

   3.5 Add Yearly-Sales to Corporate-Total

4. Print Corporate-Total
```

Narrative style

```
First print Branch-Heading and then initialize Corporate-Total value.

Next, considering each Branch separately, do the following operations:

Calculate Yearly-Sales, find Max-Sale, print Branch-Results, Add Yearly-
Sales to Corporate-Total. At the end, print Corporate-Heading and
Corporate-Total.
```

11.3 PSEUDOCODE

Pseudocode is an alternative to Structured English and it is similar to such programming codes as COBOL, PL/1, FORTRAN, or Pascal. It is therefore easy for programmers to use and to understand but is not suitable for nonprogrammers.

When SE is used, some details such as opening or closing files, initializing counters, or setting flags are usually not included. With pseudocode they are included. However, the pseudocode user is not concerned with a number of language-dependent details such as the difference between real and integer numbers in FORTRAN or DCL statements in PL/1 or the distinction between subscripts and indexes for table manipulation in COBOL, that is, the definition of data in any language.

Like SE, there is not a standard, universal pseudocode; various versions exist. In any pseudocode version, however, the three basic structures, namely sequence, selection, and iteration, are often included.

Sequence.   Sequence is a collection of various statements. Input/Output instructions are explicitly defined in pseudocode; that is, such statements as

Read data from source

and

Write data to destination

can be specified. It is also possible to group and name a number of pseudocode statements and treat them as a single block using the perform verb.

Selection.   The general form of a selection or decision pseudocode block may be written as

```
If <condition>
    then perform block-1
    else perform block-2
Endif
```

Thus a selection block begins with an *If* and ends with *Endif*.

The CASE structure is a common tool that is used if a problem involves a selection from among several alternative paths. Its general form is:

```
Selected variable
          CASE (value-1)   block-1
          CASE (value-2)   block-2
                    .
                    .
                    .
          DEFAULT CASE      block-n
Endselect
```

Iteration.   In pseudocode, one is more concerned with the various forms of repetitive logic than SE. The basic idea of repetitive logic is that a block is executed repeatedly until a termination condition is satisfied. There are three forms for repetition logic in pseudocode:

Do while structure: This is the commonly used structure for iteration. Its general form is

```
While <condition> do
          perform block
Endwhile
```

As is evident, While and Endwhile delimit the block.

Repeat until structure: Another structure for repetition logic is known as the repeat until structure. Its general form is

```
Repeat
        Perform block
Until   <condition>.
```

Do structure: Sometimes repetition logic in pseudocode is expressed similar to FORTRAN and PL/I. The general form is

```
Do index = initial to limit
        Perform block
Enddo
```

Again, please note the indentation and placement of *Enddo* statements. Statements within a block are indented and *Enddo* aligns with *Do*.

SUMMARY

The most commonly used nongraphical tools for information systems development are the Data Dictionary/Directory (DD/D), Structured English (SE), and pseudocode.

A data dictionary is a collection of information about naming, classification, representation or structure, usage, and administration of data. It is also referred to as "data about data" or metadata. Various DD/D software packages are commercially available. Use of such a system in the analysis phase improves communication among systems analysts, users, and management. A DD/D system clarifies the flow and content of data items through the information system during the design phase. A data item in a DD may be an element or a group. A set of relational operators is used to define the composition of group data.

Pseudocode is an alternative for SE. Pseudocode is similar to a programming code and therefore it is a preferable communication tool between systems analysts and programmers. Like SE, pseudocode has no universal standard; various versions exist. In any pseudocode version, however, the three basic structures—namely sequence, selection, and iteration—are often included.

EXERCISES

1. What are nongraphical tools in information systems development?
2. What is a DD/D?
3. What are the objectives of DD/D during an information system development process?
4. What is an element data item?
5. How would you define the composition of a group data item?
6. State any three of the relational operators that are used in DD composition definition.
7. What is the meaning of the following composition definition? CUSTOMER-NAME = 1{(TITLE) + FIRST-NAME + LAST-NAME} 50
8. Prepare a DD description for an employee record which consists of ID No., Social Security No., Name, Department, Position, and Starting Date.
9. Using Structured English first and then pseudocode, describe a module to calculate state sales tax charges for a customer's total purchases.

SELECTED REFERENCES

(BCS 77)   The British Computer Society. *Data Dictionary Systems Working Party Report.* DDSWPR, March 1977.

(Ca 78)   Canning, R. G. "Installing a Data Dictionary," *EDP Analyzer*, Vol. 16, No. 1 (January 1978).

(Ca 81)   Canning, R. G. "A New View of Data Dictionaries," *EDP Analyzer*, Vol. 19, No. 7 (July 1981).

(DeM 78)   DeMarco, T. *Structured Analysis and Systems Specification.* Yourdon Press, 1978.

(KL 83)   Kahn, B. K., and E. W. Lumsden. "A User-Oriented Framework for Data Dictionary Systems," *DataBase*, Fall 1983, 28–36.

(Kr 81)   Kreitzer, L. W. "Data Dictionaries—The Heart of IRM," *Infosystems*, No. 2 (1981), 64–66.

(Pes 80)   Peters, L. J. *Software Design*. Yourdon Press, 1981.

(Scl 77)   Schussel, G. "The Role of the Data Dictionary," *Datamation*, Vol. 23, No. 6 (June 1977), 129–42.

(Se 80)   Semprevivo, P. *Using Data Dictionary/Directories*. Auerbach Publishers Inc., Portfolio No: 32-04-09, 1980.

(Yo 81)   Yourdon, Inc. *Structured Analysis/Design Workshop*, Edition 7.2, July 1981.

Chapter 12

Evaluation and Refinement of Qualities of a System Design

12.1 GENERAL

As noted before in early chapters, the major concern of a structured system is that it is "modular." In other words, it should be partitioned into separately named and addressable elements or components that are integrated to meet the system requirements. Each of these elements is called a module and, depending on their level in the system, they may be defined as subordinate or superordinate modules. Analogous to the structure of business or military organizations, a modular system should also have a "hierarchy" to identify the top-level modules in charge of controlling activities and related decision-making processes and the low-level modules in charge of detailed operations. "Module independence" is another important property in addition to modularity and hierarchy of a structured information system. System development, testing, and maintenance are simplified if the modules of a system are independent or relatively so. There is a close relationship between module independence on the one hand and modularity and hierarchy on the other; in fact, one may state that module independence is a critical factor in an information system design activity.

The modularity concept in systems design is a result of the classical "divide and conquer" logic. Yet, one also feels that after a certain number of modules—that is, the number of divisions—the integration of the modules of the system becomes more difficult. Hence there should be an optimum number of modules for any system being designed. A system with a relatively small number of modules is termed "undermodular," and a system with an excessive number of modules is called "over-modular." Unfortunately, we have no formula to determine that optimum number and we are forced to use our own intuition or experience. Even if one had that number, it is not enough to finalize a design. Assume a system with five modules, m_1, m_2, . . . , m_5, to be designed. Consider three design alternatives A_1, A_2, A_3 as shown in Figure 12.1. The figure illustrates only three of the many possible configuration alternatives using five modules. A system designer must pick only one of them. Obviously then, not only the number of modules in the sytem, but also their communications and hierarchical relations should be considered in finalizing an information system design. Fortunately, there are some qualitative tools to be used as guidelines to evaluate and refine the properties of an information system design and to compare the overall system with alternatives.

Two such tools, *coupling* and *cohesion*, are used to measure module independence within the system. Considering the vital function of module independence in an information system design—and hence in information system development—one may realize the significance of coupling and cohesion. Coupling is a measure of the relative interdependence among two or more modules. Cohesion (or strength or binding) measures the degree that each module of an information system performs a single, problem-related function. In other words, it indicates the relative functional strength of a module in a system. The function of a module is a description of the input to output transformation that occurs when the module is called. The function is related not only to the operations performed in that module, but also to the functions of any modules called by that module.

Although modularity, hierarchy, module independence, and coupling-cohesion measures are the key points in information system design activities, there

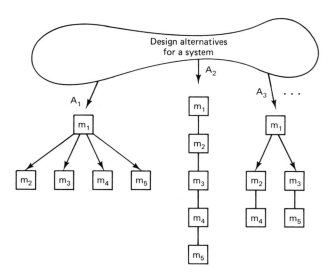

Figure 12.1   Design alternatives for a system

are some additional guidelines that one can use to evaluate and refine the qualities
of an information system design. Some of these guidelines are given here:

- Factoring and module size
- Information hiding
- Decision splitting
- System shape or system morphology
- Error reporting
- Editing
- Restrictivity/generality
- Fan-in/fan-out

The following are used for the evaluation of

a. an individual module

- its size
- fan-in/fan-out
- its cohesion level
- its information-hiding property
- its restrictivity/generality

b. a group of modules

- coupling
- factoring
- decision splitting
- error reporting
- editing

The systems design is refined by

- factoring
- combining
- rearranging

As we shall see in the following chapters, various methodologies are available for information systems development. Because these methodologies are based
on different approaches, the resulting system design alternatives will be different
for the same set of information systems requirements. The guidelines we have
listed are used to evaluate and refine the qualities of the resulting information

systems design alternatives. In the following sections we discuss these guidelines in greater detail before we go on to individual systems development methodologies. Remember that the design phase is really the crux of the whole information system development efforts.

12.2 COUPLING

Quite often coupling and cohesion concepts are presented by means of structure charts. Clearly, the use of data couples and control couples will simplify the explanation of these concepts. It is, however, incorrect to consider coupling and cohesion only in relation to structure charts. They are general concepts that are applicable to any modular system.

As noted earlier, coupling is a measure of the degree of interdependence among the modules of a system. Modularization of a system will minimize coupling and in turn facilitate understanding of how individual modules function and lessen the "ripple effect" in the system during maintenance. If some modules are highly coupled, one needs an overview of the functioning of all, even if only one is needed for maintenance purposes; and, of course, a change in one module is bound to have some effects on modules coupled to it. One may, therefore, conclude that a minimum degree of coupling between the modules of a system will result in a well-designed, better functioning system.

Data coupling, stamp coupling, control coupling, common coupling, and content coupling are coupling types. Any two modules of a system have *data coupling* if necessary data is communicated between them. The data may be a single data item or an element of an array. Data that is communicated between modules without any use is called "tramp data" and should be avoided.

Two modules of a system are said to be *stamp coupled* if they communicate a group of related data items such as a record consisting of various fields or an array consisting of elements. Obviously any change either in format or structure of a field in a record or an element in an array will have an effect on the modules that use that record and/or array. Not all but only some fields of a record or some elements of an array may be needed in a module. Still, the whole record and/or array will be communicated. Thus stamp coupling tends to expose a module to more data items than it needs. This may not always be desirable because of the high probability of error and the inefficiency of the system. Another potential problem for stamp coupling is "bundling." Bundling involves collecting fairly unrelated data and/or control into an artificial data structure. Because bundling increases the difficulty of understanding the functioning of modules, it should not be used in a structured system.

Two modules of a system are *control coupled* if one of the modules communicates a piece of information, usually a flag, intended to control the internal logic of the other module. Two types of flags are the descriptive flag and the control flag. A descriptive flag has an adjective (e.g., "code is alphabetic" or "new customer data is at the end"). A control flag, on the other hand, has a verb such as "initialize counters," or "delete customer record."

Two or more modules of a modular system are *common coupled* if they share data that is held in a common area. Here the word *common* is used in the same sense as COMMON in FORTRAN or as global variables in PL/I, and similar to the way the REDEFINES clause is used in Data Division of COBOL. Such a coupling obscures the functioning of modules and, therefore makes maintenance more difficult. Also, an error or change in a module using the common data area may be transmitted to other modules, and thus common coupling should be avoided whenever possible.

The worst type of coupling between any two modules is called *content coupling*. To express its undesirable properties, such coupling is sometimes referred to as "pathological or sick coupling." Such a coupling will occur if a module refers to or modifies data contained inside another module without communicating with that module, if it alters a statement in another module, or if it branches or falls through into another.

If two modules have more than one type of coupling, it is the lower level type that will affect the system. In practice, it is not needed to determine the precise level of coupling. Rather, it is important to minimize the coupling so that module independence is increased.

The coupling types, their relative levels, degrees, and qualities are summarized in Table 12.1.

The table indicates that any two modules of a modular system may have (1) no direct coupling or (2) any coupling ranging from data coupling to content coupling. It is impossible to have a system in which all modules have no coupling. The objective is to minimize the coupling level of modules. Level values in Table 12.1 are given only to indicate relative values; they should not be used for any numerical operations.

TABLE 12.1   Coupling Types

Coupling Type	Level	Degree	Quality
no direct coupling	0	low	best
data coupling	1		
stamp coupling	2		
control coupling	3		
common coupling	4		
content coupling (or pathological coupling)	5	high	worst

12.3 COHESION

Cohesion, module strength, and binding are all terms signifying one method of evaluating a system design. As defined earlier, cohesion is a measure of the degree by which each module carries out a single, problem-related, and well-understood function. If a module reaches that objective, it is defined as "conceptually whole" or as "functionally cohesive." Ideally we would like to have functionally cohesive modules. There are modules, however, that perform not a single function but a group of functions. Such modules are defined as "fragmented modules." Depending on the degree of fragmentation, that is, on the strength of association of elements within a module, one may define different types of cohesion for such modules.

There is a close relationship between coupling (that is, what goes on between modules) and cohesion (that is, what goes on inside individual modules). A system with highly cohesive modules will have low coupling, a much desired objective in systems design.

Stevens-Myers-Constantine (SMC 74) and Yourdon (Yo 81) have developed a scale of cohesion given as Table 12.2 which also includes a maintainability range.

In the literature, functional cohesion is also referred to as "external cohesion"; the remaining six cohesion types are grouped together as "internal cohesion." The six levels of internal cohesion may be further grouped as:

Data-Oriented Cohesion Types

- Sequential
- Communicational

A module has *sequential cohesion* if its elements are involved in a sequence of activities such that result or output of an activity is an input to the next activity of that module. Such a module is easily maintainable.

A module is said to have *communicational cohesion* if its elements contribute to activities that use the same data item as an input. Such a module is quite maintainable.

Sequential and communicational cohesion types are quite similar. The main difference between them is that order of execution is unimportant for communi-

TABLE 12.2   Scale of Cohesion

Cohesion Type			Level of Cohesion	Ordinal Values	Maintainability
External Cohesion	Functional		1	10	Best
Internal Cohesion	Sequential	Data	2	9	
	Communicational	Oriented	3	7	
	Procedural	Time	4	5	
	Temporal	Oriented	5	3	
	Logical	Suite	6	1	
	Coincidental	Oriented	7	0	Worst

cationally cohesive modules, whereas the sequential type demands a certain pattern of execution.

Time-oriented cohesion types

- Procedural
- Temporal

Modules which have *procedural cohesion* and *temporal cohesion* are called time-oriented cohesive modules. In a procedurally cohesive module, control flows from one activity to the next, and activities within the module may be different and have little relationship among them.

A module has temporal cohesion if its elements are involved in activities of different groups that are related only in time, such as an initialization module in which rewind tape, set counter, clear table, and set switch operations are performed. Similar to the difference between sequential and communicational cohesion, the order of execution of activities is more important in procedurally cohesive modules than in temporally cohesive modules.

Suite-oriented cohesion types

- Logical
- Coincidental

Modules with *logical* and *coincidental cohesion* are said to have suite-oriented cohesion. Such modules are highly dependent on other modules for their activities and decisions.

A module has logical cohesion if its elements are not related by flow of data or by flow of control, but related only to tasks of the same general category. Finally, a module has coincidental cohesion if its elements have no meaningful relation at all.

Quite often it is difficult to determine the exact level of cohesion of a module. However, this is unnecessary since the main objective is to design systems with highly cohesive modules.

12.4 ADDITIONAL DESIGN GUIDELINES

As stated earlier, we need some further guidelines in addition to coupling and cohesion to design better systems. In the following these guidelines are briefly discussed (e.g., Jo 80, Pes 81, Pr 82, and YC 79):

Factoring and module size.   Factoring is also known as decomposition, partitioning, or explosion. It is the separation of a function in one module into a new module of its own. The objectives in factoring are to reduce module size, to simplify development and implementation of individual modules, and to improve the coupling/cohesion property of modules.

Information hiding.   The principle of information hiding proposed by Parnas (Pas 72) suggests that modules should be specified and designed so that information within a module is inaccessible to other modules that have no need for such information. The practice provides benefits during the testing and maintenance of individual modules.

Decision splitting.   In general, recognition of what action to take and execution of that action are the two parts of a decision. A decision split occurs if the two parts of a decision are separated and placed into two different modules. Decision splits should be avoided as much as possible.

System shape or system morphology.   Major features of system shape are depth, width, and overall morphology (Figure 12.2). Depth of a system is defined as the number of levels in the hierarchy. Width is the maximum number of modules at any level of the system under consideration. For the overall morphology of a system, Yourdon and Constantine report that most well-designed systems have a shape that could be likened to a cigar, a flying saucer, or a mosque (YC 79, p. 157).

Error reporting.   As a general rule, errors should be reported by the module which detects the error and determines its type.

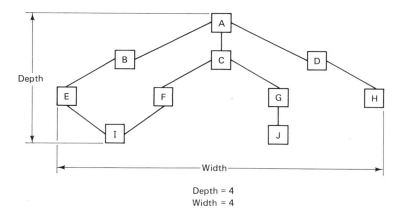

Depth = 4
Width = 4

Figure 12.2   System shape

Editing.   Editing of a piece of input data should be done in the following order (Jo 80):

- Edit known before unknown. If a person entering a field realizes that a mistake has been made, give the person a chance either to correct it or to cancel the entry.
- Edit syntactic before semantic. Check the data's format before checking its sense. For example, UT + H would be syntactically incorrect, whereas UT × H would be syntactially correct, but semantically incorrect for UTAH.
- Perform single editing before cross-editing. Cross-validate only those fields that are individually correct.
- Edit internal before external. Make sure that you verify the syntax and semantics of all the fields of a given record before trying to use that record in something else.

Restrictivity/generality.   A module of a system should not be neither too restrictive nor too general. As stated in Jones (Jo 80), a restrictive module has one or more of the following characteristics:

- It performs a needlessly specific job.
- It deals with restrictive data values, types, or structures.
- It makes assumptions about where or how it's being used.

An overgeneral module has one or more of the following characteristics:

- It performs a very broad job.
- It deals with too many data types, values, or structures.
- It reads in, or takes as a parameter, data that is unlikely to change.

Fan-in/fan-out.   Fan-in of a module is the number of modules that call it. Fan-out or span of control, is the number of direct subordinates to a module. As a general rule, fan-in of modules should be as high as possible (i.e., reusable modules) and fan-out of modules should not be more than 7 ± 2. Figure 12.3 has an example of fan-in and fan-out.

Fan-in = 3   Fan-out = 4   **Figure 12.3**   Fan-in/fan-out of modules

12.5 EXAMPLES

Consider the system described by the structure chart given in Figure 12.4. The modules of the system and their functions are as follows:

MAIN   : sends a control couple (FLAG-1) to INPUT-DATA module and another control couple (FLAG-2) to EDIT-DATA module; gets edited input record (ED-REC), passes it to PROCESS module; gets data items RESULTS from PROCESS module and passes it to FORMAT module; it receives formatted RESULTS data items, FMT-RESULTS, from FORMAT module;

INPUT-DATA   : gets input record (IN-REC), passes it to the editing module (EDIT-DATA);

PROCESS   : gets edited input record (ED-REC), processes it, and yields RESULTS data items;

FORMAT   : gets RESULTS data items and puts them into a proper format to yield formatted results (FM-RESULTS);

GET-DATA   : sends input record (IN-REC) to the calling module (INPUT-DATA);

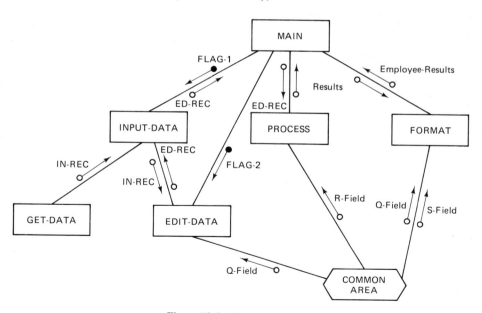

Figure 12.4 A sample system

EDIT-DATA   :   gets input record (IN-REC), edits it, and passes the
                      edited record (ED-REC) back to the calling module (IN-
                      PUT-DATA).

The coupling characteristics of the modules of the system described in Figure 12.4
may be summarized in tabular form as Table 12.3.

TABLE 12.3   Coupling Characteristics of the Sample System

Module	Module	Coupling Type	Communicated Item(s)
MAIN	INPUT-DATA	control coupling	control couple (FLAG-1)
MAIN	PROCESS	stamp coupling	record
MAIN	FORMAT	data coupling	data item (field)
MAIN	GET-DATA	—	no direct coupling
MAIN	EDIT-DATA	content coupling	control transfer into another module
INPUT-DATA	GET-DATA	stamp coupling	record
INPUT-DATA	EDIT-DATA	stamp coupling	record
INPUT-DATA	PROCESS	—	no direct coupling
INPUT-DATA	FORMAT	—	no direct coupling
PROCESS	GET-DATA	—	no direct coupling
PROCESS	EDIT-DATA	common coupling	common data items
PROCESS	FORMAT	common coupling	common data items
FORMAT	GET-DATA	—	no direct coupling
FORMAT	EDIT-DATA	common coupling	common data items

TABLE 12.4   Cohesion Types of Various Sample Modules

Sample Module Name	Function	Cohesion Type
A	gets transactions, edits them, returns them	sequential
B	using employee number, it determines employee name, determines employee address, determines employee position, and returns name, address, and position	communicational
C	performs initialization, reads data file, edits, writes, and closes the file	procedural
D	daily activities such as getting up, having breakfast, driving to the office, doing the daily chores, and returning home	temporal
E	drink tea, drink coffee, drink coke, drink water	logical
F	study, go to concert, visit friends and relatives, paint car, read paper, play tennis, and eat lunch	coincidental

Recall that module cohesion (or strength) can be classified as data-oriented cohesion (sequential or communicational cohesion), time-oriented cohesion (procedural or temporal cohesion), and suite-oriented cohesion (logical or coincidental cohesion). Some sample modules, named A thru F, are tabulated as Table 12.4 to describe their functions and specify their cohesion types accordingly.

SUMMARY

Modularity and hierarchy are two major characteristics of a structured system. In addition to them, module independence is another property that a structured system must have. In finalizing an information system design, the optimum number of modules, their communications, and hierarchical relations with the system should be considered. There are some qualitative tools available to evaluate and refine the properties of an information system design and to compare it with other system alternatives. Coupling and cohesion are two such tools.

Coupling is a measure of the degree of interdependence among the modules of a system. It should be minimized in order to facilitate understanding how individual modules function and to minimize the "ripple effect" during system maintenance. There are various coupling types; data coupling is the most desired and content coupling (or pathological coupling) is the least desired. In practice, it is not necessary to determine the precise level of coupling. Rather, it is important to try keeping the coupling at a minimal level so that module independence is increased.

Cohesion is a measure of the degree that each module carries out a single, problem-related, and well-understood function. Module strength and binding are other terms that are used for cohesion. There are various types of cohesion; functional and sequential cohesion types are the best, and coincidental cohesion is the worst for maintainability of modules of a system.

Factoring and module size, information hiding, decision splitting, system shape (or morphology), error reporting, editing, restrictivity/generality, and fan-in/fan-out are some of the guidelines that are used as tools to improve an information systems design.

EXERCISES

1. What is the modularity of a system?
2. What are the three major properties of a structured system?
3. What is coupling?
4. What is cohesion?
5. What is the relationship between coupling and cohesion?
6. What are the guidelines to be used to evaluate a module?
7. What are the guidelines to be used to evaluate a group of modules?

8. What are the guidelines to be used for refining a systems design?

9. State the coupling types.

10. What is tramp data?

11. What is bundling?

12. State the cohesion types.

13. Take an available program which has at least four modules. Determine the type of cohesion of each module and the type of coupling of each pair of modules. Use a table to show the type of coupling between the modules. (A module in PL/I is a procedure; it is a subroutine or function subprogram in FORTRAN. In COBOL, program, subprogram, section, and paragraph are examples of modules.)

14. The following modules perform the activities described by the short sentences. Determine the type of cohesion of these modules: G-PAY : Edit time record, get payroll master, and calculate gross pay. WRITE : Write by pen, write by ball-point, write by pencil.

15. Considering the structure chart given as Figure 8.3 in Chapter 8, define the coupling characteristics of modules in a tabular form.

16. Refering to the modules of Figure 12.4, define their cohesion types.

SELECTED REFERENCES

(Jo 80)   Jones, M. P. *The Practical Guide to Structured Systems Design.* Yourdon Press, 1980.

(Pas 72)   Parnas, D. L. ''On the Criteria Used in Decomposing Systems into Modules,'' *Comm. of the ACM*, Vol. 15, No. 12 (1972), 1053–58.

(Pes 81)   Peters, L. J. Software Design. Yourdon Press, 1981.

(Pr 82)   Pressman, R. *Software Engineering*. McGraw Hill, 1982.

(SMC 74)   Stevens, W. P., G. J. Myers, and L. L. Constantine. ''Structured Design,'' *IBM Systems Journal*, Vol. 13, No. 2 (1974), 115–39.

(Yo 81)   Yourdon, Inc. *Structured Analysis/Design Workshop Notes*, 1981.

(YC 79)   Yourdon, E., and L. L. Constantine. *Structured Design*. Prentice-Hall, 1979.

Chapter 13

An Overview of Information Systems Development Methodologies

13.1 A REVIEW OF TERMINOLOGY

As we noted in Section 4.1, algorithm, method, methodology, and strategy are key terms relevant to information systems development efforts.

A dictionary (Web 75) definition of the term *algorithm* is a step-by-step procedure for solving a problem. *Method* is defined as a systematic way, technique, or process of or for doing something; a body of skills and techniques. A body of methods, procedures, working concepts, rules and postulates employed by a science, art, or discipline is known as *methodology*. Finally, *strategy* is defined as the art of devising or employing plans toward a goal.

Although there is no clear distinction between these terms and they are often used interchangeably in the literature (e.g., BG 80, Go 79, Par 78), we would like to use the terms *methodology* and *strategy* synonymously, as well as the terms *method* and *algorithm*.

In engineering if one follows a method (or algorithm) carefully, he/she will surely end up with the correct solution. If, however, one follows a methodology (or strategy), chances of getting one of the possible correct solutions is high, although there is no guarantee for it. Having made this distinction between a method and a methodology, we can now make the following statement: There is not yet a unique, standard method available to be used universally for a successful information systems development; all we have are various methodologies. This clearly indicates that the success of an information systems development process still depends on the skills, experience, and understanding of the systems analyst even if he/she follows an available methodology for information systems development.

13.2 CLASSIFICATION OF AVAILABLE METHODOLOGIES

Almost all of the methodologies that we will be considering have been proposed for the systems design phase of an information systems life cycle. Most of them, however, are also used during the analysis phase of the process. For this reason we will make no distinction between phases in considering and classifying available methodologies. We may need to do so later during the presentation of individual methodologies, however.

The available methodologies for information systems development can be classified into three groups: (1) functional decomposition methodologies, (2) data-oriented methodologies, and (3) prescriptive methodologies. They are further decomposed as follows:

I. Functional Decomposition Methodologies
  1. Top-down approach
  2. Bottom-up approach
  3. HIPO
  4. Stepwise refinement approach
  5. Information-hiding approach
II. Data-Oriented Methodologies
  1. Data Flow Oriented Methodologies
     a. SADT
     b. Composite Design
     c. Structured Design
  2. Data Structure Oriented Methodologies
     a. Jackson's Methodology
     b. Warnier/Orr Methodology
III. Prescriptive Methodologies
  1. Chapin's approach
  2. Design by Objectives (DBO)
  3. Problem Analysis Diagram (PAD)
  4. Problem Statement Language (PSL)/Problem Statement Analysis (PSA)
  5. Others

Functional decomposition methodologies emphasize the relevant dissection of a system into smaller subsystems such that the resulting elementary systems are not so complex to understand, design, and implement. System functions are considered the major concern—therefore, the name ''functional approach.'' The most common examples of functional decomposition methodologies are top-down and bottom-up approaches.

Data-oriented methodologies mainly emphasize the characteristics of the data to be processed. Data flow oriented methodologies and data structure oriented methodologies are two different types of methodologies within that category. Data flow oriented methodologies are generally based on decomposition of a system into modules by considering the type of data elements and their logical behavior within the system. The logical organization of the system is based on the data flow logic and functional relationships between the modules of the system. Data structure oriented methodologies mainly emphasize the output/input data structures of the system. These structures form a base for the structure of the system. The functional relations between the modules or elements of the system and their decompositions are then realized in terms of the system structure.

Prescriptive methodologies are generally computerized procedures to help system development efforts, especially during software system development. The major objective of such a methodology is to free analysts from the detailed technicalities of program design by providing them with a prescriptive approach to analyze the system specifications and to generate the needed software.

In the following chapters these three groups of methodologies are discussed and specific references are cited. The following are some of the general references for the available methodologies: Bergland and Gordon (BG 80), Brookes et al. (BGJL 82), Davis (DaW 83), Freeman and Wasserman (FW 80), Gilbert (Gi 83), Gomaa (Go 79), Griffiths (Gr 78), Leathrum (Lea 83), Parker (Par 78), Peters (Pes 81), Peters and Tripp (PT 78), Pressman (Pr 82), Richardson et al. (RBT 80), Riddle and Fairley (RF 80), Weinberg (Wei 80), and Ziegler (Zi 83).

As a final remark for the available methodologies, one may quote from Riddle and Fairley (RF 80, p. 117):

> . . . any commercial enterprise or government agency that adopts one of these methodologies will do so with a great concerted effort and will make the technique a standard throughout the organization. To do otherwise would not let the technique take hold in the organization, and would allow programmers and managers to fall back on their old methods. Once a method has been adopted by an organization and found to be beneficial, there will be extremely strong resistance to change, no matter how many faults may appear with the methodology. This situation is similar to the adoption of certain programming languages by organizations in the past and has been one of the major deterrents to acceptance of new and better languages.

SUMMARY

There is often no distinction between the terms *algorithm*, *method*, *methodology*, and *strategy*. Although the terms are often used interchangeably, one can group them into two as method (and algorithm) and methodology (and strategy). Normally if one has a method and follows it very carefully, he/she will surely end up with the correct solution. By contrast, following a methodology will most likely lead to one of the possible correct solutions, although there is no guarantee for it.

There is no one single method available to guarantee the successful development of an information system; all we have are various methodologies. This is why the success of an information systems development process still depends on the skills, experience, and understanding of the systems analyst even if he/she follows one of the available methodologies.

The available methodologies for information systems development may be classified as functional decomposition methodologies, data-oriented methodologies, and prescriptive methodologies.

EXERCISES

1. What is the basic difference between a method and a methodology?

2. How are available methodologies presently being classified?

SELECTED REFERENCES

(BG 80)   Bergland, G. D., and R. D. Gordon. *Tutorial: Software Design Strategies.* IEEE Computer Society, 1981.

(BGJL 82) Brookes, C. H. P., P. J. Grouse, D. R. Jeffery, and M. J. Lawrence. *Information Systems Design.* Prentice-Hall, 1982.

(DaW 83)   Davis, W. S. *Systems Analysis and Design.* Addison-Wesley, 1983.

(FW 80)   Freeman, P., and A. I. Wasserman. *Tutorial: Software Design Strategies.* IEEE Computer Society, 1980.

(Gi 83)   Gilbert, P. *Software Design and Development.* Science Research Associates (SRA), 1983.

(Go 79)   Gomaa, H. "A Comparison of Software Engineering Methods for System Design," *Proc. of National Electronics Conference*, Chicago, October 1979, 464–69.

(Gr 78)   Griffiths, S. N. "Design Methodologies," in *Infotech: Structured Analysis and Design*, Vol. 2, Infotech International, Ltd. Maidenhead Berkshire, UK. 1978, 133–66.

(Lea 83)   Leathrum, J. F., *Foundations of Software Design.* Reston/Prentice-Hall, 1983.

(Par 78)   Parker, J. "A Comparison of Design Methodologies," *ACM SIGSOFT*, Software Eng. Notes, Vol. 3, No. 4 (October 1978), 12–19.

(Pes 81)   Peters, L. J. *Software Design.* Yourdon Press, 1981.

(PT 78)   Peters, L. J., and L. L. Tripp. "Some Limitations of Current Design Methods," in *Infotech: Structured Analysis and Design*, Vol. 2 (1978), 249–64.

(Pr 82)   Pressman, R. *Software Engineering*. McGraw Hill, 1982.

(RBT 80)   Richardson, G. L., C. W. Butler, and J. D. Tomlinson. *Structured Program Design*. Petrocelli, 1980.

(RF 80)   Riddle, W. E., and R. E. Fairley. *Software Development Tools*. Springer Verlag, 1980.

(Web 75)   Webster's New Collegiate Dictionary, G. & C. Merriam, 1975.

(Wei 80)   Weinberg, V. *Structured Analysis*. Prentice-Hall, 1980.

(Zi 83)   Ziegler, C. A. *Programming Systems Methodologies*. Prentice-Hall, 1983.

Chapter 14

Functional Decomposition Methodologies

14.1 INTRODUCTION

As stated earlier, some of the available methodologies such as the top-down approach, the bottom-up approach, HIPO, SR (Stepwise Refinement), and information hiding are classified as *functional decomposition methodologies*. The following sections discuss these methodologies very briefly.

14.2 THE TOP-DOWN APPROACH

The top-down approach is also called "decision analysis" when it is applied to the analysis phase of the systems development life cycle; it is, however, the best known method for systems design. Some other methodologies such as HIPO and SR are special applications of the top-down approach.

In the top-down approach, the highest level decisions of the system are made first and lower level decisions are handled later. If we think of a tree of data structures, the upper branches and leaves (i.e. upper level modules) would be designed and implemented first.

14.3 THE BOTTOM-UP APPROACH

The bottom-up approach is also known as "data analysis" when it is applied to the analysis phase; it is a classical approach in systems design.

In the bottom-up approach one makes the lower level decisions first and higher level decisions are gradually handled later. Again, considering the system structure as a tree in data structures, in the bottom-up approach we design the lower leaves and branches, first.

14.4 HIPO

As we already noted in Chapter 5, HIPO (Hierarchy plus Input-Process-Output) is a documentation tool developed by IBM. Although it is primarily a documentation tool, it is sometimes referred to as a design methodology. Instead of using it as an independent methodology, HIPO is often used to document other methodologies such as composite design or structured design which are discussed later.

14.5 SR (STEPWISE REFINEMENT)

Stepwise Refinement or Iterative Stepwise Refinement (SR or ISR) assumes that an exact and constant problem statement is available and a set of available design alternatives or solutions is presented first. After selecting one of the same level solutions as optimal, we proceed to the next level alternative solutions and repeat the process. Two disadvantages are that there is no rule available when to stop the lower level refinements; also it is difficult to pick the ''best'' among the presumable equivalent solutions (e.g., Pes 81). Ledgard (Led 73) and Wirth (Wi 71) may be cited as the proper references for SR.

14.6 INFORMATION HIDING

Although information hiding is also referred to as a methodology, it is rather a guideline to be used to improve systems design, as discussed in Section 12.4. The key idea is to specify and design the modules so that the procedures and data contained within a module are not accessible to modules not directly involved with that data. The direct result of this idea is to increase the cohesion of individual modules and minimize the coupling between modules. Recall that these are the major design considerations in systems development. The fundamental concepts of information hiding were proposed by Parnas (Pas 72, Pas 79).

   As a simple example consider a family database. Access to information on the family in the DB should be limited to identifying the family wanted, then accessing information on the individual members.

SUMMARY

Typical functional decomposition methodologies are the top-down approach, the bottom-up approach, HIPO, stepwise refinement, and information hiding. In the top-down approach, the highest level decisions of the system are made first and lower level decisions are handled later. In the bottom-up approach one makes the lower level decisions first and only gradually adds the higher level decisions. In both of these approaches guidelines are lacking on how to conduct the analysis and design of a system, except for some general considerations.

HIPO, which is included as a functional decomposition methodology, is actually a documentation tool instead of a methodology. It is often used to document the top-down approach. It may also be used together with some other methodologies.

Stepwise refinement is an application of the top-down approach. Development of alternative solutions, selection of the "best" alternative, and when to stop the refinement are the major difficulties in applying this approach.

Finally, information hiding is also referred to as a design methodology. Basically, its objective is to develop systems with highly cohesive modules having low coupling between them.

EXERCISES

1. What are the examples of functional decomposition methodologies?
2. What is the basic idea in the top-down approach?
3. What is the basic idea in the bottom-up approach?
4. What are the major characteristics of HIPO?
5. What are major difficulties in applying SR?
6. What is the relationship between information hiding and cohesion/coupling?

SELECTED REFERENCES

(Led 73) Ledgard, H. "The Case for Structured Programming," *BIT*, Vol. 13 (1973) 45–47.

(Pas 72) Parnas, D. L. "On the Criteria to be Used in Decomposing Systems into Modules," *Comm. of the ACM*, Vol. 15, No. 12, (December 1972), 1053–58.

(Pas 79) Parnas, D. L. "Designing Software for Ease of Extension and Contraction," *IEEE Transactions on Software Engineering*, Vol. SE-5, No. 2 (March 1979), 128–37.

(Pes 81) Peters, L. J. *Software Design*. Yourdon Press, 1981.

(Wi 71) Wirth, N. "Program Development by Stepwise Refinement," *Comm. of the ACM*, Vol. 14, No. 4 (April 1971), 221–27.

Chapter 15

Data-Oriented Methodologies

15.1 INTRODUCTION

Data-oriented methodologies may be divided into two classes: Data Flow Oriented Methodologies and Data Structure Oriented Methodologies. SADT, Composite Design, and Structured Design are typical examples of Data Flow Oriented Methodologies; Jackson System Design and the Warnier/Orr approach are two typical examples of Data Structure Oriented Methodologies. This chapter is devoted to the discussion of these typical methodologies.

15.2 DATA FLOW ORIENTED METHODOLOGIES

15.2.1 SADT (Structured Analysis and Design Technique)

SADT is a methodology designed by D. T. Ross in the early seventies and supported and developed by SofTech Corporation since 1974. The methodology can be applied to both small and large information systems; there is, however, a relatively limited amount of published information about it (e.g., Co 80, RB 76, RDMcG 77, and Ro 80).

SADT can be applied to both the analysis and design phases of systems development; it is a diagramming technique using the graphical tools of actigrams (activity diagrams) and datagrams (data diagrams) that were presented earlier in

Chapter 8. Each of these diagrams consists of three to six rectangular boxes connected in various ways by horizontal and vertical arrows. Descriptive texts may
also be added to the diagrams. For higher level diagrams, descriptive texts may
be two to three pages and lower level diagrams should have at most one page of
descriptive texts for optimum clarity of diagrams. An example of a SADT activity
diagram is given in Figure 15.1, which illustrates major activities, data flows,
support mechanisms, and constraints of a hospital information system.

The basic concepts on which SADT is based may be summarized as follows
(Pes 81, StB 77):

1. Models are the best means for solving complex problems.
2. Analysis and general design of any information systems problem should be
   performed in a top-down, modular, hierarchic, and structured fashion.
3. The model used should be graphical to represent the whole structure, its
   elements, and their interrelationship.
4. The model should represent both happenings (or activities) and things (or
   data) of the system using two different sets of diagrams.
5. The results of analysis and general design activities must be documented for
   review, proper feedback, and future maintenance efforts.
6. A disciplined and coordinated team work should be provided in applying the
   model for analysis and general design of an information system.

The use of "reader-author cycle" in SADT provides the opportunity for
disciplined and coordinated teamwork in applying SADT methodology (Figure
15.2). The parties in the cycle are represented by circles, and the communications
between them are expressed by directed arcs.

As shown in Figure 15.2, in applying SADT methodology to develop an
information system, various people are expected to participate in development efforts. Author, commenter, reader, user, and manager are the titles of some of these
individuals. An author is the systems analyst, that is, the individual who applies
the SADT model to systems development. A commenter is another systems analyst
whose job is to review the SADT models prepared by another systems analyst and
to prepare a written comment. A reader is an individual who receives the models
for verbal comments or for information only. Users of the system being developed
are expected to review the models and submit their written comments on the
models. Managers of the cycle are the project manager and users manager(s). For
a large system, various other personnel titles may be needed as given in Peters
(Pes 81) and Connors (Co 80).

The author prepares an SADT kit—that is, a set of diagrams—and sends them
to commenters, readers, users, and managers with a cover letter. Their oral and,
in particular, written comments and suggestions for the diagrams are sent back to
the author. As the author goes over these comments and suggestions, he/she may
agree with some and make needed changes or additions, as well as reexamine
certain concepts. Sometimes he/she may need to discuss the comments with the com-

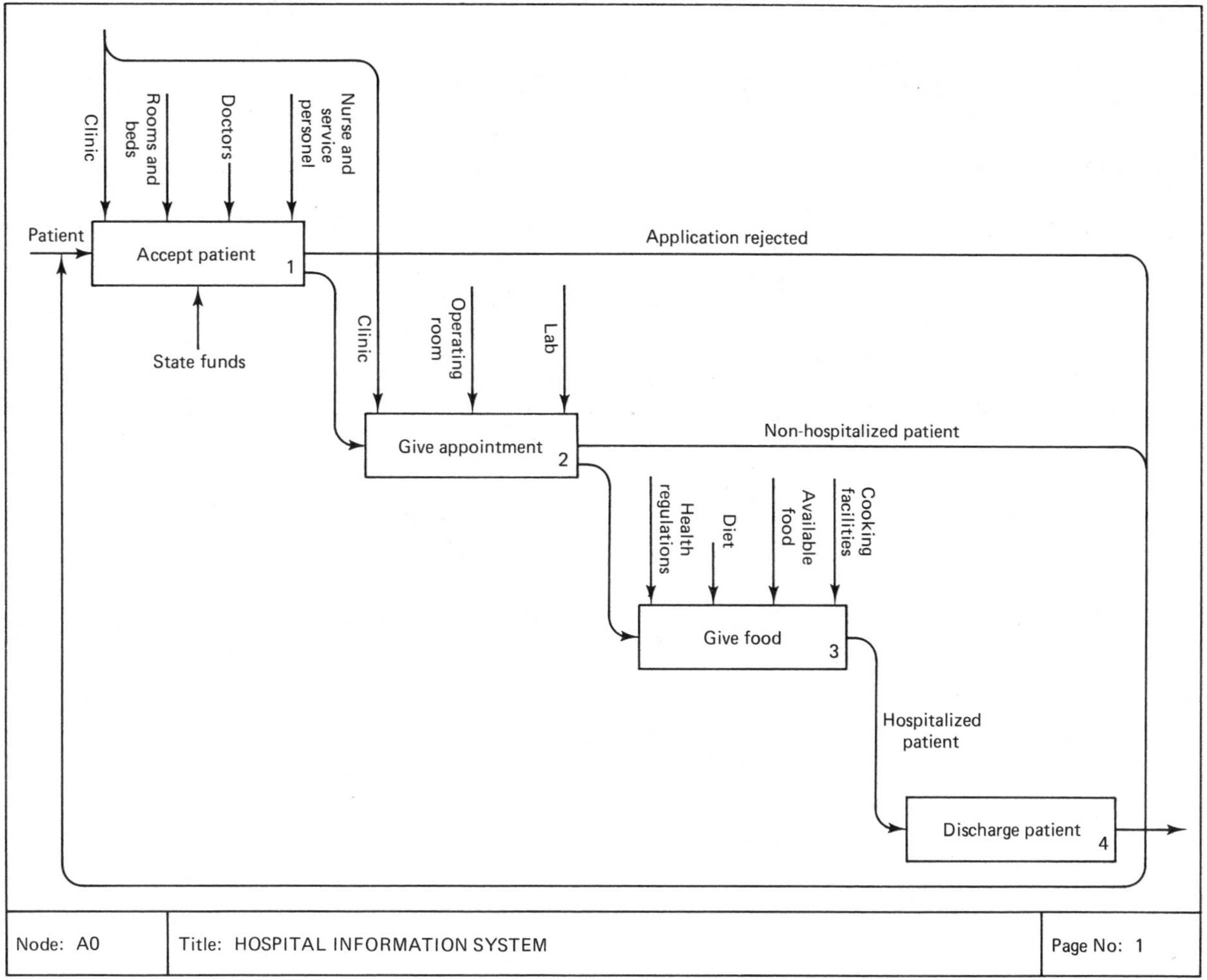

Figure 15.1 Example of an SADT activity diagram

| Node: A0 | Title: HOSPITAL INFORMATION SYSTEM | Page No: 1 |

141

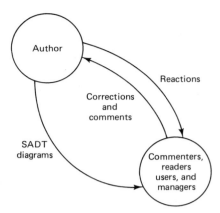

Figure 15.2 Author/reader cycle of SADT

menter, user, or manager. In case a disagreement occurs between the parties, an experienced author or a special committee called TRC (Technical Review Committee) may arbitrate. The author is supposed to prepare written reactions, corrections, and modifications after the comments and suggestions and send them back to commenters, readers, users, and managers once again for additional comments, suggestions, and constructive criticism. That cycle is repeated until the design is finalized and diagrams are put into their final form and printed.

SADT methodology may be summarized as follows: The project team starts with a top-level functional description of the system, that is, a context diagram or activity model. When the author is satisfied that the model represents an accurate view of the required system, the activity boxes of the context diagram are further decomposed at various levels. Remember that activity diagrams represent functional elements and the relevant data elements and data structures of the system. The activity model is only half the job. The author next develops the data model.

Some of the advantages of SADT are as follows:

1. It is teachable.
2. It is an excellent vehicle for communicating with users during the development process.
3. The resulting system design is very well documented as a result of earlier modeling activities.
4. Given the same specifications, most systems designers would end up with the same or similar solutions.

Some of the disadvantages of SADT, on the other hand, are:

1. It may require more time and more personnel for application, resulting in higher costs.

2. The methodology may be used only for the analysis and general (or systems) design phase of the systems development life cycle; for a detailed design, the systems analyst must use another tool or methodology.
3. The processes within the modules are not described.
4. The application of the methodology requires a certain level of skill and experience on the part of the systems analyst.

15.2.2 Composite Design

Composite Design (CD) and Structured Design (SD) were first proposed as software tools to make coding, debugging, and modification easier, faster, and less expensive by reducing complexity. These concepts were later expanded to include information systems development activities. The major ideas of Composite Design and Structured Design belonged to a few people mainly from IBM, L. L. Constantine being the major name among them. The first significant publication on the subject, authored by Stevens, Myers, and Constantine, appeared in 1974 (SMC 74). Although the concepts of Composite Design and Structured Design were quite similar, Myers publicized his approach under the name "Composite Design" (e.g., MyG 73, MyG 75). Myers pointed out the significance of modularity in software design and proposed to use module coupling and module strength (i.e., module cohesion) to obtain modularity.

15.2.3 Structured Design

Although the basic concepts of Structured Design (SD) were identical to Composite Design (CD), SD introduced some additional terminology and concepts such as "transform design" and "transaction centered design," as well as "afferent modules," "efferent modules," and "transform modules." SD also uses the term "module cohesion" for "module strength" of CD. Compared to CD, SD is much more popular and widely used for information systems development activities. There are various publications on SD (e.g., DeM 78, Dic 81, StW 81, YC 79, and Yo 81). Structured Design may be summarized simply as follows:

1. Prepare a DFD (data flow diagram) of the system.
2. Use some or all of the following to develop a structure chart of the system:
   • Transform analysis
   • Transaction analysis
   • Decomposition (factoring or top-down approach)

Thus the objective of SD is to produce a structure chart of a given system using its DFD. One may demonstrate this process in terms of DFD notation as in Figure 15.3 (Yo 81).

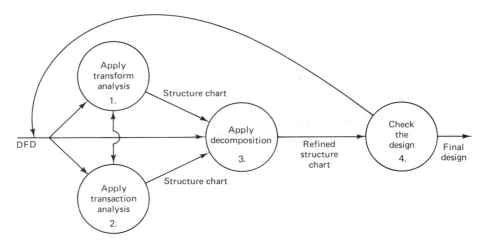

Figure 15.3   Summary of structured design methodology

The process described in Figure 15.3 should be repeated several times until a satisfactory design is obtained.

The basic steps of SD, using transform analysis and decomposition as tools, may be summarized as follows (e.g., Jo 80, Wei 80):

1. Draw a DFD of the system, as illustrated in Figure 15.4a.
2. Identify all of the major input and output data streams in the DFD.
3. Follow each input data stream until it has reached a point at which the stream can no longer be considered input. Identify each such point; the bubbles between such points and source(s) of the system are named afferent (or input) bubbles. They are included in the afferent module of the system.
4. Trace each output data stream backward until it can no longer be considered output. Identify each such point; the bubbles between such points and sink(s) of the system are named efferent (or output) bubbles. They are included in the efferent module of the system.
5. Identify the transformation bubbles (known as "central transforms") in the middle as shown in Figure 15.4b. Transformation bubbles are distinguished from afferent and efferent bubbles by being included in the central transform module.
6. Draw the top two levels of a structure chart; in Figure 15.4c, the function of modules M_C, M_A, M_T and M_E are as follows:
    - M_C is the main module and it acts as a coordinate (or control) module— one that coordinates and manages the activities of other modules.
    - M_A is the afferent module, whose major function is to transform the physical input of the system into logical input; it is therefore sometimes called an input module.

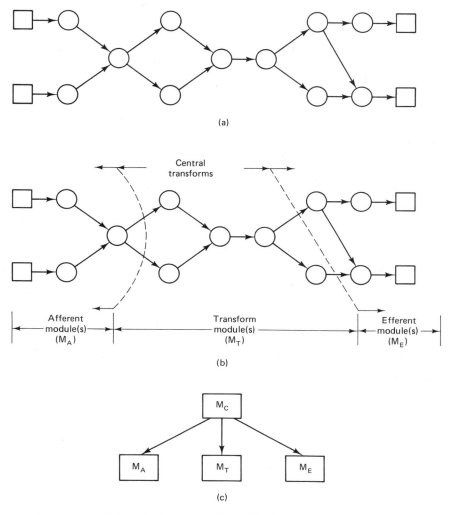

Figure 15.4 (a) A DFD of a system, (b) Identification of the central transforms, and
(c) High-level structure chart

- M_E is the efferent module, whose major function is to transform the logical
  output of a system into physical output; it is therefore sometimes called
  an output module.
- M_T is the central transform module; it transforms the logical input of a
  system into logical output.
7. Decompose the second-level modules (i.e, M_A, M_T, M_E) into their components.
8. Refine the decomposition.

An application of the transform analysis is presented in the case study in the Appendix.

Transaction (e.g., Yo 81) may be defined as a data flow that

1. comes in different "flavors"
2. contains a data element to identify the flavor
3. performs different actions depending on the flavor.

So far, we may summarize the steps of SD using transaction analysis and decomposition as tools as follows (e.g., Wei 80):

1. Draw a DFD of a system, such as the one in Figure 15.5a that shows different transactions and their processes.

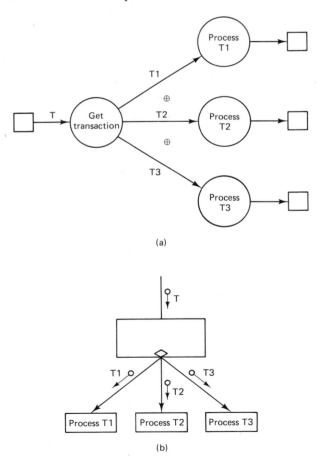

(a)

(b)

Figure 15.5   (a) A DFD of a system, (b) Structure chart

2. Identify any bubbles where an input data stream produces several mutually exclusive data streams by transaction type. Such bubbles are called "transaction centers"; some examples would be addition, deletion, or modification of existing records due to daily transactions.
3. Identify the transactions and their defining actions.
4. Draw a structure chart showing decisions and major transaction modules.
5. Decompose transaction modules.
6. Refine the decomposition.

Some of the advantages of SD are as follows:

1. There are quite a number of publications on the subject and even some companies (e.g., Yourdon Inc., in both the USA and Europe) teaching the methodology.
2. Comparison of various design alternatives is possible because of coupling and cohesion criteria.
3. Resulting structure charts are excellent tools for systems development and for user communication.
4. Although the methodology is not so easy to learn, it is relatively simpler than other available methodologies.

Some disadvantages of SD are:

1. SD does not provide the user with a tool for detail design so another tool must be used.
2. Coupling and cohesion criteria are still qualitative or subjective.
3. The methodology is not so easy to learn.
4. Various users may not end up with the same or similar design results even if they use the same system specifications.

15.3 DATA STRUCTURE ORIENTED METHODOLOGIES

As noted earlier in Chapter 13 and in Section 15.1, the most common methodologies in this group are JSD (Jackson System Development) and W/O (Warnier/Orr or LCS/SSD). Both of these methodologies are discussed in this section and applications are presented in the case study included as an Appendix.

15.3.1 Jackson System Development

Jackson first proposed his approach to software development in 1975 (Ja 75). He extended his ideas for information systems development recently (Ja 83). This subsection is a brief summary of JSD based on M. Jackson (Ja 83, Hic 85).

JSD differs from the other available information systems development methodologies in that its principles combine modelling the real world environment with modelling the functions of a system. JSD is, therefore, more appropriate for developing dynamic systems where the time dimension is a vital factor in contrast to static systems.

As we might expect, the basic terms of JSD such as entity and action have definitions related to time. An entity is defined as an object in the real world which participates in a time-oriented set of actions. An action is an event in which one or more entities participate by performing or suffering the action. The real world is described in terms of entities, actions they perform or suffer, and the orderings of those actions. One may note that the JSD definition of entity is different from that used in a database system where it may be defined as a person, place, thing, event, or concept about which information is recorded.

The development steps of JSD are summarized as follows:

1. Specification Development Phase
   - Specification of the Real World Model
     - Abstract Description of Real World
       a. Entity-Action Step
       b. Entity-Structure Step
     - Realization of the Model
       c. Initial Model Step
   - Specification of System Functions
       d. Function Step
       e. System Timing Step
2. Implementation Phase
       f. Implementation Step

In the first step, the entity-action step, the system analyst describes the real world area of interest by listing the entities and actions with which the system will be concerned. No description of entities is provided at this time. However, for each action, an informal description is given and a list of tentative attributes for that action are provided. The attribute list will be modified and extended in the later development steps.

In the next step, namely, the entity-structure step, the set of actions for each entity is ordered by Jackson Diagram notation that is discussed earlier in Section 11.2. These diagrams, so-called "Structure Diagrams (SD)," together with the list of entities, the list of actions, and their descriptions and attributes, form an integral part of system specification.

The result of the two previous steps is an abstract description of the real world—that is, a model—described in terms of sequential processes. The third step, the initial model step, has the task of stating diagrammatically how the real world process is to be connected to the model process using a new set of symbols given in the Appendix of Jackson's book (Ja 83). The resulting diagram is called a "System Specification Diagram" (SSD). In addition to describing the connection between the real world and the model in this step, the system analyst is supposed to specify the model process by writing a "Structure Text or Meta Code" using the Structure Diagrams of the entity-structure step and considering the System Specification Diagram. Structure Text is a pseudocode that consists of three basic structures: sequence, selection, and iteration.

In the next step, the function step, functions are tied to system outputs, and additional processes are added to the specification as elaborations of Structure Diagrams and/or Structure Text as necessary. The output of the function step is a specification of each of the required functions. This specification is documented using System Specification Diagram or using Structure Text.

The fifth step is the system timing step. In this step the systems analyst considers some potential delays in implementation of different parts of the system and determines, with the system's users, what delays are acceptable for the various parts of the system. The resulting decisions are informally documented, and they provide input to the implementation step; they constrain the implementation alternatives to those which will allow satisfactory response time and satisfactory time lags in the system.

The last step in JSD is the implementation step. In this step, the system analyst considers what hardware or software components are available or will be needed to run the developed system. Documentation of this step is not intended for communication with the system's users, and a new set of symbols will be developed for the "System Implementation Diagram," symbols which are given in the appendix of Jackson's book (Ja 83). JSD structure diagrams are applied in the case study in the Appendix.

Some of the advantages of JSD are:

1. It is a teachable methodology, promoted by two software companies, InfoTech in England and SofTech in USA.
2. It is often the case with JSD that a consensus can be reached on problems.
3. The resulting design is relatively easy to code if the system is a software system.

Some of the disadvantages of JSD are:

1. The heavy emphasis on programming is the major disadvantage; Structure Text that is used for algorithm description is more difficult than pseudocode or Structured English.
2. The system to be considered should be time-dependent; in other words, it should be a dynamic system.
3. Many different symbols in various diagrams (e.g., Structure Diagrams, System Specification Diagrams, System Implementation Diagrams, as well as

the Structure Text) make the methodology too confusing for user communication.

15.3.2 Warnier/Orr Methodology

J. D. Warnier is a French mathematician who has worked in the field of set theory. One of the analytical tools he has developed is a diagram consisting of braces and resembling a horizontal tree structure of a hierarchy chart. The basics of this tool have already been discussed in Chapter 10. The methodology was first proposed as LCP (Logical Construction of Programs) (Wa 74) and later as LCS (Logical Construction of Systems) (Wa 81). The American K. Orr has modified the Warnier Diagrams and applied them to a large class of problems including databases. Orr used the acronyms SSD (Structured Systems Development) (Orr 77) and DSSD (Data Structured Systems Development) (Orr 81b) for his methodologies. Nonetheless, all these methodologies may be referred to as Warnier/Orr or W/O methodologies.

Recall that W/O methodology, similar to JSD, is a data-centered or data-structured design approach, different from functional decomposition and data flow oriented methodologies. W/O methodology enforces the study of a system's outputs as the first step. Once the output of an information system is agreed upon by the system analyst and the user and represented in terms of Warnier diagrams, the data structure of the system is developed next. Once again, the vehicle for both development and documentation is the same type of diagram, only in this case it is used to represent the data structure. A very important property of this methodology is that the resulting design facilitates coding in a software system.

Table 15.1 summarizes the individual steps of some variations on W/O methodology.

Some of the advantages of W/O methodology are:

1. It is teachable.
2. It is relatively simple.
3. It is very convenient for direct coding.
4. The same set of symbols is uniformly used in the development.
5. There is a company teaching the methodology (K. Orr & Associates in the USA).

Some of its disadvantages are:

1. It may get complicated for a large system.
2. Its simple appearance may be misleading.
3. The steps given in Table 16.1 are not that easy to apply for real life system problem.

TABLE 15.1 Summary of W/O Methodologies

Approach / Step	LCP	LCS	(SSD) Orr (77)	(SRD) Orr (81)	Higgins (79)	Higgins (83)
1	Define the logical output file	General study (DBs needed)	State the general problem	Logical planning	Define the process outputs	Actual output definition
2	Define the logical input file	Primary data	Identify the structure (and frequency) of the system outputs	Physical planning	Define the logical DB	Logical output definition and design
3	List the logical sequences (flow chart)	Secondary and operational data	Identify the logical database of the system	Logical requirements definition	Define entities and attributes (event analysis)	Logical input design
4	Define the executable operations	Operational output groups	Place the system requirements into a basic system flow hierarchy	Physical requirements definition	Develop the physical database	Logical process design
5	Locate operations in the logical sequence		Check if data required already exists	Logical design	Design the logical process	Physical process—augment
6			Identify events in the real world which affect the DB	Physical design	Design the physical process	Output mapping design
7			Place logical updating actions into basic system hierarchy			Input mapping design
8						Coding
9						Testing

SUMMARY

SADT, Composite Design, and Structured Design are the typical examples of Data Flow Oriented Methodologies. SADT is applied to both the analysis and general design phases of the systems development process. It is a diagramming technique using the graphical tools of actigrams and datagrams. The reader-author cycle is an important tool for the application of SADT methodology. Author, commentater, reader, user, and manager are some of the personnel needed to develop an information systems project. The SADT process involves first preparing activity models and later a data model of the system. Its teachability, its efficiency in user communication, and the good documentation of the resulting system are some of its advantages. Two of its disadvantages are its higher cost and the need for another tool for detailed design.

Composite Design (CD) and Structured Design (SD) were first proposed as software tools. Their use was later extended to information systems development. Basically, Composite Design relies on module coupling and module strength (i.e., module cohesion) as two basic tools to develop modular systems.

Structured Design (SD) is more popular and widely used for information systems development activities. The objective in SD is to produce a structure chart of a system using its DFD. Transform Analysis, Transaction Analysis, and Decomposition are the tools used in SD. Some of the advantages of SD are the relatively high number of available publications, the use of coupling and cohesion for system design measurement or comparison, and its efficiency for user communication. Some of its disadvantages are the facts that it needs another tool for detailed design, that coupling and cohesion are still subjective tools and that it is relatively difficult to learn the methodology.

JSD (Jackson System Development) and Warnier/Orr methodologies are the two methodologies that are grouped under Data Structure Oriented Methodologies. JSD requires that the time dimension of activities of a system or its dynamic quality, be taken into account. Entity and action are the basic terms relevant to JSD. An entity is an object in the real world which participates in a time-ordered set of actions. An action is an event in which one or more entities participate by performing or suffering the action.

The development steps of JSD methodology are entity-action step, entity-structure step, initial model step, function step, system-timing step, and implementation step. JSD is quite teachable and the resulting design is very easy to code if the system is a software system. Heavy emphasis on programming and a plethora of symbols in various diagrams are its disadvantages.

Warnier/Orr methodology is actually comprised of several variations—LCP, LCS, SSD, DSSD, and so on. The output, and user agreement on the output, have the major emphasis in this methodology. Its teachability and simplicity, convenience for coding, and uniformity of symbols are some of the advantages of the methodology. However, the methodology may be complicated for a large information system, and its simple appearance may be misleading. The individual steps of the methodology are neither uniform nor well defined.

EXERCISES

1. What are the methodologies classified as data flow oriented methodologies?
2. What are the major characteristics of SADT?
3. Can you use descriptive texts together with SADT?
4. Comment on the basic concepts on which SADT is based.
5. Describe the author/reader cycle of SADT.
6. Who are the major personnel involved in the author-reader cycle of SADT?
7. Summarize SADT methodology.
8. State some of the advantages of SADT.
9. State some of the disadvantages of SADT.
10. What is the basic idea behind composite design?
11. What are the differences between CD and SD?
12. How can you summarize SD methodology?
13. What are the tools that are used in SD?
14. Describe the steps of Transform Analysis.
15. What is the definition of a coordinate, a transform, an afferent, and an efferent module?
16. What is a transaction?
17. Describe the steps of Transaction Analysis.
18. State some of the advantages of SD.
19. State some of the disadvantages of SD.
20. What are the methodologies that are classified as data structure methodologies.
21. What is the significance of the time dimension in JSD?
22. What is an entity and an action in JSD?
23. Are the definitions of an entity in JSD and in database applications the same?
24. What are the steps of JSD?
25. What types of symbols and diagrams are used in JSD?
26. What is Structure Text? How do you compare it with a pseudocode?
27. State some of the advantages of JSD.
28. State some of the disadvantages of JSD.
29. Who first proposed the W/O methodology?
30. What is the contribution of K. Orr to Warnier's approach?
31. What is the significance of output in W/O methodology?
32. State some of the advantages of W/O methodology.
33. State some of the disadvantages of W/O methodology.

SELECTED REFERENCES

(Co 80)   Connor, M. F. *Structured Analysis and Design Technique.* SofTech May
               1980.

(Dic 81)   Dickinson, B. *Developing Structured Systems.* Yourdon Press, 1981.

(DeM 78)   De Marco, T. *Structured Analysis and Systems Specification.* Yourdon
               Press, 1981.

(Hic 85)   Hiçyilmaz, C. *Jackson System Development Methodology and an Appli-
               cation.* M.S. Thesis, METU, Dept. of Computer Eng., March 1985.

(Hig 79)   Higgins, D. *Program Design and Construction.* Prentice-Hall, 1979.

(Hig 83)   Higgins, D. *Designing Structured Programs.* Prentice-Hall, 1983.

(Ja 75)   Jackson, M. *Principles of Program Design.* Academic Press, 1975.

(Ja 83)   Jackson, M. *System Development.* Prentice-Hall, 1983.

(Jo 80)   Jones, M. P. *The Practical Guide to Structured Systems Design.* Yourdon
               Press, 1980.

(MyG 73)   Myers, G. J. "Characteristics of Composite Design," *Datamation*, Vol.
               19, No. 9 (September 1973), 100–102.

(MyG 75)   Myers, G. J. *Reliable Software Through Composite Design.* Petrocelli,
               1975.

(Orr 77)   Orr, K. *Structured Systems Development.* Yourdon Press, 1977.

(Orr 81b)   Orr, K. *Structured Requirements Definition.* K. Orr and Associates, 1981.

(Pes 18)   Peters, L. J. *Software Design.* Yourdon Press, 1981.

(RB 76)   Ross, D. T., and J. W. Brackett. "An Approach to Structured Analysis,"
               Computer Decisions, Vol. 8, No. 9 (September 1976), 40–44.

(RDMcG 77)   Ross, D. T., M. E. Dickover, and C. McGowan. *Software Design Using
               SADT.* Auerbach Publishers, Inc., Portfolio No: 35-05-03, 1977.

(Ro 80)   Ross, D. T. "Structured Analysis (SA): A Language for Communicating
               Ideas," in *Tutorial on Software Design Techniques*, ed. P. Freeman and
               A. I. Wasserman. IEEE Computer Society, 1980, 107–25.

(SMC 74)   Stevens, W. P., G. J. Myers, and L. L. Constantine. "Structured Design,"
               IBM System Journal, Vol. 13, No. 2 (1974), 115–39.

(StB 77)   Stevens, B. M. "Structured System Design Review," National Bank of
               Detroit, 1977.

(StW 81)   Stevens, W. P. *Using Structured Design.* Wiley, 1981.

(Wa 74)   Warnier, J. D. *Logical Construction of Programs.* Van Nostrand Reinhold,
               1974.

(Wa 81)   Warnier, J. D. Logical Construction of Systems. Van Nostrand Reinhold,
               1981.

(Wei 80)   Weinberg, V. *Structured Analysis.* Prentice-Hall, 1980.

(YC 79)   Yourdon, E., and L. L. Constantine. *Structured Design.* Prentice-Hall,
               1979.

(Yo 81)   Yourdon, Inc. *Structured Analysis/Design Workshop*, Edition 7.2, July
               1981.

Chapter 16

Prescriptive Methodologies

16.1 INTRODUCTION

The methodologies that dictate procedures to be followed during the information systems development process are classified as prescriptive methodologies. Some of these methodologies are in the form of commercially available software packages. The major contribution of such packages is their support for other methodologies by complementing or enhancing the system requirements definition and software development activities of information system development.

In the following sections, some of the commercially available information systems development packages are described. They are ISDOS (PSL/PSA), PLEXSYS, PRIDE, SDM/70, SPECTRUM, and SRES/SREM.

In addition to these software packages, some other methodologies such as Chapin's approach, DBO (Design By Objectives), PAD (Program Analysis Diagram), HOS (Higher Order Software), MSR (Meta Stepwise Refinement), and PDL (Program Design Languages) are classified as prescribed methodologies and they are described by Peters (Pes 81) and Aron (Ar 83).

16.2 ISDOS PROJECT (PSL/PSA)

ISDOS, Information System Design and Optimization System, is a software project being developed at the University of Michigan (e.g., TH 77). The objective of ISDOS is to automate the information systems building process. Its two components are PSL and PSA (Ar 83, Ca 79, and Te 79).

PSL, the major component of ISDOS, is a language for recording user requirements in a machine-readable form. PSL was designed so that its output could be analyzed by the software package PSA. PSL is a language to describe systems, it is not a procedural programming language; PSA is a software package similar to a data dictionary and it is used to check the data as it is entered, to store it, to analyze it, and produce various reports as output. PSA utilizes a DBMS to store the user requirements. PSA analyzes PSL for correct syntax and produces a large number of reports. A data dictionary, a function dictionary, and an analysis of precedence relationships of processes are some of the reports that are produced by PSA. A graphical report is also available; it illustrates all relationships of a given process including whether a process is part of another process or the process has components. PSA performs network analysis to check for the completeness of all relationships between data and processes. It also performs an analysis of time-dependent relationships of the data and an analysis of volume specifications. When the PSA analysis of PSL is error-free, the requirements are passed to system designers to build the system.

As noted by Nunamaker and Konsynski (NK 81), the ISDOS concept was originally intended to automate the system development process; however, very little emphasis has actually been devoted to activities in systems building other than problem definition.

16.3 PLEXSYS PROJECT

The objective of the PLEXSYS Project is to have a system-building system, developed to transform a high-level language problem statement to an executable code for a target hardware configuration. PLEXSYS is really an extension of IS-DOS. While ISDOS has concentrated on nonprocedural aspects of requirements definition, PLEXSYS has concentrated on the automatic code-generation aspects of software systems building.

16.4 PRIDE

PRIDE is an automated system design methodology to be used for information systems development which is offered by the American firm, M. Bryce & Associates. It is described as a thoroughly integrated approach to structured systems analysis/design, data management, project management, and documentation/communications. It provides a Computer Aided Design (CAD) tool for systems development. The software package can actually prepare systems design for manual and/or automated applications. The evaluation of alternatives is just a matter of modifying parameters (BrT 82).

16.5 SDM/70

SDM/70 or Systems Development Methodology/70 is developed and marketed by the American firm, Atlantic Software, Inc. SDM/70 is a comprehensive set of methods, estimation, documentation, and administrative guidelines to help users to develop and maintain effective systems.

16.6 SPECTRUM

SPECTRUM is a systems development methodology developed and marketed by the U.S. firm SII (Spectrum International, Inc.). It has various versions for different purposes such as SPECTRUM-1 (for conventional life cycle), SPECTRUM-2 (the structured project management system), and SPECTRUM-3 (on-line interactive estimator).

16.7 SRES AND SREM

SRES, Software Requirement Engineering System, was developed by TRW for the Software Development System (SDS) of the U.S. Air Force (NK 81).

In SRES, the requirements are stated in the RSL (Requirements Statement Language). REVS (Requirement Engineering and Validation System) is used for analysis of the RSL definition and maintenance of the database. The underlying methodology is called SREM (Software Requirements Engineering Methodology). The system was first implemented on the Texas Instruments Advanced Scientific Computer in 1976. SRES has some concepts similar to those of the ISDOS project discussed earlier.

SUMMARY

Prescriptive methodologies are those that dictate procedures to be followed. Chapin's approach, Design By Objectives (DBO), Program Analysis Diagram (PAD), Higher Order Software (HOS), Meta Stepwise Refinement (MSR), and Program Design Language (PDL) are some of these methodologies.

There are also some commercially available information systems development packages such as PSL/PSA, PLEXSYS, PRIDE, SDM/70, SPECTRUM, and SRES/SREM. The major use of such software packages is to support other methodologies for systems requirement definition and software development activities.

EXERCISES

1. What is the basic property of the prescriptive methodologies?

2. What are the main contributions of prescriptive methodologies in systems development?

3. State the names of some prescriptive methodologies.

4. What is the objective of the ISDOS project?

5. Describe the major components of the ISDOS project.

6. What is the objective of the PLEXSYS project?

7. What is the difference between the ISDOS and PLEXSYS projects?

8. Describe briefly PRIDE, SDM/70, SPECTRUM, and SRES/SREM.

SELECTED REFERENCES

(Ar 83)   Aron, J. D. *The Program Development Process*, Part II. Addison-Wesley, 1983.

(BrT 82)   Bryce, T. Private communication.

(Ca 79)   Canning, R. G. "The Production of Better Software," *EDP Analyzer*, Vol. 17, No. 2, (February 1979).

(NK 81)   Nunamaker, J. F., and B. Konsynski. "Formal and Automated Techniques of Systems Analysis and Design," in Cotterman et al., *Systems Analysis and Design*. North Holland, 1981, 291–320.

(Pes 81)   Peters, L. J. *Software Design*. Yourdon Press, 1981.

(TH 77)   Teichroew, D., and E. A. Hershey. "PSL/PSA: A Computer Aided Technique for Structured Documentation and Analysis of Information Processing Systems," *IEEE Transactions on Software Engineering*, Vol. SE-3, No.1 (January 1977), 41–48.

(Te 79)   Teichroew, D. "The PSL/PSA Approach to Computer-Aided Analysis and Documentation," Auerbach Publications, Inc., Portfolio No: 32-04-04, 1979.

Chapter 17

Contemporary Research

17.1 INTRODUCTION

The need to single out some measurable properties of programs—for example, their size or complexity—and to use such measures to evaluate and compare the product software has led to the development of "software science." Similarly, there is a growing need to develop some techniques to evaluate and compare information systems quantitatively. Recall that most of the structured tools and methodologies for information systems were first utilized for software development. Similarly most of the measurement and evaluation techniques for software are now being generalized to information systems. In the following sections, we define software science briefly and cite some of the recent research in measurement and/or evaluation of information systems in order to indicate future research activities that might be undertaken.

17.2 SOFTWARE SCIENCE

Software science may be defined as a system of statistically derived formulas that relate measurable properties of computer programs to their length, the time taken to code the programs, and the expected number of errors discovered in the debugging process (HS 80). The late Prof. M. Halstead of Purdue University developed most of these formulas. Some of these statistically derived measures are the vocabulary, program length (or Halstead Length), program volume, program level, language level, programming effort (time), and number of bugs (or program errors during development). We use the following variables to define the various measures:

η_1 = number of unique or distinct operators
η_2 = number of unique or distinct operands
N_1 = total usage of all operators
N_2 = total usage of all operands

The measures are defined as follows (e.g., Gr 84, Ha 78):

1. The vocabulary is

$$\eta = \eta_1 + \eta_2 \tag{17.1}$$

   It is the vocabulary of a specific program under consideration.
2. The program length is

$$N = N_1 + N_2 \tag{17.2}$$

   It represents the length of an expression of an algorithm.
3. The program volume is

$$V = N \log_2 \eta \tag{17.3}$$

   It is a measure of the number of bits required to specify the program.
4. The program level is

$$L \sim \frac{\eta_2}{N_2} \tag{17.4}$$

   It is the ratio of potential volume to actual volume.
5. The language level is

$$\lambda = L^2 V \tag{17.5}$$

   It is a measure of the power of a programming language.
6. The estimated value of programming effort in time is

$$T = \frac{\eta_1 N_2 N \log_2 \eta}{2 S \eta_2} \tag{17.6}$$

   Here S is the Stroud number, and it is defined as the number of the most elementary discriminations that the human brain can perform per second.
7. The estimated total number of bugs is

$$B = V/3000 \tag{17.7}$$

Christensen et al. (CFS 81) have developed the following rules in terms of the above measures:

1. The length of a program is a function of the vocabulary of that program.
2. The lines of code, length, and volume are equally valid as relative measures of program size.

As we shall see in the next section, similar measures may be developed and applied to information systems. Quite a few researchers are working on these objectives at the present time.

17.3 MEASUREMENT OF INFORMATION SYSTEMS

In a study, Troy and Zweben (TZ 81) tried to express the quality of design (in terms of program errors) as a function of 21 independent metrics including coupling, cohesion, complexity, modularity, and size of programs. Examining a set of basic relationships among various software development variables, Basili and Freburger (BF 81) plotted software size against productivity. Similar relations and equations can be used to measure information systems.

Michelson and coworkers (Mic 80) have proposed the following measures to be used for user/system interfaces: reliability, correctness, learnability, usability, flexibility, performance, applicability, security and protection, and cost effectiveness. In a different paper, Cruickshank and Gaffney (CG 80) proposed a set of quantifiable metrics or indicators to measure software design characteristics. Similar to these, Aktas (Ak 82) proposed three groups of metrics relating to the structure, completeness, and resource characteristics of information systems for measurements (Figure 17.1).

In Figure 17.1, the structural characteristics are reliability, flexibility, per-

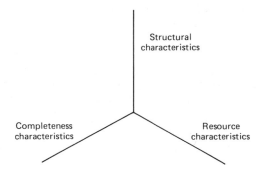

Figure 17.1 Characteristics of an information system

formance, applicability, relative complexity, coupling, cohesion, design logic and presentation clarity, and security and protection. The completeness characteristics are relative requirements, documentation, and completeness; and the resource characteristics are the necessary equipment and cost effectiveness.

Basili and Reiter (BR 81) conducted a small-scale experiment on software development approaches and indicated that a disciplined methodology effectively improved both the process and product of software development. They also verified that methodological discipline has a key influence on the general efficiency of the software development process and significantly reduces the material costs of software development. Similar experiments need to be performed on information systems development projects to quantify procedures and to minimize, if not eliminate, abstract feelings and subjective experiences (Ak 82).

Henry and Kafura (HK 81) defined and validated a set of software metrics which were appropriate for evaluating the structure of large-scale systems, particularly those that are defined for procedure complexity, module complexity, and module coupling.

17.4 OTHER RESEARCH AREAS

Ferrentino (Fe 81) discusses an approach for making good estimates of time and human resources needed to develop a software system. Peercy (Pee 81) described an implemented procedure for evaluating a program's documentation and source code for maintainability characteristics. Harrison and colleagues (HMKK 82) proposed the use of software complexity metrics such as those for program size, data structures and data flow, and program control structures, for program maintenance. Another study on the quality assessment of a software system design is reported by Mohanty (Moh 81). The several metrics used for this purpose are based on the entropy function of communication information theory. These studies also seem applicable to information systems.

Information systems performance evaluation—and various models available for that purpose—is a subject of recent interest as well. In a research paper, Anderson (An 84) reported an application of five performance evaluation methodologies on a relatively small information system.

The problem-solving capability of systems analysts is another interesting area. A relatively recent paper discusses several problem-solving behaviors exhibited by highly regarded and less highly regarded systems analysts and draws some conclusions about the relationship of those behaviors to successful performance (VD 83). Another study has as its subject the behavior of system designers and users in the design and implementation stages (DW 83). Obviously, systems analysts need to understand social and psychological factors for efficient system development.

SUMMARY

Software science may be defined as a system of statistically derived formulas that relate measurable properties of computer programs to their length, the time taken to code the programs, and the expected number of errors discovered in the debugging process. Using the same or similar metrics, various authors have arrived at a number of "quality characteristics" of software and information systems. In addition to information systems metrics, two other topics of recent research are the problem-solving characteristics of systems analysts and user behavior.

EXERCISES

1. Define software science.
2. What are the statistically derived measures for software?
3. What are the metrics to be used to measure some properties of a program?
4. What are the three groups of metrics that can be used to define an information system?
5. What are the results of experiments of disciplined methodologies on software development?
6. State any two recent research topics.

SELECTED REFERENCES

(Ak 82)   Aktas, Z. "Discussion of Structured Systems Analysis and Design Strategies for Information Systems." Paper presented at the ACM Tenth Annual Computer Science Conference, Indianapolis, February 1982.

(An 84)   Anderson, G. E. "The Coordinated Use of Five Performance Evaluation Methodologies," *Comm. ACM*, Vol. 27, No. 2 (February 1984), 119–25.

(BF 81)   Basili, V. R., and K. Freburger. "Programming Measurement and Estimation in the Software Engineering Laboratory," *The Journal of Systems and Software*, Vol. 2, No. 1 (February 1981), 47–57.

(Bo 81)   Boehm, B. W. "An Experiment in Small-Scale Application Software Engineering," *IEEE Transactions on Software Engineering*, Vol. SE-7, No. 5 (September 1981).

(BR 81)   Basili, V. R., and R. W. Reiter. "A Controlled Experiment Quantitatively Comparing Software Development Approaches," *IEEE Transactions on Software Engineering*, Vol. SE-7, No. 3 (May 1981), 299–320.

(CFS 81)   Christensen, K., G. P. Fitsos, and C. P. Smith. "A Perspective on Software Science," *IBM Systems Journal*, Vol. 20, No. 4 (1981), 372–87.

(CG 80)   Cruickshank, R. D., and J. E. Gaffney. "Indicators for Software Design Assessment," Software Cost Eng. Dept., IBM, 1980.

(DW 83) Dagwell, R., and R. Weber. "System Designers' User Models: A Comparative Study and Methodological Critique," *Comm. ACM*, Vol. 26, No. 11 (1983), 987–97.

(Fe 81) Ferrentino, A. B. "Making Software Development Estimates Good," *Datamation*, September 1981, 179—82.

(Gr 84) Gremillon, L. L. "Determinants of Program Repair Maintenance Requirements," *Comm. ACM*, Vol. 27, No. 8 (1984), 826–32.

(HK 81) Henry, S., and D. Kafura. "Software Structure Metrics Based on Information Flow," *IEEE Transactions on Software Engineering*, Vol. SE-7, No. 5 (September 1981), 510–18.

(HMKK 82) Harrison, W., K. Magel, R. Kluczny, and A. D. Kock. "Applying Software Complexity Metrics to Program Maintenance," *Computer*, September 1982, 65–79.

(Ha 78) Halstead, M. H. *Elements of Software Science.* North Holland, 1978.

(HS 80) Halstead, M. H., and V. Schneider. "A Self-Assessment Procedure Dealing with Software Science," *Comm. ACM*, Vol. 23, No. 8 (August 1980), 475–80.

(Mic 80) Michelson, C. D., et al. "A Methodology for the Objective Evaluation of the User/System Interfaces Using Software Engineering Principles," 18th Southeast Regional ACM Conference, Tallahassee, Florida, March 1980.

(Moh 81) Mohanty, S. N. "Entropy Metrics for Software Design Evaluation," *The Journal of Systems and Software*, Vol. 2, No. 1 (February 1981), 39–46.

(Pee 81) Peercy, D. E. "A Software Maintainability Evaluation Methodology," *IEEE Transactions on Software Engineering*, Vol. SE-7, No. 4 (July 1981), 343–51.

(TZ 81) Troy, D. A., and S. H. Zweben. "Measuring the Quality of Structured Designs," *The Journal of Systems and Software*, Vol. 2 (1981), 113–20.

(VD 83) Vitalari, N. P., and G. W. Dickson. "Problem Solving for Effective Systems Analysis: An Experimental Exploration," *Comm. ACM*, Vol. 26, No. 11 (1983), 948–56.

Appendix A

A Case Study

A.1 INTRODUCTION

In addition to the examples and exercises provided in the relevant chapters of the textbook, we offer a case study to help clarify the use of some of the tools and methodologies used in an information system development process. Our objective is to demonstrate the application of Structured Design, Warnier/Orr, and Jackson methodologies to the information system of a relatively small, real-life company. In order to ensure privacy and objectivity, we have changed the functions, identities, and locations.

For a better view of the tools and methodologies and for an ease of comparison, the information systems development life cycle that was discussed in Chapter 2 will be followed. The first three phases, namely, planning, analysis, and physical design activities are discussed in sequence.

A.2 CASE COMPANY: THE CAST IRON VALVE COMPANY (CIV CO.)

CIV Company was founded in 1970 as a small workshop with 15 workers. In the following years, because of the high quality of their products, the eagerness of their salespeople and, in particular, the various patent contracts that the company received, both company size and the volume and range of products have increased.

Today CIV Company is working in a new and larger factory complex that houses 250 workers producing various types of valves and fittings for the domestic and international markets. The present organization chart of the CIV Company is given as Figure A.1.

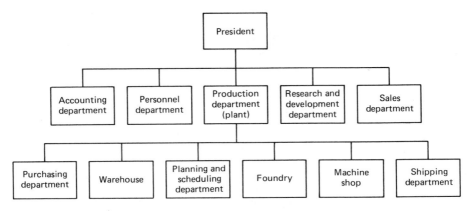

Figure A.1   Present organization chart of the CIV Company

The president of the company, Mr. Schreiber, a talented and a very successful businessman in the region, has long realized the significance of computerization. He is, however, not sure how computers and computerization will be beneficial for his company. For the time being, the most critical problem that bothers him in CIV Company is the delay in meeting customer orders. He is, therefore, anxious to see whether computerization will solve or at least ease this problem.

Mr. Schreiber now hires a system analyst to investigate the feasibility of installing a computer-based inventory control system and to develop and implement it, if feasible. Obviously, if this first application is successful, other applications will follow and eventually a management information system will be realized for the company. However, for the sake of brevity, we are interested only in the inventory control system.

A.3 CASE PROBLEM: INVENTORY CONTROL SUBSYSTEM

Inventory is a subsystem of the information system of a manufacturing organization, along with other subsystems such as sales and invoicing, production and profit planning, accounting, purchasing and accounts payable, and personnel and payroll. An inventory has usable but idle resources—human resources, materials, finished or unfinished machines, monetary assets.

When the resource involved is materials or goods at any stage of completion, the inventory may also be called stock. In many organizations, the ratio of inventory to total assets is estimated to be about 20 to 30 percent. Optimum utilization of inventory is, therefore, vital for a company's profitability, and inventory management and control thus becomes one of the most common applications of information systems.

As noted by Burch and Strater (BS 74), an organization with inventory problems needs an inventory control system to accomplish two things:

1. To make certain that approximately all items are available in the correct quantity when they are needed; that is, to prevent or minimize shortage or stockout. The objective is to maintain sales and customer satisfaction.
2. To prevent an overstock, which is an increase of inventory beyond proper limits. The objective is to reduce investment cost, storage space, and spoilage.

To reach an optimum balance between stockout and overstock situations of inventory, a proper inventory control mechanism must handle the two critical problems of determining the reordering point in replenishing the stock and deciding how much to order, or the value of classical EOQ (Economic Order Quantity). EOQ is the amount of inventory to be ordered at one time for purposes of minimizing annual inventory costs.

The controlling factors in reordering are the lead time (the time interval between placing an order and receiving the product in the firm), the rate of inventory usage, and the safety stock. Safety stock is the level of minimum stock before reordering a particular product to avoid or minimize stockouts and back orders. Back order is a customer order that is not met because of stockout. Some graphical, mathematical, statistical, and forecasting techniques are used to determine the reorder point (e.g., MU 76). The periodic system and the reorder point system are two approaches to replenish inventories. In the periodic system, which is more often used, an order is placed on a specific date. In a reorder point system, an order is placed when the inventory level of an item reaches a predetermined reorder point.

There are various methods of determining how much to order. The commonly used model is the classic EOQ model (e.g., BS 74) which calculates the reorder quantity. In determining that value two opposite types of costs should be considered:

1. Cost for carrying insufficient inventory
2. Cost for carrying too much inventory

The cost elements for carrying insufficient inventory include costly changes in the firm's production rate; extra purchasing, handling and transportation costs; lost sales and penalty costs; and failure in customer relations. On the other hand, the cost of invested capital, handling and storage costs, taxes and insurance cost, deterioration and obsolescence of stocks are some of the cost elements that should be considered in holding or carrying excess inventory. Clearly, then, the objective in determining EOQ is to reach a trade-off that will minimize these costs.

An inventory can simply be modelled as an input/output model such that items that are purchased and/or manufactured and placed in stock are considered input, while those that are sold and/or scrapped are output. The model to be used should also continuously update quantity on hand and make available all sorts of other information.

Although inventory problems may arise in different contexts, finished goods inventory, which is at the hub of the firm's purchasing, production, and sales activities, is one of the most common types of inventory and one that is particularly relevant to the case study at hand. Therefore, in the following sections, inventory will be taken to mean finished goods inventory.

A.4 INFORMATION SYSTEMS DEVELOPMENT PROCESS

The main phases of an information system development process are planning, analysis, physical design, implementation, and maintenance. The individual steps of these phases were already given in Chapter 2 and summarized in Table 2.1 and Figure 2.1. The key considerations and end product of each of these steps are summarized and presented as Table A.1.

The first phase, planning, consists of "study type" activities. The feasibility study is the key activity of this phase, and the resulting report, called a Feasibility Report, will recommend either no change to the existing system, modification of the existing system, or a new system. If a new system is recommended, an outline of the proposed system, proposed requirements, and project schedule will be included in the Systems Proposal which is another end product of Feasibility Study.

The next two phases are the analysis and physical design stages, and the last two are implementation and maintenance. These four phases are all "doing type" of activities compared to the "study type" activities of the planning phase.

The major emphasis of this book and of the case study is on the analysis and physical design phases. We, therefore, assume that the planning phase has already been conducted, that a computer-based system has been shown to be feasible, and that top management has given the go-ahead to begin the analysis phase. After the analysis and general design steps, the detailed design and the next two phases—namely, implementation and maintenance—can be performed in the actual organization. We shall not deal with them in the case study since they are outside the scope of our text.

Section A.5 looks at the case company, Cast Iron Valve Company, from the standpoint of the analysis and design activities for the inventory control subsystem. These phases will be performed according to the model, and wherever there is a need for a structured tool, the three tools—Data Flow Diagram, Jackson Diagram, and Warnier/Orr Diagram—will be applied individually. In the general design step,

TABLE A.1   A Summary of the Information Systems Development Process

Phase	Key Considerations	End Product
I. Planning		
1.1 Request for a system study	•Organization objectives •User department objectives	•Request memo/form to initiate study
1.2 Initial investigation	•Priority of the requested system study •Resource requirements of the requested system •Overall budgeting of the organization/information systems department	•Resource estimate statements •Information Systems Department budget •Statement of objectives and scope
1.3 Feasibility study	•Problem definition •Alternative solutions •Feasibility criteria and cost/benefit analysis •Recommended solution(s)	•Feasibility report •Systems proposal
II. Analysis		
2.1 Redefine the problem	•What is the actual problem?	•Problem definition
2.2 Understand the existing system	•Data gathering •Data analysis	•Data dictionary •General algorithms

2.3 Determine user requirements and constraints on the new system	•Current/future requirements of the new system
	•Time/resource restrictions
	•Control points of the system
		•Identification of
		  •Outputs/inputs
		  •Operations
		  •Resources

2.4 Logical (or conceptual) model of the solution	•Specification of user needs
	•Implementation considerations
	•Training needs
		•Logical system design report
		  •Output specifications
		  •Input specifications
		  •Edit, security, and control specifications
		  •Logical data model
		  •Implementation strategy

III. Physical design		
3.1 General design (or systems design)	•How will the system be implemented? •Alternative physical solutions	•General design report •Systems flowchart •List of physical components •Cost/benefit/analysis •Implementation schedule
3.2 Detailed design	•Dividing the work among team members •Report, form, and screen design •Procedures preparation	•The detailed design report •Technical specifications for I/O and storage •Implementation plan •A revised cost/benefit evaluation

TABLE A.1   A Summary of the Information Systems Development Process (*cont.*)

Phase	Key Considerations	End Product
IV. Implementation		
4.1 Systems building	•Planning/scheduling •Hardware/software procurement •Staffing	•The new system
4.2 Systems testing	•Module test •Systems tests	•Test results and feedback
4.3 Installing and conversion	•Conversion strategy	•Changeover plan
4.4 Operations and post-implementation audits	•Training •Procedures preparation •Postimplementation review	•Trained personnel •Procedures •Review Report
V. Maintenance		
5.1 Maintenance and review	•System errors •Business needs •Enhancements	•Corrected/modified system

the three structured methodologies—Structured Design, Jackson System Development, and Warnier/Orr methodologies—are again considered separately.

A.5   SYSTEM ANALYSIS AND DESIGN OF THE CASE PROBLEM

A.5.1   Analysis Activities

Redefine the problem.   The first step in the analysis phase is to review the problem once more. Here we assume that the president of CIV had already requested a feasibility study of computerization in the company, which had revealed that a computer application would have a significant impact on CIV's customer order processing system. This system is a combination of production, warehousing, sales, and purchasing activities. The major bottleneck, warehousing activities, creates serious dissatisfaction in management, harms customer relations, and causes loss of profits.

The warehouse contains raw materials, parts, and finished goods. The whole inventory system is manually operated. Inventory count, performed twice a year, is neither accurate nor timely. It, therefore, becomes clear that CIV's critical problem is inventory management and control, and the objective of the study is to develop a computer-based-inventory control system.

Understand the existing system.   The system analyst had to understand the existing physical and logical information system for inventory control in order to propose a new logical model at the end of the analysis phase. That model will be used to develop physical design in the phase following analysis.

In order to gain that understanding, the system analyst interviewed Mr. Schreiber, the president, and other managers of the CIV. The analyst held various observation sessions for the activities, in particular inventory flow, of the company and also read some textbooks on the subject of inventory control and management.

The systems analyst collected the existing data and presented them in the following tables and figures of this section.

The existing forms and reports that are relevant to order processing are presented graphically in Figure A.2. As shown in the figure, Customer Order Form (F1) is prepared in the Sales Department and sent to the Production Planning and Scheduling Department. Similarly, the Stock List of Finished Valves Form (F2) and Stock List of Parts Form (F3) are prepared in the Warehouse and sent to the Production Planning and Scheduling Department. The flow of other forms, F4 through F9, are also shown in Figure A.2. Title, description, source, destination, frequency, number of copies, and comments about each of the existing forms (F1–F9) of the order processing system of CIV Co. are listed as Table A.2. In that figure D stands for daily, and M stands for monthly frequency. "Reversible" means that the particular form is sent back to the source from the destination after a certain processing.

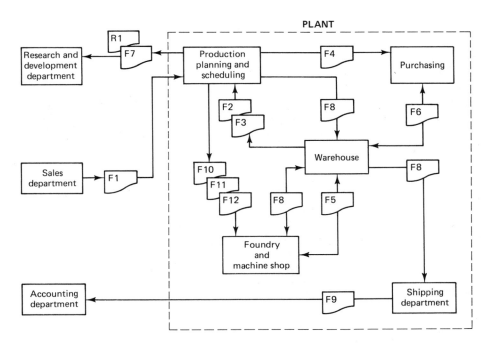

Figure A.2 CIV Company existing order processing form/report flow diagrams

TABLE A.2 CIV Co. Existing Forms Summary Sheet

Title	Description	Source	Destination	Frequency	Number of Copies	Comments
F1	Customer Order Form	Sales	Production Planning and Scheduling	D	1	
F2	Stock List of Finished Valves	Warehouse	Production Planning and Scheduling	M	3	
F3	Stock List of Parts	Warehouse	Production Planning and Scheduling	M	3	
F4	Materials/Parts Purchase Form	Production Planning and Scheduling	Purchasing	D	4	
F5	Warehouse Entry Form for Finished Valves/Parts	Warehouse	Foundry and Machine Shop	D	3	reversible
F6	Warehouse Entry Form for Purchased Material	Warehouse	Purchasing	D	3	reversible
F7	New Product Request Form	Production Planning and Scheduling	Research and Development	D	2	

F8	Warehouse Exit Form	Warehouse	• Shipping • Foundry and Machine Shop • Production Planning and Scheduling	D	3	reversible
F9	Delivery Receipt	Shipping	Accounting	D	2	
F10	Monthly Parts Production Schedule	Production Planning and Scheduling	Foundry and Machine Shop	M	2	
F11	Foundry Work Program	Production Planning and Scheduling	Foundry and Machine Shop	M	2	
F12	Work Shop Work Program	Production Planning and Scheduling	Foundry and Machine Shop	M	2	

(D: daily, M: monthly)

TABLE A.3   CIV Co., Existing Reports Summary Sheet

Title	Description	Source	Destination	Frequency	Comments
R1	New Product Definition and Technical Specifications	Production Planning and Scheduling	Research and Development	M	
R2	Valve Stock Level Summary	Warehouse	Production Planning and Scheduling	Y	
R3	Order Summary	Sales	Production Planning and Scheduling	Y	
R4	Materials Stock Level Summary	Warehouse	Production Planning and Scheduling	Y	

(M: monthly, Y: yearly)

Figure A.2 also shows the flow of existing reports of the order processing system. In addition to the New Products Request Form (F7), the New Product Definition and Technical Specifications Report (R1) is sent to the Research and Development Department from the Production Planning and Scheduling Department. The other reports (R2 through R4) are a tabular summary of product stock level, order, and materials stock level of CIV Co. Frequency of these reports are monthly (M) or yearly (Y). Title, description, source, destination, frequency, number of copies, and comments about the reports of the order processing system are summarized as Table A.3. A data element list that summarizes data items in various forms is given in Table A.4.

The existing data items, records, and files are next defined in a manual or a computer-based DD/D (Data Dictionary/Directory) system that is discussed in Chapter 11. Just as an example of the content of DD, the data item "Customer Name" is considered and, using the format of the example in Figure 11.1, it is given as Figure A.3.

Another task in this step of the analysis phase is to present the general algorithms of the existing system. Referring to Figure A.2, we now attempt to summarize the warehouse activities of CIV Co. The existing inventory management system of CIV Co. is given as Figure A.4.

The stock lists produced monthly in the warehouse are not accurate; besides those monthly lists never keep pace with the production scheduling work of the Production Planning and Scheduling Department of CIV Co.

TABLE A.4 CIV Co., Existing Data Items Summary Sheet

Information Systems Development Co.	DATA ELEMENT LIST	Page 15 of 45
Activity No. 003-005	Activity Name: Analysis of the Existing System	Prepared by
Project No. 002-0084-003	Project Name: CIV Co., Order Processing System	Date: 3/15/84

APPEARS IN THE FOLLOWING FORMS

No.	Data Item	F1	F2	F3	F4	F5	F6	F7	F8	F9	F10	F11	F12
1	Date	X	X	X	X		X	X	X	X			
2	Valve Type	X	X	X					X	X		X	X
3	Quantity	X			X			X	X		X	X	X
4	Technical specifications	X	X										
5	Delivery date	X			X			X		X			
6	Customer name	X						X		X		X	
7	Salesperson	X								X			
8	Comments		X		X								
9	Part Name			X					X		X	X	X
10	Status Code			X									
11	Material name				X		X		X				
12	Unit				X	X	X		X				
13	Requesting Unit				X								
14	Manager				X								
15	Warehouse Supervisor				X								
16	Plant Director				X								
17	Code No.					X	X		X				
18	Valve/Part Name					X							

TABLE A.4 CIV Co., Existing Data Items Summary Sheet (cont.)

Information Systems Development Co.	DATA ELEMENT LIST	Page 15 of 45
Activity No. 003-005	Activity Name: Analysis of the Existing System	Prepared by
Project No. 002-0084-003	Project Name: CIV Co., Order Processing System	Date: 3/15/84

APPEARS IN THE FOLLOWING FORMS

No.	Data Item	F1	F2	F3	F4	F5	F6	F7	F8	F9	F10	F11	F12
19	Entering Quantity					X	X						
20	Stock Level					X	X		X				
21	Unit Price					X	X		X				
22	Value					X	X		X				
23	Vendor Company						X						
24	Order Date						X						
25	Materials Group						X						
26	Shipment Form No.						X						
27	Transportation						X			X			
28	Product Definition							X					
29	Leaving Quantity							X					
30	Driver's Name									X			
31	Month										X	X	X
32	Operation Code										X		
33	Processing Time in hr.										X		
34	Foundry Unit No.											X	
35	Machine No.												X

176

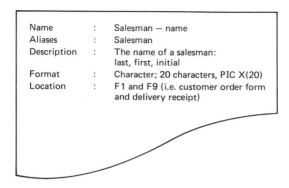

Name	:	Salesman — name
Aliases	:	Salesman
Description	:	The name of a salesman: last, first, initial
Format	:	Character; 20 characters, PIC X(20)
Location	:	F1 and F9 (i.e. customer order form and delivery receipt)

Figure A.3   Example of DD use

At present all the available forms are filed in file cabinets in the warehouse. Clearly, such an application has retrieval and storage area problems.

Determine user requirements and constraints on the new system.
In the existing system, the Purchasing Department, Warehouse, and Planning and Scheduling Department are separate departments. These highly interrelated departments may be combined in a single department, say, Production Control and Management Department, for a relatively small company like CIV Co. The internal operations of the organization, particularly those of purchasing and stocking of materials and finished product, must be subjected to a system of internal control to prevent or minimize waste and fraud.

The new system to be developed should be a modular and hierarchical system; it should also be maintainable, flexible, and testable—in short, a structured system. CIV Co. is a relatively small company. The proposed system should, therefore, be a low-cost system for installation and operation in terms of hardware, software, and personnel. Considering user requirements and constraints on a new system, one may propose some changes in the organization chart as well. The proposed chart, given as Figure A.5, has a significant change compared to Figure A.1 and it should result in greater efficiency.

Logical model of the solution.
As noted earlier, the three commonly used approaches, namely Structured Design, Warnier/Orr, and Jackson System Development, are discussed in the analysis and design phases. In the analysis phase, only the relevant diagrams will be used to represent the logical structure of the proposed system. The relevant diagram for the Structured Design approach in this phase is the Data Flow Diagram. The proposed inventory management system is given in terms of Data Flow Diagrams (Figure A.6), Warnier/Orr Diagrams (Figures A.7 and A.8), and Jackson Diagrams (Figure A.9). Table A.5 is the data flow diagram narrative for CIV's inventory control system.

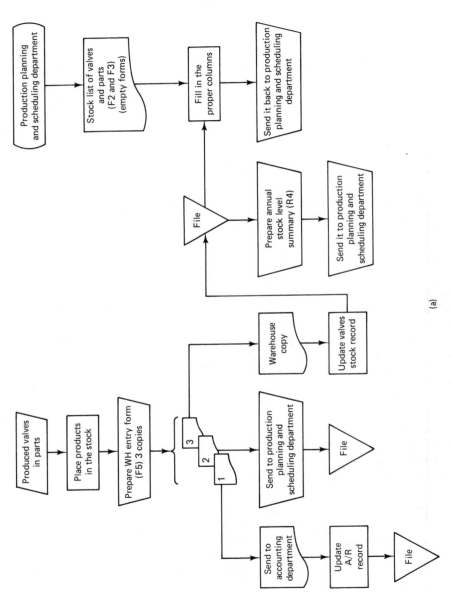

Figure A.4 Existing inventory management system

(a)

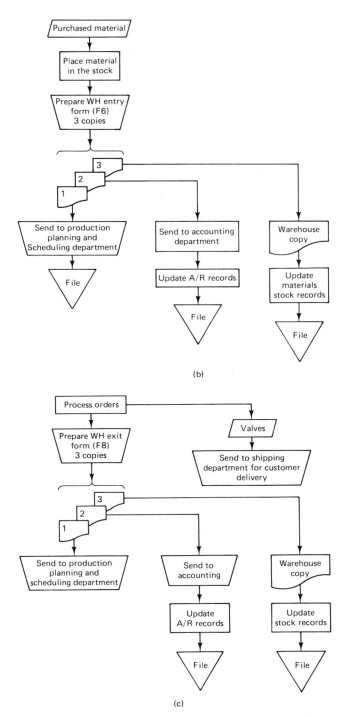

(b)

(c)

Figure A.4 *(cont.)*

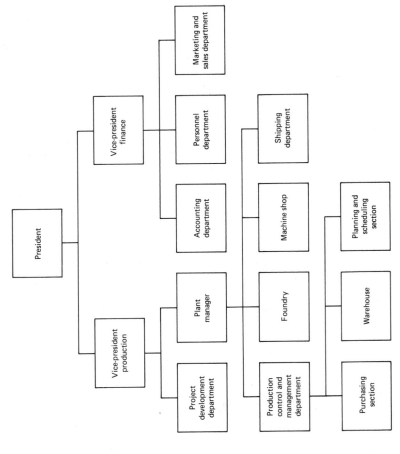

Figure A.5 Proposed organization chart of the CIV Company

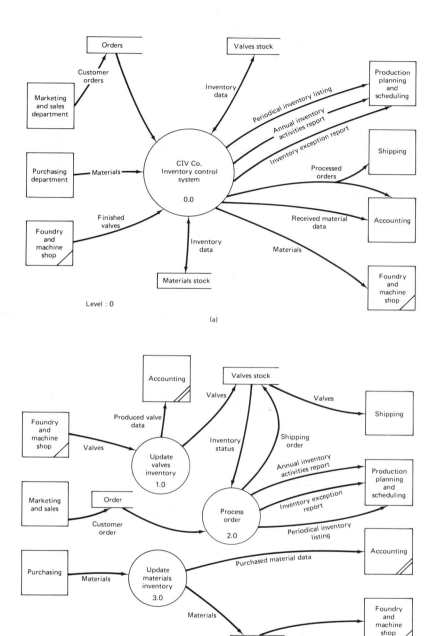

Figure A.6 (a) Context diagram for CIV Company's inventory control system, (b) Overview diagram for CIV's inventory control system, (c) Process order function (explosion of bubble no. 2) in CIV's inventory control system, (d) Process transaction function (explosion of bubble no. 2.2) in CIV's inventory control system.

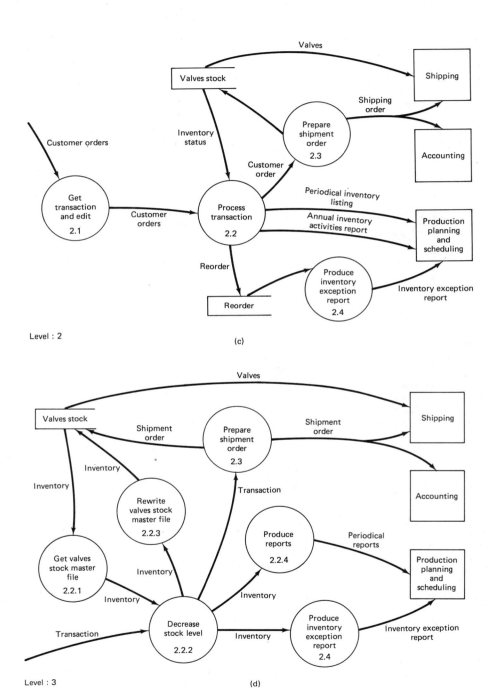

Level : 2

(c)

Level : 3

(d)

Figure A.6 (cont.)

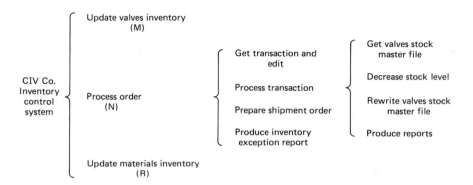

Figure A.7   Warnier/Orr diagram representation of CIV Company's inventory control system

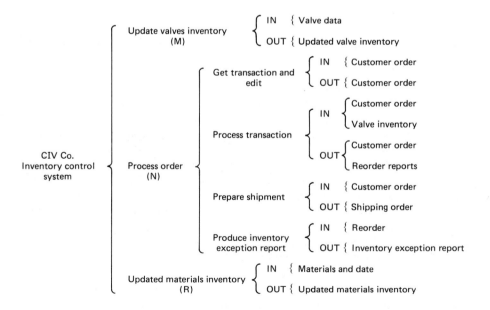

Figure A.8   Warnier/Orr representation of CIV Company's major inputs, outputs, and process of inventory control system

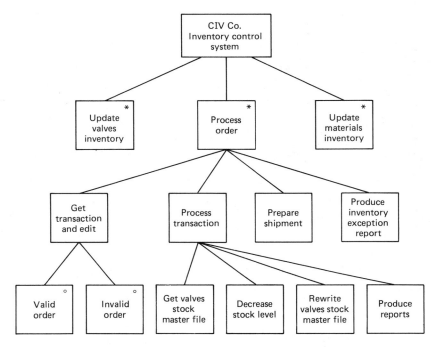

Figure A.9   M. Jackson diagram representation of CIV Company's inventory control system

A.5.2 Physical Design Activities

System design.   The major concern of the system design step of the physical design phase is to study how to implement the new system physically using the logical model proposed in the analysis phase. Various alternative physical solutions should be discussed and one of them should be recommended.

One alternative is to perform manual operations on the proposed system; another is to develop an information system using a database management system. One could take these alternatives as two extreme cases. A third alternative, which will be recommended, is to use an on-line file management system with sufficient terminals and magnetic disk memory as in Figure A.10.

Detail design.   The next step in the physical design phase is the detail design step. Our objective is simply to demonstrate how to apply Structured Design, Warnier/Orr, and Jackson System Development; therefore, we are going to look at the detail design of one subfunction, namely, "process transaction" of the Inventory Management System of CIV Co.

The first application uses Structured Design. Referring to Figure A.6c and

TABLE A.5   Data Flow Diagram Narrative for the Inventory Control System of CIV Co.

1.0	**Update Valves Inventory**	
	Process	Receives produced valves from machine shop and updates valves inventory
	Input	Valves and their data
	Output	Processed valve data for Accounting Dept. and produced valves to stock
	Performance Criteria	Average ten valves per day
	Problems/Comments	During peak production periods, the process is delayed; there is no checking mechanism
2.0	**Process Order**	
	Process	Receives the customer orders, gets the inventory status and processes the order
	Input	Customer Order, Inventory Status
	Output	Shipping Order, Annual Inventory Activities Report, Inventory Exception Report, Periodical Inventory Listing
	Performance Criteria	Daily average 20 customer orders
	Problems/Comments	Manual processing of customer orders is slow; inventory status is not timely; therefore, unfulfilled shipping orders are sometimes possible
2.1	**Get Transaction and Edit**	
	Process	Customer orders are received from Marketing and Sales Department and orders are edited
	Input	Customer Order
	Output	Edited Customer Order
	Performance Criteria	
	Problems/Comments	
2.2	**Process Transaction**	

defining the transform center as in Figure A.11, we end up with the higher level structure chart of Figure A.12. That diagram would further be decomposed and data/control couples would be indicated as we did in Chapter 8.

Similarly, referring to Figure A.7, we rewrite the "process transaction" function of the inventory control system as Figure A.13 in Warnier/Orr Diagram. Later each of the subfunctions shown in Figure A.13 will be decomposed and their elements expressed in terms of W/O Diagrams (see Higgins, Hi 83).

Finally, referring to Figure A.9, we may define the "process transaction" function as in Figure A.14 in terms of Jackson Diagram. Exploding the model further, we can describe each subfunction using Structure Text of Jackson System Design (Ja 83). Remember, Structure Text is very similar to pseudocode and it is used for algorithm description.

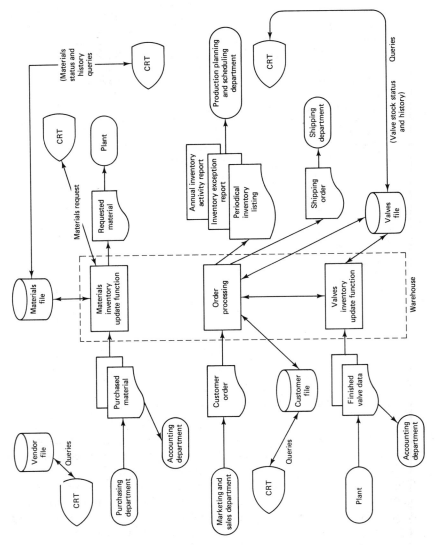

Figure A.10 Recommended system alternative

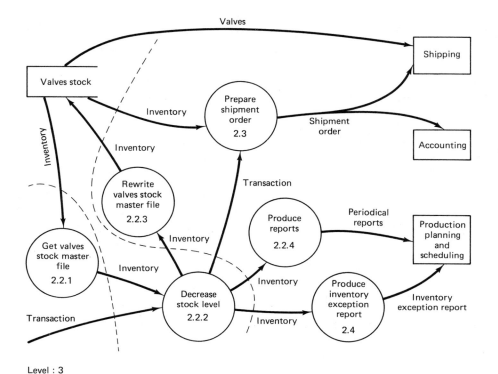

Level : 3

Figure A.11   Main modules of process transaction function

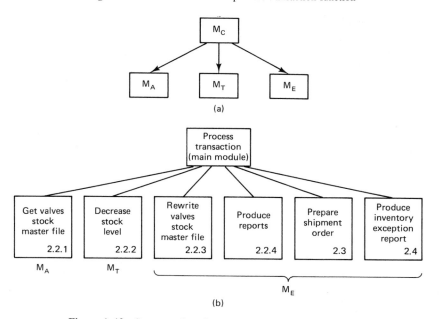

Figure A.12   Structure chart for process transaction module

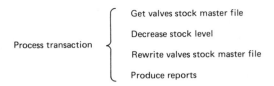

Figure A.13 Process transaction function of inventory control system in Warnier/Orr diagram

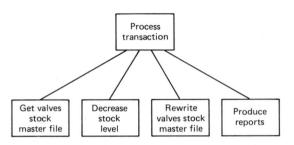

Figure A.14 Process transaction function in Jackson diagram

SELECTED REFERENCES

(BS 74)   Burch, J. G., and F. R. Strater. *Information Systems: Theory and Practice.* Wiley, 1974.

(Hi 83)   Higgins, D. *Designing Structured Programs.* Prentice-Hall, 1983.

(Ja 83)   Jackson, M. *System Development.* Prentice-Hall, 1983.

(MU 76) Matz, A., and M. F. Usry. *Cost Accounting*, 6th ed. Southwestern Publishing Co., 1976.

Index